# TELEVISION PRODUCTION HANDBOOK

## SECOND EDITION

# TELEVISION PRODUCTION HANDBOOK

## SECOND EDITION

### Herbert Zettl

San Francisco State College

Wadsworth Publishing Company, Inc., Belmont, California

L.C. Cat. Card No.: 68-19446

Printed in the United States of America

Grateful acknowledgment is made to the following people and organizations for their courtesy in supplying and permitting reproduction of the illustrations appearing on the pages indicated.

*Photographs:*
Albion Optical Company: pages 33, 42, 59, 65, 66, 67, 68.
Ampex Corporation: pages 11, 322, 323, 326, 327, 329, 331, 467, 468.
Bill Bishop, San Francisco State College: pages 129, 142, 144, 145, 146, 188, 397.
Century Lighting, Inc.: page 79.
Chrono-Log Corporation: page 319.
ColorTran Industries: pages 126, 131, 133, 135.
Peter Dart, San Francisco State College: page 268.
Electro-Voice, Inc.: pages 81, 91, 92, 95, 101.
Gates Radio Company: page 115.
General Electric: page 11.
Houston Fearless Corporation: pages 32, 33.
Imagination, Inc.: page 256.
Kliegl Brothers: pages 126, 127, 131, 132, 133, 136.
KNXT, CBS Affiliate, Los Angeles: pages 416, 457.
KPIX, Westinghouse Group W Station, San Francisco: pages 46, 77, 84, 140, 159, 186, 211, 231, 232, 233, 234, 236, 237, 238, 245, 305, 392.
Marconi Company, Ltd.: page 8.
NBC: page 30.
North American Philips Company: pages 16, 19, 23.
RCA: pages 3, 4, 6, 7, 13, 14, 20, 21, 22, 25, 26, 27, 28, 29, 31, 41, 59, 60, 61, 62, 64, 76, 83, 85, 95, 96, 104, 314, 315, 317, 318, 324, 325, 397.
Shure Brothers, Inc.: pages 83, 91, 93, 103.
Sony Corporation of America: pages 326, 327, 469.
Vega Electronics Corporation: pages 98, 99.
Visual Electronics Corporation: pages 5, 104.

*Script Samples:*
Benjamin Draper, San Francisco State College: page 444.
KPIX, Westinghouse Group W Station, San Francisco: pages 447, 448, 449.
Larry Williams, Lawren Productions: pages 446, 450, 451.

*Charts:*
Max Factor and Co.: pages 374, 375.

All other illustrations are the work of the author.

**To Erika**

# Preface

Before we can hope to communicate effectively through television, we must attain a thorough understanding of the medium—that is, we must learn what production elements there are, what each element can and cannot do, and how it can be used in relation to others.

In this second edition of *Television Production Handbook,* all major production equipment has been updated and, wherever appropriate, illustrated with photographs or sketches. Color equipment and color operations are emphasized throughout the text. A four-page color insert (opposite page 200) shows the basic workings and the internal optical system of color cameras as well as some basic aspects of color compatibility. And since monochrome television is still widely used (though not always still manufactured), the descriptions of the most prevalent monochrome equipment and operations have been retained in this edition.

The organization of chapters has again been guided by the characteristics and functions of the television camera. All other television equipment, even the television studio and all basic operations, depend directly on what the camera can see and how it functions. With the exception of an additional chapter on television lenses, the sequence and headings of the chapters of the first edition have been retained in this edition.

To keep the book manageable for the reader, several areas of television production, such as camera shading, computer-controlled television equipment, and the whole realm of television aesthetics, have been purposely omitted. Also, the reader should realize that the *do's* and *don'ts* of television production techniques as expressed in this text are intended only to give him a basic frame of reference; under specific conditions, the *don'ts* may very well become the *do's*, and vice versa.

The first edition of the *Handbook* benefited especially from the generous help of Richard J. Goggin of New York University; Charles F. Hunter of Northwestern University; James E. Lynch of Ohio State University; and Martin Corbett of RCA. Much of their initial guidance has once again influenced the preparation of the second edition.

Special thanks should go to Tom C. Battin of the University of Houston; Barry J. Cronin of the University of Missouri; Donald W. MacLennan of Brooklyn College; Quinn Millar, Paul Courtland Smith, and David Wiseman of San Francisco State College; and to Rebecca Hayden and Konrad Kerst of Wadsworth Publishing Company, all of whom have given invaluable information and suggestions for the second edition.

I am also greatly indebted to the following people and organizations who have assisted me with specific information or materials: ABC; Albion Optical Company, Inc.; Ampex Corporation; ColorTran Industries, Inc.; Jim Bishop of San Francisco State College; CBS; Ed Chavanette of NBC; Chrono-Log Corporation; Peter Dart of San Francisco State College; Gotham Audio Corporation; Paul A. Greenmeyer of RCA; Raymond M. Holtz of the Group W Station KPIX, Westinghouse Broadcasting Company; Houston Fearless Corporation; Kliegl Brothers Lighting, Western Corporation; Donald E. Lincoln of the Group W Station KPIX; NBC; North American Philips Company, Inc.; RCA; Shure Brothers, Inc.; Sony Corporation of America; Charles Steinheimer of the Sicular X-Ray Company; Ray M. Swenson of the Group W Station KPIX; Paul Turner of KQED; Vega Electronics Corporation; and Visual Electronics Corporation.

Once again my wife, Erika, deserves much credit for her patience and constant encouragement during the writing of this edition.

*Herbert Zettl*

# Contents

# TELEVISION PRODUCTION HANDBOOK

## SECOND EDITION

# 1

## The Camera

Everything you see on your television screen has been "pre-seen" by a television camera. The images that appear on your set are determined by what the camera can see and how it can see them. The camera is thus the most important single television production element. All other elements and techniques are geared to the physical and electronic characteristics of the camera. Lighting, scenery, audio, writing, and directing all depend more or less on the potential of the camera.

# TYPES OF TELEVISION CAMERAS

There are two major types of broadcast television cameras: (1) the monochrome or black-and-white camera, and (2) the color camera. Both camera types work on the same basic principle: the conversion of an optical image into electrical impulses, and the reconversion of these impulses into a picture of that image on the television screen.

Also, both camera types consist of three main parts: (1) the optical system, which selects a certain field of view and produces a small optical image of this view, (2) the camera itself, with its electronic components that convert this optical image into electrical impulses, and (3) the viewfinder, which converts these electrical impulses back into a television picture of the view as seen by the lens.

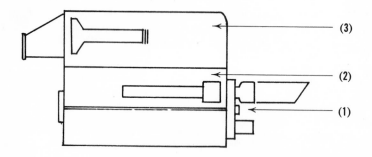

However, there are important optical, electronic, and operational differences between the monochrome and the color camera; you must be familiar with these differences in order to understand properly the various techniques of television production. Although the color camera will eventually replace altogether the monochrome camera even in small station operation, the monochrome camera still holds an important place in television production and will be used side by side with the color camera for some time to come. We will therefore discuss the various types of monochrome cameras as well as the color camera.

## The Monochrome Camera

The three types of monochrome television cameras are (1) the image-orthicon camera, usually called the I-O camera, (2) the vidicon camera, and (3) the Plumbicon* camera.

---

*Plumbicon is a registered trade mark by Philips' Gloeilampenfabrieken, Eindhoven, Netherlands.

### The image-orthicon camera

We can classify image-orthicon cameras by the size of their pickup tubes: the 3-inch I-O and the 4½-inch I-O cameras.

In general, the 4½-inch I-O camera produces a higher-quality picture and is electronically more stable than its 3-inch I-O counterpart. The 4½-inch camera is larger and heavier than the 3-inch I-O, and it also costs more to operate; but since picture quality is always of primary importance in television, the 4½-inch camera is definitely preferred in monochrome television production. Nevertheless, some of the old 3-inch I-O cameras are still in use in many commercial and educational stations, and new, highly improved 3-inch I-O cameras are still put into operation on a fairly large scale.

*The 3-inch image-orthicon camera.* The most widely used 3-inch I-O cameras are the General Electric PE-28, the Sarkes Tarzian 3000-L, the Visual Zoom Mark 10, and the outmoded but very durable RCA TK-11 and TK-14. Although out of production for quite some time, the early RCA TK-11 and TK-14 models are still operating in many

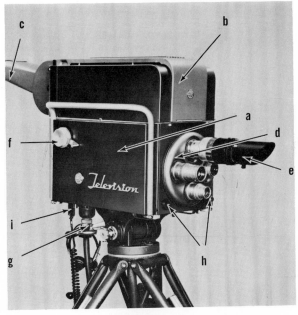

RCA TK-11:
a) camera; b) viewfinder (detachable); c) viewfinder hood (detachable); d) lens turret (detachable); e) lens; f) focusing knob; g) camera cable; h) tally lights; i) intercom outlet.

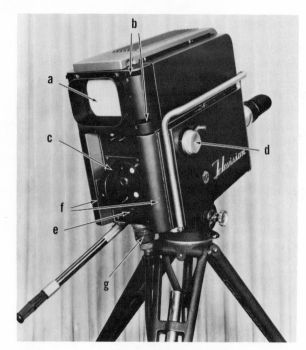

Cameraman's view of camera:
a) 7-inch viewfinder with attachment for viewfinder hood; b) viewfinder controls; c) control handle for rotating lens turret; d) focusing knob; e) tally light; f) electronic camera controls; g) camera cable.

television stations. Both models have a four-lens turret and a detachable viewfinder. The control handle for rotating the lens turret is on the back of the camera, and the focus knob is on the right-hand side of the camera.

With few exceptions, the newer and more sophisticated 3-inch I-O cameras, such as the PE-28 or the Sarkes Tarzian 3000-L, work on the same operational principles as the TK-11. Both of these newer cameras have the turret control handle on the back of the camera and the focus knob on the right-hand side. However, the PE-28 camera has a five-lens turret instead of the customary four-lens turret, and the Sarkes 3000-L has a remote iris control. (See the section on lenses for more detailed information on remote iris control.) Electronically, all new cameras are "solid state" (fully transistorized).

The Visual Zoom Mark 10 camera by the Visual Electronics Corporation differs radically in concept, design, and operation from the RCA prototype. Instead of the customary multilens turret, the

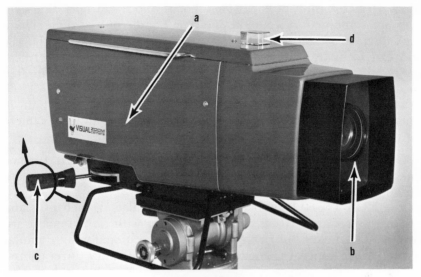

Visual Zoom Mark 10:
a) camera and built-in viewfinder; b) built-in
10:1 zoom lens; c) zoom and focus control handle:
push or pull to zoom, rotate to focus.

Cameraman's view of Visual Zoom Mark 10:
a) viewfinder screen; b) zoom and focus control
handle; c) zoom (lens angle) indicator; d) electronic camera controls; e) viewfinder controls.

Mark 10 has a built-in zoom lens. Focus and zoom operating controls are combined in a motorcycle-type handle on the right side of the camera. You can zoom in or out by pulling or pushing the handle and can focus by rotating the handle. A small thumb wheel near the handle permits you to lock the zoom lens into various calibrated zoom (focal length) positions.

This camera is relatively light and quite rugged. With its built-in zoom lens, it makes a good studio camera as well as an ideal camera for remote operations.

*The 4½-inch image-orthicon camera.* The most widely used 4½-inch image-orthicon cameras are the RCA TK-60, the General Electric PE-29, and the British-made Marconi Mark V.

The RCA TK-60 is probably the most popular 4½-inch I-O camera in this country. It has a four-lens turret with an automatic iris control. This heavy but rugged camera is operationally quite similar to the earlier 3-inch I-O models. It has the customary turret control

RCA TK-60:
a) camera and viewfinder; b) viewfinder hood;
c) turret with "TV-88" mounts; d) lens; e) remote iris control motor; f) tally light.

Cameraman's view of TK-60:
a) viewfinder; b) control handle for rotating lens turret; c) focusing knob; d) electronic camera controls; e) neutral density filter selector; f) camera cable; g) tally lights; h) intercom outlet.

in back, a panning handle on the left, and the focus knob on the right-hand side of the camera. Special effects, such as a super or split-screen effect, can be fed from the control room into the camera's viewfinder. This is a great advantage to the cameraman, who now can line up his shot properly for the intended effect.

The General Electric PE-29 is quite similar to the TK-60 in its operation. It has, however, a five-lens turret with remote iris control.

The Marconi Mark V camera has a zoom lens instead of the customary turret. The zoom control either is mounted with the focus control on the left panning handle or is attached to a special bar, which looks like a second panning handle on the right of the camera.

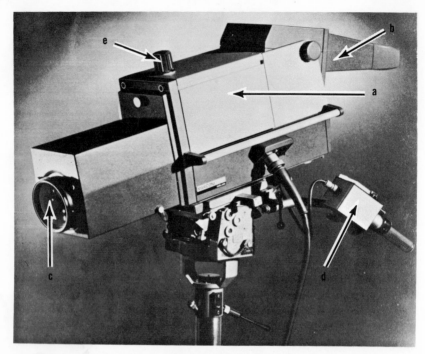

Marconi Mark V:
a) camera (4½-inch I.O. monochrome); b) view-finder and hood; whole assembly tilts up and down; c) 10:1 zoom lens; d) zoom controls; e) tally light.

A unique feature of the Mark V camera is a tilting viewfinder. If you have to elevate or lower the camera much beyond your eye level, you can tilt the whole viewfinder assembly toward your eyes for a better view.

Of course all the multilens turret cameras can have a zoom lens attached in the "taking lens" or "on-the-air lens" position. These positions vary sometimes from camera to camera. The diagram on page 9 shows the "on-the-air lens" positions for the cameras discussed above.

### Electronic characteristics of the image-orthicon camera

Although the transistorized image-orthicon cameras are much more stable—that is, they need less attention during operation by the video engineers than do their tube-type predecessors—image-orthicon equipment is still highly sensitive and, at times, temperamental. To learn the potentials and limitations of these cameras, and to ensure

RCA TK-11 or TK-14 (monochrome 3-inch I-O)

General Electric PE-28 (monochrome 3-inch I-O)

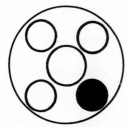

Sarkes Tarzian 3000-L (monochrome 3-inch I-O)

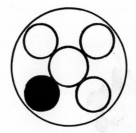

RCA TK-60 (monochrome 4½-inch I-O)

smooth coordination with engineering personnel, you should be aware of at least three basic electronic characteristics of the I-O camera. These are (1) operating light level, (2) burn-in, and (3) contrast range.

1. *Operating light level.* The image-orthicon camera needs a certain amount of light to perform at peak efficiency. If the camera is used under lighting conditions that are below the operating light level, picture quality will suffer. Even for the newer and very light-sensitive I-O tubes, the operating light levels for the 4½-inch and 3-inch I-O cameras range generally from 75 to 100 foot-candles. We will discuss the operating light levels in more detail in Chapter 4.

2. *Burn-in.* The image-orthicon tube has a limited service life. Although some stations have stretched the service life of a 3-inch I-O tube to 2,000 hours, the normal service time averages between 750 and 1,000 hours. The 4½-inch I-O tube has an even shorter "life." The older the tube gets, the more sensitive it becomes to "burn-ins" or "sticking." A "burn-in" means that the tube remembers the picture it has taken and carries a gray negative image of that particular picture over the following shots taken. This very undesirable image retention is usually caused in two ways: (1) the camera is focused on one object for a period of time with no movement of camera or object; or (2) the camera is focused on an object with strong black and white contrast.

In order to avoid a burn-in, most cameras have an electronic orbiter device that moves the image very slowly on the surface of the
pickup tube, although the camera and the object may be stationary.
New "non-stick" tubes, however, are less susceptible to burn-ins and
make the orbiter device often unnecessary. If a burn-in has occurred,
you must know how to eliminate it quickly without damaging the
tube. When you notice a burn-in, you can quickly remove it by
panning the camera back and forth on a neutral surface, such as
the studio floor. In cases of extreme emergency, you can take the
camera out of focus and aim it at a diffused light. This method,
however, can be harmful to the television tube and should be used
with care.

Old I-O tubes can sometimes be reused if given a period of rest—
anywhere from a week to two or three months. Some experiments
have been conducted by local stations in "revitalizing" I-O tubes.
The tubes are put into a deep freeze with the hope of "freezing out"
old age. The benefits from such or similar treatments, however, are
rather doubtful.

3. *Contrast range.* The image-orthicon tube is highly sensitive to extreme black and white contrast. A somewhat limited contrast range
will greatly enhance picture quality. However, if you show nothing
but a variety of medium grays, your picture will look, indeed, "medium." There is nothing wrong with using very dark colors in your
set, so long as you don't put something extremely bright and highly
reflecting directly in front of it. As a matter of fact, your video
engineer will probably appreciate having something white and something black in the set so that he has a reference for his shading adjustment. Generally, the new 4½-inch I-O tube can tolerate a much
higher picture contrast range than can the older 3-inch tubes. The
larger tube also helps to minimize the "halo-effect"—the black rim
around shiny and highly polished objects, such as brass instruments
or jewelry.

### The vidicon camera

Out of the great variety of existing vidicon cameras, we can distinguish two basic types: (1) the small, "industrial" vidicon camera, which has no viewfinder, and (2) the larger, studio vidicon
camera, which resembles the I-O camera in design, size, and operation.

Although the industrial-type vidicon camera is used extensively
in education, it is generally employed for simple observations rather
than for studio productions.

General Electric TE-20 closed circuit camera

General Electric TE-20 closed circuit camera

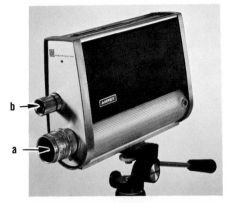

b →
a →

Ampex CC-6400 closed circuit camera with
(a) camera lens and (b) optical viewfinder lens

General Electric TE-23 closed circuit camera

On some occasions, these small cameras have been used during special-event telecasts, such as political conventions. In these circumstances, the camera operator carries not only the camera itself but also the power supply and the transmission equipment. The low powered R-F (radio-frequency) signal is then picked up in the control room and made compatible with the regular broadcast signal. In spite of many such uses, however, this "creepie-peepie" camera, as it has been facetiously called, has not succeeded in replacing the bulkier yet ultimately more useful studio-type camera. We shall therefore consider only those models that are designed for television studio operation. The vidicon film-chain camera will be discussed in more detail in Chapter 8.

Since the vidicon pickup tube is much smaller than the I-O tube, studio vidicon cameras are lighter and generally smaller than I-O cameras. There are several other operational advantages of vidicon cameras over image-orthicon cameras. One of these advantages is the stability of picture alignment. The vidicon camera's video controls are fairly easy to handle. Once a vidicon camera is properly aligned, it will retain this alignment for several days with only minor adjustments.

The service life of the vidicon tube exceeds that of the image-orthicon tube by far. Also, the cost of a vidicon tube is considerably lower than that of an image-orthicon tube. And in general, vidicon equipment requires less maintenance than image-orthicon equipment. All these operational advantages help to establish vidicon equipment as an important tool in college operation.

Small stations use vidicon cameras sometimes for newscasts but rarely for their entire operation. The reason for the vidicon camera's unpopularity in professional television production is its inferior picture quality and characteristics when compared to the I-O camera, especially the 4½-inch I-O. One of the reasons for this quality difference is, besides the more intricate electronic structure, simply the size of the vidicon tube.

The light-sensitive front surface of the vidicon tube is about half as big as that of the 3-inch image-orthicon tube and considerably smaller than that of the 4½-inch image-orthicon tube. Let's use a familiar example and compare picture quality of different-sized film. If we make a print from a small negative, such as a 16mm film, we will not achieve the quality we will get by using a 35mm or 70mm negative. The vidicon tube surface corresponds approximately to the size of a 16mm film; we therefore use 16mm film lenses for vidicon cameras. The 3-inch image-orthicon tube, on the other hand, corresponds to a 35mm film; hence, 35mm lenses are used for image-orthicon cameras. The 4½-inch image-orthicon tube corresponds to an even larger negative and produces, therefore, clearer and better pictures, although 35mm lenses are also used for this camera since the image enlargement occurs within the I-O tube.

### Electronic characteristics of the vidicon camera

Let us now consider the three basic electronic characteristics that we previously discussed with image-orthicon equipment: operating light level, burn-in, and contrast range.

1. *Operating light level.* The necessary light level for vidicon cameras exceeds the operating light level of the image-orthicon camera. Approximately 150 to 200 foot-candles of illumination are needed for the vidicon monochrome camera. This illumination is just about twice as much as is needed for the I-O cameras.

2. *Burn-in.* The vidicon camera is comparatively insensitive to burns and can be focused on stationary objects for a considerable length of time without noticeable picture retention.

3. *Contrast range.* The vidicon camera is capable of handling high black and white contrasts without substantially lowering picture

quality. Especially in the lighter ranges of the gray scale, the vidicon camera renders excellent and subtle grays. In the dark end of the gray scale, however, the vidicon tube has a "fast fall-off," which means that it does not differentiate well between light and very dense shadow areas. Generally, the vidicon camera shows all shadows equally black.

Another major disadvantage of the vidicon camera is the "lag" or "following image." If the object in front of the camera or the camera itself moves too quickly, the vidicon tube will show a lag— a smear in the picture that always trails the moving object. This lag occurs especially under low lighting levels.

### Types of studio vidicon cameras

One of the most durable vidicon cameras, and the one that most closely approximates operationally the I-O camera, is the old RCA TK-15. Although this tube-type camera is no longer manufactured, it is still widely used by many educational institutions and even by some television stations.

The most popular transistorized vidicon cameras manufactured for studio use are (1) the Sarkes Tarzian 2500-L, (2) the General Electric PE-23, and (3) the RCA PK-330.

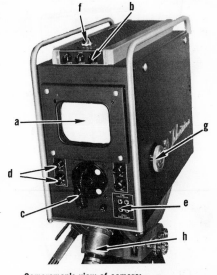

RCA TK-15:
a) camera and viewfinder (viewfinder is not detachable); b) focusing knob; c) lens turret (detachable); d) lenses; e) tally lights; f) cable.

Cameraman's view of camera:
a) 7-inch viewfinder; b) viewfinder controls; c) turret handle; d) camera controls; e) intercommunication outlets; f) tally light; g) focusing knob; h) camera cable.

All but the PK-330 have standard operational features. All have a four-lens turret that can hold a zoom lens, a turret control handle on the back of the camera, and a focus knob on the right-hand side. Although the vidicon cameras operate with 16mm lenses, the PE-23 has an optional accessory turret that can hold regular I-O (35mm) lenses.

The RCA PK-330 is a cross between an industrial camera and a studio camera. It has no lens turret but has a built-in zoom lens that tilts with the entire vidicon assembly. The rest of the camera remains in a horizontal position when you are tilting up or down. The PK-330 has very simple electronic zoom controls. Also, when you pan from extreme dark to extreme light, the camera does most of the video adjusting itself, thus eliminating the need for complex video operations. The camera is designed for simple operations in educational institutions, for which it is more than adequate. However, its operational flexibility and picture quality are not quite good enough for professional television production.

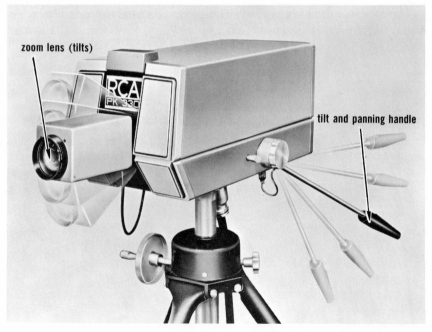

RCA PK-330 vidicon camera

The following diagram shows the location of on-the-air lenses for the cameras discussed.

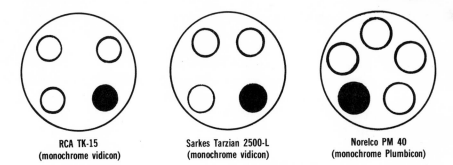

| RCA TK-15 | Sarkes Tarzian 2500-L | Norelco PM 40 |
| (monochrome vidicon) | (monochrome vidicon) | (monochrome Plumbicon) |

### The Plumbicon monochrome camera

Plumbicon refers to a tube that is basically a vidicon tube with a different photoconducting surface. Although the Plumbicon tube is used primarily in color cameras, there are some manufacturers that produce Plumbicon monochrome cameras. The most popular Plumbicon cameras are the Norelco PM 40, by North American Philips Company, and the Sarkes Tarzian 2700-L. Both cameras are very similar to vidicon cameras in design and operation. They are fully transistorized and have multiple-lens turrets that can also hold a zoom lens. The PM 40 has a five-lens turret, the Sarkes 2700-L a four-lens turret. Both cameras use 16mm lenses. The Sarkes 2700-L can also be adapted for I-O (35mm) lenses.

There are certain advantages and disadvantages in using the Plumbicon tube for monochrome operations. The advantages lie in the basic electronic characteristics discussed previously: operating light level, burn-in, and contrast range.

1. *Operating light level.* The Plumbicon tube is much more light sensitive than the vidicon tube and can operate on approximately the same light levels as the I-O cameras—between 75 and 100 foot-candles. Under certain circumstances, the Plumbicon camera can produce acceptable pictures with an illumination of a mere 20 foot-candles.

2. *Burn-in.* The Plumbicon tube is virtually insensitive to burn-in and has, therefore, little or no need for orbiting devices.

3. *Contrast range.* Like the vidicon, the Plumbicon tube has an excellent contrast range, which means that it can tolerate a great latitude of light and dark.

There are four main disadvantages of the Plumbicon monochrome camera. (1) The picture does not have a very high resolution; in other words, it is not so crisp and sharp as the I-O picture. (2) The

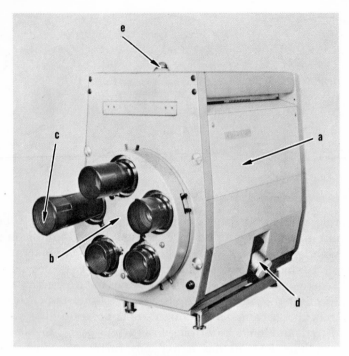

Norelco PM 40:
a) camera and viewfinder; b) 5-lens turret;
c) lens; d) cable outlet; e) tally light.

Norelco PM-40:
a) 10:1 Angenieux zoom lens; b) turret rotation
control (if turret lenses are used); c) focus
control (for turret operation); d) zoom control.

tube has a limited red sensitivity, which can also cause lack of picture definition. (3) The Plumbicon tube is susceptible to "speckling" —an imperfection on the tube surface, which shows up in the television picture as a light, dark, or even twinkling spot. (4) Similar to the vidicon tube, the Plumbicon shows some lag under unfavorable lighting conditions. However, the Plumbicon lag is much less severe than that of the vidicon tube, and with a perfect tube may not be noticeable at all.

## The Color Camera

Color television is technically much more complex than monochrome television. Although you don't need to know all about the intricate electronics of the color television process, you should know at least some of the basic workings of the color camera. This basic knowledge will help you greatly in understanding the specific production techniques for color television.

We will, therefore, briefly discuss some basic points relative to the color television camera. These are (1) primary colors, (2) chrominance and luminance channels, (3) color camera pickup tubes and optical systems, (4) electronic characteristics of the color camera, and (5) types and operational characteristics of color cameras.

### Primary colors

In color television, light is split into its basic color components of red, green, and blue—the primary colors of light. They are also called *additive primary colors,* because when you combine red, green, and blue light you get normal white light (see the color illustration following page 200). The primary colors of pigment, such as paint, are called *subtractive primary colors;* they are red, yellow, and blue. Since it is light, not paint, that enters the color camera, we must deal with the additive primary colors.

### Chrominance and luminance channels

The color camera contains in effect three "cameras," each of which is responsible for a primary color. Thus, we have a red, a green, and a blue camera. These three cameras, or channels, are called the chrominance (color) channels.

Most color cameras also contain a fourth "camera," the so-called luminance (light) channel. The luminance channel produces a monochrome picture, which is used for two purposes. (1) It provides the color picture with a bright and crisp outline, which helps to separate and highlight the subtle color differences; it gives the color picture crispness and snap. (2) It produces the monochrome picture seen on monochrome sets. In a three-tube color camera, the monochrome picture is produced by matrixing (basically mixing) the red, green, and blue signals together again. There is no special luminance channel. One camera, however, the Norelco PC-70 (which we will discuss in more detail later), produces the luminance channel out of the green camera. This type of luminance channel is appropriately called "contours-out-of-green."

Generally, the three tubes for the chrominance channels are located on one side of the camera, the tube for the luminance channel on the other side.

### Pickup tubes and optical systems in the color camera

*Pickup tubes.* Although we spoke of red, green, and blue "cameras" or channels within the color camera, the image pickup tubes necessary for these chrominance channels are the standard tubes used in the monochrome cameras. The various types and models of color cameras use a variety of tubes in various combinations. Some of the old color cameras use 3-inch I-O tubes; some of the newer cameras use vidicon tubes or Plumbicon tubes. Various tubes are also used for the luminance channels, ranging from vidicon to 4½-inch I-O tubes.

*Internal optical system.* All color cameras must have a complex internal optical system that splits the image as captured by the camera lens optically into the three primary colors for the three chrominance tubes and, in most cases, also into a luminance channel. This optical system consists of a combination of prisms, mirrors, relay lenses, and color filters (see the color illustration of the internal optical system on Plate II following page 200).

The *prism* behind the lens is a "beam-splitter," which doubles the image as seen by the lens. One of these images is split and goes into the chrominance channels; the other goes into the luminance channel.

The regular *mirrors* divert the image into the luminance channel or into *dichroic mirrors,* which separate the image into red, green, and blue images. From the dichroic mirrors, the color images are sent into the relay lenses, and from there into the pickup tubes.

The *relay lenses* help to keep the images sharp and clear until they reach the pickup tubes.

The *filters* correct the color as provided by the dichroic mirrors and prepare the color for the chrominance pickup tubes.

Sometimes, the entire internal optical system is combined in a small prism block that contains dichroic layers and color-correction filters. Since the pickup tubes can be attached directly to the prism block, relay lenses are not needed (see the illustration below and also the color illustration following page 200).

Beam-split prism block of the Norelco PC-70 Plumbicon color camera.

### Electronic characteristics of the color camera

Since the color camera consists literally of three or even four cameras, it is extremely complex in its color alignment and electronic operation. However, since color cameras use standard pickup tubes, some of the basic electronic characteristics of monochrome television still prevail.

*1. Operating light level.* More light is needed for color cameras than for monochrome cameras, because the color camera has many more optical components through which the light must travel. Also, the light entering the main lens is split several ways and redirected many times before it finally hits the pickup tube. Most color cameras use the vidicon and Plumbicon tubes, which again need somewhat more light than the highly light-sensitive I-O tubes. The three-tube color camera needs somewhat less light than the four-tube camera, since the incoming light is not split for the luminance channel.

Generally, the operating light level of the color camera is at least three times that of the monochrome camera, ranging anywhere from 250 to 500 foot-candles. Of course, in some cases the color camera must, and does, manage to produce acceptable pictures at much lower levels, even as low as 50 foot-candles. If the light levels are too low, however, the color camera is subject to lag, especially when vidicon tubes are used, and the colors look distorted.

*2. Burn-in.* The color camera, like the monochrome camera, is susceptible to burn-in. However, since both the vidicon and the Plumbicon tubes have a relatively high resistance to burn-in, this problem is not so severe with color cameras as it is with I-O monochrome cameras. If the luminance channel has an I-O tube, the same precautions against burn-in must be taken as with the monochrome I-O camera.

3. *Contrast range.* Although the vidicon and Plumbicon tubes have a great contrast latitude, it is often difficult to maintain true color when panning from a very bright scene to a dark scene—such as when panning from the sunlit side of a football stadium to its shadow side. Proper video shading, however, can compensate somewhat for this color change.

### Types and operational characteristics of color cameras

The more common types of color cameras are (1) the old RCA TK-40 and TK-41, one of the first color cameras put into broadcast service, (2) the RCA TK-42 and TK-44A, (3) the General Electric PE-350, (4) the Marconi Mark VII, (5) the Sarkes Tarzian Series 88, and (6) the Norelco PC-70.

Of these cameras, the RCA TK-40 and TK-41 are no longer manufactured. They are, however, still used in some NBC stations. The

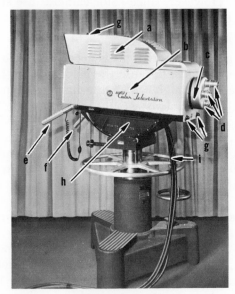

RCA TK-41 Color Camera:
a) viewfinder; b) camera; c) lens turret;
d) lenses; e) camera panning handle with focus
grip; f) camera panning handle; g) tally lights;
h) cradle head; i) three camera cables.

TK-40 and TK-41 are the only cameras that have three 3-inch I-O tubes and a four-lens turret that moves in and out for focusing.

All new color cameras have a zoom lens instead of the multilens turret. There are two main reasons for this single-lens system. (1) The zoom lens is easier to operate. (2) Every lens has a slightly different color response to light. Previously, each time the cameraman rotated the turret to another lens, the video engineer had to work quite hard to maintain the previous color balance. A single lens system eliminates this problem altogether.

All color cameras are similar in their operation, even though the various models have different tube combinations and optical systems. For example, all common types of color cameras have a monochrome viewfinder and a zoom lens, which is either built in or replaceable by a single fixed-focal-length lens. Most color cameras have two panning handles, one on each side of the camera. The zoom control is located either on one of the panning handles or, as with the G.E. PE-350, on the side of the camera, resembling the old focus knob. The focus controls are attached either to the second panning handle or right next to the zoom control. Most color cameras will operate properly on a cable length of 1,000 feet, although some cameras will take up to 2,000 feet with little or no reduction in performance.

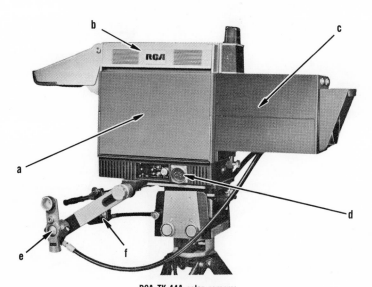

RCA TK-44A color camera:
a) camera; b) viewfinder (detachable for servicing);
c) 10:1 zoom lens (removable); d) camera cable
outlet; e) zoom control; f) focus control.

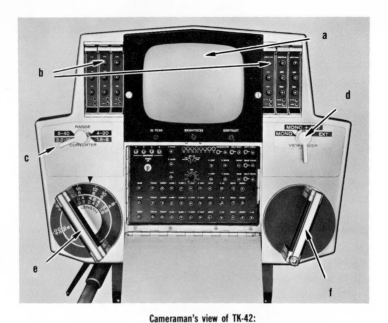

**Cameraman's view of TK-42:**
a) viewfinder; b) electronic camera and viewfinder controls; c) lens range converter (changes focal length range of built-in zoom); d) viewfinder selector; e) zoom handle (now replaced by panning handle zoom control); f) focus control (now replaced by panning handle focus control).

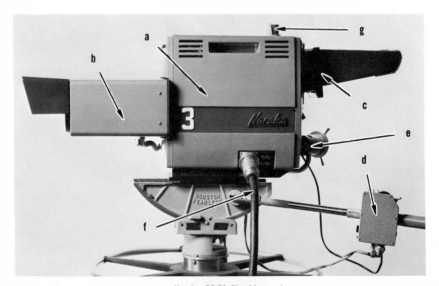

**Norelco PC-70 Plumbicon color camera:**
a) camera and viewfinder; b) 10:1 zoom lens; c) viewfinder hood; d) automatic zoom control (shot box); e) focus control; f) camera cable; g) tally light.

Norelco PC-70, cameraman's view:
a) viewfinder hood; b) viewfinder controls;
c) focus control; d) camera cable; e) tally light;
f) space for hanging shot sheet.

RCA TK-44 color camera for remote operations:
a) camera with 3 Plumbicon tubes (chrominance
channels) and 1 Isocon tube (3-inch I-O type
tube for luminance channel); b) detachable
viewfinder; c) 10:1 zoom lens; d) tally light.

The following table lists important data on the common color cameras: tube complements, lenses used, and camera weight.

| Type | Luminance Channel | Chrominance Channel | Lens | Weight (in pounds) |
|---|---|---|---|---|
| RCA TK-42 | 4½-inch I-0 | 3 vidicons | 10:1 zoom 4-40 inches; with wide-angle adapter: 1.6–16 inches. | |
| RCA TK-44A | | 3 Plumbicons | 10:1 zoom 4-40 inches; can have adapters | 140 |
| G.E. PE-350 | Plumbicon | 3 Plumbicons | 10:1 (18mm-180mm) equivalent to I-0 1.4–14 inches | |
| Marconi Mark VII | Plumbicon | 3 Plumbicons | 10:1 zoom; various ranges; uses 35mm I-0 lenses | 175 |
| Sarkes Tarzian 88 | various; Plumbicon or I-0 | various; 3 Plumbicons or 3 vidicons | 10:1 zoom | |
| Norelco PC-70 | none; "contours-out-of-green" | 3 Plumbicons | 10:1 zoom 18-180mm; equivalent to I-0 1.4–14 inches; accepts other 16mm zoom lenses | 130 |

## CAMERA MOUNTING EQUIPMENT

Ease and fluidity of camera movement are essential factors in the art of television photography. Good and flexible mounting devices for television cameras are thus extremely important.

Since color television cameras are very similar to monochrome cameras in their actual handling and operation, the same camera-mounting equipment is used for both types of cameras.

Three basic units have been developed that enable the camera-man to move the camera freely and smoothly about the studio. These units are (1) the tripod dolly, (2) the studio pedestal, and (3) the studio crane.

## The Tripod Dolly

The tripod dolly consists of a wooden or metal tripod usually fastened to a three-caster dolly base. The three casters are always free-wheeling, which ensures quick and easy repositioning of the camera in all directions. Various cable guards in front of the casters help to prevent rolling over or hitting the camera cable. The tripod and, in most cases, the wheel base are collapsible, which makes them the ideal camera mount for remote operations. The tripod can also be adjusted to the height of the cameraman. Quick and easy elevation of the camera, however, is not possible.

cable guards ——►

tripod dolly (collapsible)

Metal tripod (collapsible)

## The Studio Pedestal

The studio pedestal enables smooth dollying and quick elevating and lowering of the camera by the cameraman. Depending on the type of studio pedestal used, the cameraman can raise and lower the camera while it is on the air. This up and down movement adds a new and important dimension to the art of television photography.

Of the great variety of available studio pedestals, we will consider only those that seem especially fit for small station operation. These are (1) the PD-10 lightweight hydraulic camera pedestal, (2) the PD-7 lightweight camera pedestal, (3) the PD-3 studio camera pedestal—or, as it is sometimes called, the Sanner counterweight pedestal—and (4) the PD-8 pedestal.

The *PD-10 camera pedestal* is a cross between a tripod and a studio pedestal. There are two advantages to this pedestal: (1) it is light and easily collapsible; (2) it has a hydraulic pump, built into the light center column, which allows quick and easy height adjustments to accommodate short and tall cameramen. This adjustment device is especially important in college productions, where several cameramen will have to work with the same camera within the relatively short time of a class period. The camera cannot be elevated on the air, however.

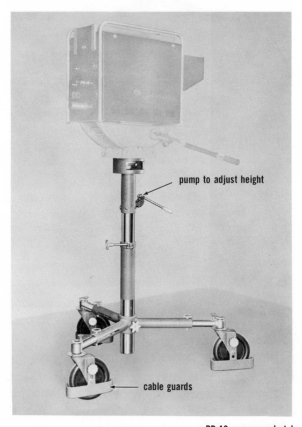

PD-10 camera pedestal

The *PD-7 lightweight camera pedestal* is a very flexible studio pedestal. By turning a crank, you can raise and lower the camera approximately 2½ feet. Some skilled camera operators manage to do this while the camera is on the air, but generally the cranking is not smooth enough to move the camera vertically while it is on the air.

Two types of steering are available: (1) synchronized steering, in which all wheels are locked parallel; and (2) tricycle steering, in which only the forward wheel turns with the steering wheel. A steering handle is conveniently located at the front of the dolly.

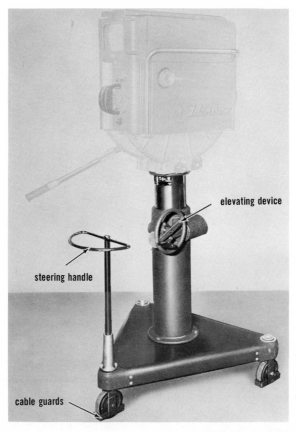

elevating device

steering handle

cable guards

PD-7 camera pedestal

The *PD-3 (Sanner counterweight) studio camera pedestal* offers complete mobility to cameras for normal studio requirements. This studio pedestal allows smooth dolly shots and smooth raising and lowering of the camera while on the air. You can raise or lower the camera simply by lifting the studio pedestal's steering wheel or by pushing it down. The pedestal will elevate the camera from about 4 feet to 6½ feet above the studio floor. A smaller, inner ring locks the pedestal at any desirable height. Parallel synchronized steering and tricycle steering are both possible.

The disadvantages of this excellent professional studio pedestal for small station operation and especially college operation are (1) it is very heavy to move about, (2) it cannot be used for remote television operation, (3) it is comparatively expensive, and (4) although the counterweights can be adjusted, it needs a fairly heavy camera to function with top efficiency.

PD-3 camera pedestal

The *PD-8 pneumatic studio pedestal* is designed specifically for the heavier color cameras. It is very similar in design and operation to the PD-3 pedestal, except that the elevation is based on pneumatic (air pressure) principles.

The more advanced pedestals, such as the PD-9, a motor-driven pedestal, are not commonly used in small station operation. You can get detailed information on such specialized equipment from the Houston Fearless Corporation, Los Angeles, California.

## The Panoram Dolly

A step between the pedestal and the studio crane is the panoram dolly. This small crane dolly permits the camera to be raised from about 18 inches to about 7 feet off the studio floor. Vertical boom-up and boom-down movements can be made smoothly and effectively while the camera is on the air. There are two disadvantages to this dolly, however: (1) it takes at least two men to operate it, and (2) it needs a large area of floor space for proper operation. If space is restricted, the panoram dolly cannot do much more than the studio pedestal—which is, therefore, preferred in small station operation.

handle for raising and lowering boom

handle for rotating turntable

handle for turning wheels on front end

steering handle for wheels on rear end

turntable for rotation of boom

Panoram dolly

## The Studio Crane

There are several types of studio cranes in use. All of them work on similar principles. Although a crane is desirable for creative camera work, it is of little use in small studio operation. In most cases, limited floor space and ceiling height prohibit the use of a big (3 × 13 feet base) studio crane. Also, a studio crane needs at least one dolly operator in addition to the cameraman—which again helps to explain its unpopularity in small stations. If motor-driven, the crane needs two operators besides the cameraman: the driver and the boom operator. In colleges and universities, however, where studio facilities and manpower may very well permit the use of a crane, important research in production techniques may necessitate the use of a studio crane.

A studio crane permits fast and multiple camera repositioning. The camera can be lowered to approximately 2 feet off the studio floor and raised to about 10 feet above the floor. The crane boom can be panned a full 360 degrees, still allowing the camera a panning radius of 180 degrees. All movements can be carried out simultaneously, allowing excellent opportunities for creative camera work.

If a studio crane is used, it is desirable to install a monitor directly on the crane for the aid of the dolly operator. The coordination of dolly operator and cameraman is essential for smooth and effective camera handling. The dolly operator will be greatly aided in his job if, in addition to listening to the director's signals, he can actually see the pictures the camera is taking.

counterweight

Studio crane

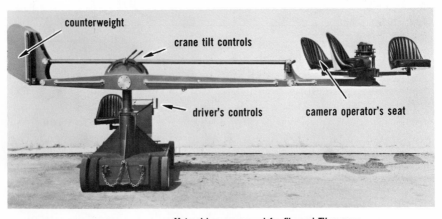

counterweight

crane tilt controls

driver's controls

camera operator's seat

Motor-driven crane used for film and TV cameras

## Camera Mounting Heads

The camera mounting head, which usually fits all types of standard tripods, pedestals, and cranes, allows the camera to be vertically tilted and horizontally panned. There are three types of mounting heads: (1) the camera friction head, (2) the camera cradle head, and (3) the camera "cam" head.

1. The *camera friction head* counterbalances the weight of the camera by a strong spring. This spring can be adjusted to the specific weight of the camera used. Friction heads are rarely used anymore, and then only for the lighter monochrome cameras.

panning handle

vertical locking device

horizontal locking device

Friction head

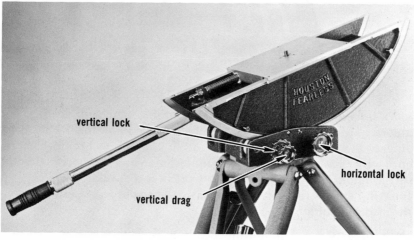

vertical lock

horizontal lock

vertical drag

Cradle head

2. The *camera cradle head* assures excellent camera balance at all times, and thus prevents the camera from overbalancing even at the most extreme tilting angle. The cradle head can accommodate any camera without special adjustments. The cradle head is extensively used for the heavy color cameras.

Houston Fearless also produces a remote-control cradle head, the MCH-5, which can be operated by a "joy-stick"—a little lever that can move in any direction, thereby causing the camera head to pan and tilt in that direction.

Remote control heads are sometimes used for television news, where the few camera movements remain fairly constant from day to day. However, remote control equipment is generally quite expensive and the cost too prohibitive for its limited application.

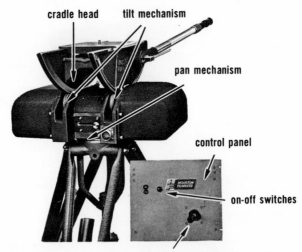

"joy-stick" pan and tilt control

MCH-5 remote control TV cradle head

3. The *cam head* uses two cams, one on each side of the head, to assure balanced, smooth tilting and panning even with the heaviest camera. The cam head is especially designed for the heavy color camera, but you can also use it for lighter monochrome cameras simply by changing the set of counterbalancing cams. Besides the British-made Vinten head, which works on a similar principle, the Houston Fearless cam head is probably the smoothest-operating camera head available.

All three types of mounting heads have horizontal and vertical locking devices and drag controls that can be adjusted to the desired

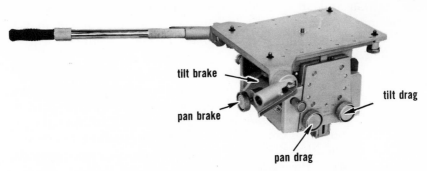

tilt brake

pan brake

tilt drag

pan drag

Houston Fearless cam head

pan (horizontal lock)

tilt (vertical lock)

Vinten camera pan and tilt head

panning and tilting drag necessary for smooth, jerk-free camera operation.

Contrary to the friction and cam heads, the cradle head will balance the camera, even though the mounting head is not locked and the camera is left temporarily unattended. This additional safety factor is especially important in college operation.

## BASIC CAMERA OPERATION TECHNIQUES

In most television stations, the camera is operated by television engineers rather than by people of the production department. This procedure may seem somewhat unreasonable. You may argue that the production people will probably have a better feeling for picture composition and, in general, a better artistic conception than most of the more technically minded engineers. This argument may be partially true, although there are many excellent engineers with artistic flair.

The primary reason for using engineers as cameramen is that the television camera is a highly temperamental technical instrument, which needs constant technical supervision and adjustment, a job that could hardly be adequately done by even the most artistic member of the production crew. In case of a camera failure, the cameraman can frequently tell by the way the picture breaks down what particular part of the camera circuit has become defunct. Thus, he can help to restore the camera quickly to normal functioning. In most stations around the country, engineers are designated under union jurisdiction to operate all electronic equipment, including the television camera.

In colleges and small stations, however, production people are frequently doubling as cameramen. Especially in college operation, it is impossible to have only engineering students run the cameras, while the production students take care of the production chores.

The following summary of procedures on camera handling is not meant to be exhaustive. It is intended merely to familiarize you with basic camera operation techniques. Good camera work, like so many other things, can be achieved only through extensive practice.

Most of the basic camera operation techniques for zoom-lens cameras differ very little from the more complex operation of the turret cameras. We will, therefore, concern ourselves primarily with the operation of turret cameras. The specific focus operation of the zoom camera is discussed in Chapter 2.

1. Put on the earphones and uncap your lenses. Most cameras are electronically capped—that is, you will not see a picture on your viewfinder since the picture has been electronically removed from the camera pickup tube. The video engineer will usually tell you to uncap your lenses with a switch on your camera, or he will uncap the lenses from the video-control position.

Some lenses have rubber or metal caps over them for additional protection. In these cases, remove the lens caps as soon as the video engineer is ready to attend to the shading.

2. Unlock the panning head for horizontal (panning) and vertical (tilting) movements of the camera.

3. Adjust the friction of the panning head until you get a small amount of drag, which makes panning and tilting easier and much smoother.

4. Watch for the tally lights to go out before you change lenses. Change your lenses quickly but as quietly as possible. Careless lens racking can be very noisy, especially when the camera is close to the microphone. Be especially careful with your racking if you have long lenses on the turret. Abrupt lens changes can easily damage the turret mechanism.

5. Between takes, if your camera is not used for awhile, defocus your camera and move it occasionally in a slow circular motion. This is just an additional precaution against burn-ins, even though your electronic orbiter is your chief burn-in protection.

6. If you have to eliminate a burn within a short time, defocus your camera and pan it back and forth on a light plain surface. Some cameramen even point the defocused camera briefly into a soft light. But remember that this procedure is hard on the tube and should be done only in cases of emergency.

7. In general, keep your eyes on your viewfinder. Between shots, if the show's format allows, you can look around for something interesting to shoot; your director will appreciate new and original approaches. But you should do this only during ad-lib shows in which the shots have not been previously rehearsed. At any other time, don't try to outdirect the director.

8. When dollying, your left hand should have a firm grip on the panning handle; your right hand should usually be on the focusing knob. Sometimes you can help to push the camera by pressing your head firmly against the viewfinder hood.

9. When you dolly in, turn your focusing knob counter-clockwise. When you dolly back, turn the focus knob clockwise. Always turn the focusing knob against the direction you are dollying. In general, you do not dolly with a zoom lens. If you must change your camera position and zoom while on the air, you need a floorman to push the pedestal for you. As the floorman is moving your camera, you must operate the focus device, which is usually mounted on the left panning bar, and zoom with the zoom device on the right of your camera. If you anticipate a dolly, you preset your focus at the midpoint of your dolly distance (see Chapter 2 for presetting a zoom lens). This presetting will make the focusing somewhat easier.

10. If you have to change your dolly direction, you will have to work the dolly steering with your right hand. This you can do only when your focus needs no adjustment. Sometimes on long arc dollies your floorman can help to steer the camera properly.

11. Always watch for obstacles in your dolly path, such as scenery, properties, microphone booms, floor lights, and (particularly) people who stand in your way. Be especially careful when dollying back. A

good floor manager can help to clear the way for you. He can also tap on your shoulder to prevent you from backing into a piece of equipment.

12. Always make sure you know the positions of the second and third cameras. It is your responsibility to keep out of the field of view of the other cameras.

13. Be sure you know the approximate length of your camera cable. Know how much cable you have left before you start a fast dolly in. Cable drag on the camera can be irritating when it prevents you from achieving a smooth dolly. To ease cable tension, some cameramen carry the cable over their shoulder. You may prefer to tie the cable to the camera pedestal, leaving enough slack so that you can freely pan, tilt, and pedestal.

14. When you are operating a free-wheel dolly, always have the wheels preset in the direction of the intended camera movement. This presetting will prevent the camera dolly from moving temporarily in the wrong direction.

15. If the director does not call for a specific lens, use a 75mm or 90mm lens for shooting easel cards.

16. At the end of the telecast, wait for the "all clear" signal before you deburn your camera and lock your panning head.

17. If you have a lens cap, don't leave a camera uncapped (although the capping may have been done electronically from the control room). Be sure your camera is deburned before capping your lens.

18. After your lens is capped, take off your phones and push the camera into a corner of the studio. Never leave the camera in the middle of the studio floor; the camera can easily be damaged by a piece of scenery being moved or by any other kind of studio traffic.

19. Always coil your camera cable as neatly as possible.


## DEFINITIONS OF THE MOST COMMON CAMERA MOVEMENTS

PAN: Turning the camera horizontally, from left to right or from right to left.

TILT: Tilting the camera up and down. Sometimes also called *pan up* and *pan down*.

PEDESTAL: Elevating or lowering the camera on a studio pedestal.

TONGUE: Moving the whole camera from left to right and from right to left on a boom dolly.

CRANE OR BOOM: Moving the whole camera up and down on a camera boom.

ZOOM: Changing the focal length of the lens through the use of a zoom control while the camera remains stationary.

DOLLY: Moving the camera toward or away from an object by means of a mobile camera mount.

TRUCK: Laterally moving the camera by means of a mobile camera mount.

ARC: Moving the camera in a slightly curved dolly or truck movement with a mobile camera mount.

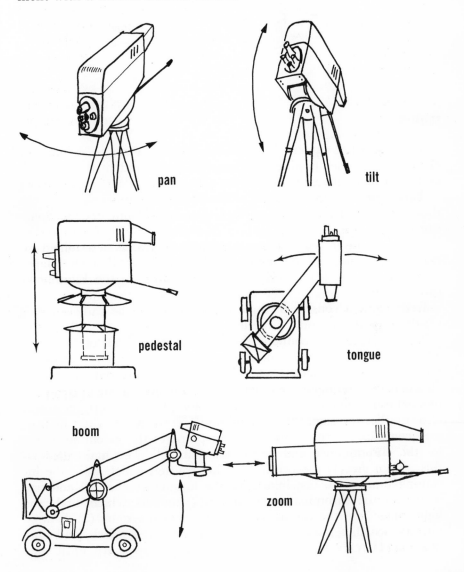

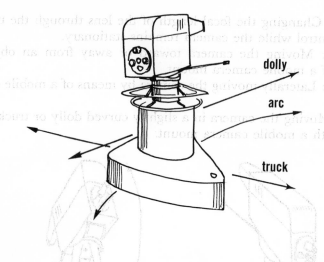

dolly

arc

truck

## SUMMARY

The television camera is the most important single production element. All other production elements are geared to the physical and electronic characteristics of the camera.

There are two major types of broadcast television cameras: (1) the monochrome, or black-and-white, camera, and (2) the color camera.

There are three types of monochrome cameras, as determined by the camera pickup tube used: (1) the 3-inch or 4½-inch image-orthicon camera, (2) the vidicon camera, and (3) the Plumbicon camera.

Each camera consists of three basic parts: (1) the camera itself, (2) the viewfinder, and (3) the lens or lenses.

The color camera contains three channels for each of the three additive (light) primary colors: red, green, and blue. These channels are called chrominance channels. Most cameras also contain a fourth channel, the luminance channel. The luminance channel provides a monochrome picture that gives the color picture its crispness and also supplies the signal for monochrome receivers.

A complex internal optical system prepares the incoming image for the chrominance and luminance channels. The main parts of this system are (1) the prism, or beam-splitter, which splits the incoming image into one image for the luminance channel and one image for the chrominance channels; (2) mirrors, which direct the light image into the various parts of the optical system; (3) dichroic mirrors, which separate the light image into red, green, and blue images; (4) relay lenses, which keep the images sharp until they reach the pickup tubes; and (5) color filters, which correct the color for the pickup tubes.

The three basic electronic characteristics of all cameras are (1) operating light level, (2) burn-in, and (3) contrast.

The studio cameras are usually put on different camera mounts: (1) tripod dollies, (2) studio pedestals, and (3) studio cranes.

**EXERCISES**

1. Name the three main parts of a television camera.
2. Describe and diagram the internal optical system of a color camera.
3. What is the difference between chrominance and luminance channels?
4. Differentiate between additive and subtractive primary colors.
5. What are the main advantages and disadvantages of the vidicon camera and the I-O camera?
6. What is the difference between a dolly and a truck?
7. What is lag and how can you avoid it?

# 2

## Lenses

Lenses are used in all fields of photographic art. The function of a lens is mainly to produce a small, clear image of the viewed scene on the film or, in the case of television, on the television picture tube.

The particular lens used determines how close or how far away an object will appear (assuming a fixed distance from camera to object). Some television lenses make an object or action seem far away, although the camera is comparatively close to it; other lenses show the object or action at close range, although the camera may be located at some distance from it.

Zoom lenses can make a "far" object appear to move continuously closer and a "close" object continuously farther away. Since the zoom lens can, to some extent, duplicate the characteristics of several lenses, it is often preferred over the multilens turret operation. As mentioned before, color cameras operate almost exclusively with a single zoom-lens system.

Both types of lenses, the turret lenses (fixed focal length) and the zoom lenses (variable focal length), incorporate similar basic optical characteristics. We will discuss some of these general characteristics before going into a more detailed discussion of the various types of turret and zoom lenses.

At this point, it is important for you to realize some obvious differences between "old" and "new" television lenses. On the old I-O cameras, such as the TK-14 and the TK-40, standard photographic (mostly Eastman Kodak) lenses are still used. Except for the long lenses, these "old" lenses are C-mount lenses—they can be screwed into the turret. Also, these lenses have adjustable distance and f-stop calibrations. The ring close to the mount gives distance in feet; the ring close to the cap gives the f-stop numbers. The distance calibration helps to focus on a particular distance. The f-stop numbers help to regulate the amount of light striking the tube. Both lens adjustments are manually set.

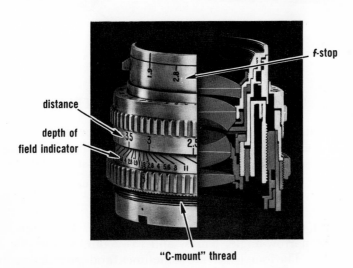

"C-mount" thread

Several lens manufacturers have come up with improved lenses specifically designed for television use. The British Rank Taylor Hobson lenses, the French Angenieux lenses, and the German Schneider lenses now enjoy wide acceptance in the television field.

These newer lenses come in slightly different focal lengths from those
of the older Eastman lenses (see the lens comparison chart on page
52); they have no distance calibration, since they are all set permanently at infinity; and they have a remote iris control—that is,
the *f*-stop is remotely controlled by the video-control engineer. Instead of the C-mount, the newer lenses have a "TV 88" mount,
which permits a fast "plugging in" of the lens into the turret. However, some vidicon lenses still come with the customary C-mount.

remote iris control

## OPTICAL CHARACTERISTICS OF LENSES

To find out when and why you should use a specific lens, you will
have to acquaint yourself with some basic characteristics of television
lenses. These are (1) focal length, (2) focus, (3) *f*-stop, and (4) depth
of field.

### Focal Length

In general, we can group lenses into (1) short, or wide-angle, lenses,
(2) long, or narrow-angle, lenses, and (3) zoom, or variable focal-
length, lenses. The long lenses are sometimes (and quite ambiguously)
referred to as close-up lenses.

The "short" and the "long" in this connection refer to the focal
length of a lens. Focal length is the distance from the optical center
of the lens (the midpoint between the front and back lens elements)
to the point where the image as seen by the lens is in focus.

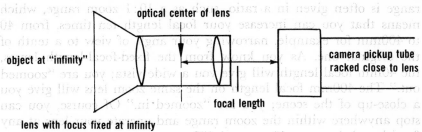

object at "infinity"

optical center of lens

camera pickup tube racked close to lens

focal length

lens with focus fixed at infinity

A thorough knowledge of how to measure focal length is not too important for a proper usage of camera lenses. Fortunately, short lenses actually look short and long lenses look long, so it is easy to tell whether the cameraman is using a short- or a long-focal-length lens.

With a short, or wide-angle, lens you can see more; you have a wider vista. What you see looks comparatively small. With a long, or narrow-angle, lens you see less; you have a narrower vista. But what you see is greatly magnified.

A short lens creates an effect similar to looking through binoculars the wrong way. A long lens is similar to binoculars used the right way.

Normal turret lenses have a fixed focal length: you cannot change the angle of view. That is why you need several lenses on a turret. Turret lenses are usually marked according to their focal length, which is given either in millimeters (mm) or in inches (in.). There are 25mm to one inch. The smaller the focal-length number, the wider the angle of view.

Contrary to the turret lenses, the zoom lens has a variable focal length, allowing you to change the focal length of the lens from long to short and from short to long in one continuous operation. A complicated series of lenses interact and keep the object in focus at all times during the zooming operation. To "zoom in" means to change the lens gradually from a wide-angle lens to a narrow-angle lens. On the television screen, a zoom appears as though the camera is moving quite smoothly and rapidly (depending on the speed of the zoom) toward the object. To "zoom out or zoom back" means to change the lens from a close-up to a distant shot. The camera seems to move magically away from the object during a zoom out. Of course, the camera actually remains stationary throughout the zooming process.

The degree to which you can change the focal length (and thereby the angle of view) of a zoom lens is the *zoom range* of your lens. This range is often given in a ratio, such as a 10:1 zoom range, which means that you can increase your focal length ten times, from 40 to 400mm for example, narrowing your angle of view to a tenth of the original one. As you know from the fixed-focal-length lenses, the 40mm focal length will give you a wide vista; you are "zoomed out." The 400mm focal length on the same zoom lens will give you a close-up of the scene; you are "zoomed in." Of course, you can stop anywhere within the zoom range and operate your lens at any focal length between 40mm and 400mm.

In this discussion of focal length it is important to recall the differences between the lenses used for image-orthicon cameras and those used for vidicon and Plumbicon cameras.

All monochrome I-O cameras use lenses comparable to the lenses used for 35mm film. Sometimes these lenses are called "Ortal" lenses, a name coined for this lens type by the Rank Taylor Hobson Company.

Vidicon and Plumbicon cameras generally use lenses of the 16mm-film type. These lenses are sometimes called the "Vidital" lenses. However, some Plumbicon cameras can use 35mm-type lenses, provided they have appropriate image-reducing adapters.

Most color cameras that use vidicon or Plumbicon tubes use zoom lenses of the 16mm type. Some color cameras, however, can also use I-O (35mm) lenses.

Of course, these different lens types have quite different focal-length characteristics. What is ordinarily called a wide-angle lens for the I-O camera is not at all a wide-angle lens for a vidicon camera, even when the lenses have the same focal length. For example, an I-O lens with a focal length of 50mm is generally considered a wide-angle lens, but a vidicon lens with a focal length of 50mm is considered a long, narrow-angle lens. Although the following example is not a precise optical theory, it may nevertheless help you to understand this focal-length difference: since an I-O lens has a fatter barrel—that is, a larger diameter—than a vidicon lens, the I-O lens allows a larger angle of view even though both lenses are equally long.

## Focus

A picture is "in focus" if the projected image is sharp and clear. The focus depends on the distance from lens to film (in a still camera) or camera tube (in a TV camera). Simply changing the distance from lens to film brings a picture into focus or takes it out of focus.

In television photography, the camera tube takes the place of the film. To keep in focus you must adjust the distance between lens and camera tube. You can change this distance in several ways. (1) You can adjust the lens itself—such as when you move the distance calibration of the lens anywhere from 2 feet to infinity on a short lens. This adjustment is the same as on any still camera or motion picture camera. (2) You can move the camera tube toward and away from the lens by turning a focusing knob on the side of the camera. (3) When using a zoom lens, you can focus anywhere within the zoom range by moving certain lens elements; these elements are adjusted by mechanical or electrical focus devices attached to the lens and to the camera. Each of these methods is examined in more detail below.

### Distance calibration

Generally, all turret lenses are set at infinity and the necessary focus adjustment is made by rotating the focus knob, thereby changing the distance from lens to camera-tube surface. However, as pointed out before, some of the older I-O lenses and some vidicon lenses can be prefocused from the usual infinity setting to a closer distance, say 10 feet. This prefocusing procedure of a lens is helpful if you want to make a fast change from a distant to a close object—for instance, from an actor in a far corner of the studio to an easel card close to the camera. Without prefocusing, the switch would involve not only a fast change of lenses but quick refocusing; if both lenses were set on infinity, you would have to turn the focus knob several times before you could bring the easel card into focus. You can avoid this time-consuming refocusing simply by prefocusing the narrow-angle lens on the distance from camera to easel card. This prefocusing is accomplished by adjusting the lens calibration to the desired distance. Prefocusing is successful, however, only if the particular lens is not used for anything but this one easel shot. In an unrehearsed show, prefocusing of lenses is not recommended.

Since prefocusing has more operational disadvantages than advantages, you will understand now why lens manufacturers have largely done away with the distance calibration on television lenses and have fixed the distance at infinity. With the newer turret lenses, all focusing is accomplished exclusively by operating the focus knob.

### Moving the camera tube

You focus monochrome turret cameras by moving the camera tube toward or away from the lens, a procedure accomplished simply by turning the focus knob or crank on the side of the camera. Depending on the speed of the camera or object, the focal length, and the lens opening, several turns of the knob may be necessary to keep the I-O picture in focus. Plumbicon and vidicon cameras usually require less turning of the focusing knob. Vidicon cameras are faster to focus, but the focusing becomes more critical and delicate. Generally, when you dolly in, you turn the focus knob counter-clockwise; when you dolly back, you turn the focus knob clockwise.

There are still some focusing knobs that prevent quick and accurate focusing because they are poorly designed. One of the most workable focusing knobs was designed many years ago by the late Larry West, a KPIX-CBS engineer. This knob, which unfortunately has never been produced commercially, is a large plastic wheel with finger notches and a large hole. The notches along the periphery of the wheel (labeled *a* in the illustration) give you a firm grip and allow fast and precise turning of the wheel with one finger. The hole in the wheel (*b*) is for fast racking with one finger.

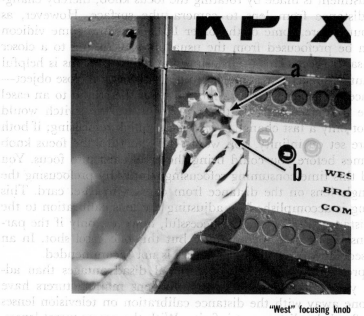

"West" focusing knob

Because the travel of the camera tube is obviously restricted within the camera, there are limitations to focusing, especially when long lenses are used. For example, you cannot take an extreme close-up of a postage stamp with a long lens, because you cannot rack into focus when you are close enough to the object to fill the screen with it. The reason for this dilemma is that long lenses have a long focal length: that is, the picture comes into focus relatively far behind the optical center of the lens. Operationally, you must rack the camera tube back a considerable distance to align the sharp image from the lens with the front surface of the camera tube. The closer the camera gets to the object, the farther back the tube has to travel in order to stay in focus. If the tube cannot go back any farther, the picture will be out of focus until either the object or the camera backs up. So an extreme close-up of a very small object requires a

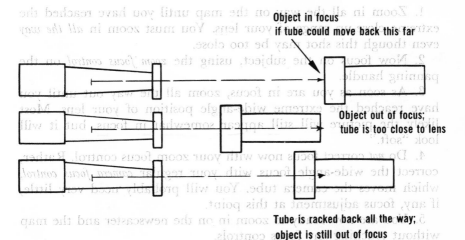

**Object in focus if tube could move back this far**

**Object out of focus; tube is too close to lens**

**Tube is racked back all the way; object is still out of focus**

wide-angle lens, which has a shorter focal length and for which the tube travel within the camera is sufficient. Of course, extreme close-ups with wide-angle lenses cause lighting problems, because the camera has to be quite close to the object; close-ups of this nature must be carefully planned before the show.

### Zoom-lens focusing

A zoom lens has several internal lens elements that move in relation to one another when you zoom as well as when you focus. One set of the sliding lens elements, normally at the front end of the lens, takes care of the focusing. The zoom-lens focus controls, which come in various configurations, are usually mounted on one of the panning handles or on a short bar attached to the rear of the camera.

Assuming that neither the object nor your camera moves very much, and that you have properly preset your zoom, you should not have to adjust the focus at all while zooming in or out. Prefocusing or presetting the zoom is a fairly simple procedure for monochrome cameras; but it is a little more complex for color cameras. We will, therefore, discuss prefocusing for the two types of cameras separately.

*Zoom prefocusing for monochrome cameras.* Let us assume your zoom camera is in one corner of the studio and your newscaster in the other. Since you will have to zoom in and out on the newscaster and on the map behind him, you must preset your zoom focus. This you do in the following steps:

1. Zoom in all the way on the map until you have reached the extreme close-up range of your lens. You must zoom in *all the way* even though this shot may be too close.

2. Now focus on the subject, using the *zoom focus control* on the panning handle.

3. As soon as you are in focus, zoom all the way out until you have reached the extreme wide-angle position of your lens. Most likely the picture will still appear somewhat in focus, but it will look "soft."

4. Do *not* correct focus now with your zoom focus control. Rather, correct the wide-angle focus with your regular *camera focus control,* which moves the camera tube. You will probably need very little, if any, focus adjustment at this point.

5. You are now ready to zoom in on the newscaster and the map without touching any focus controls.

Close-up focusing with your zoom focus control is sometimes called "front focus"; wide-angle focusing with the camera focus control is called "back focus."

*Zoom prefocusing for color cameras.* The "front-focus" operation for color cameras is identical to that for monochrome cameras. The important difference in prefocusing a zoom lens for color cameras lies in the "back-focus" operation. Since the color camera has three or four tubes whose alignment with the complex optical system within the camera is highly critical, the tubes are not moved back and forth within the camera in the way that the tube is moved in a monochrome camera. Although the color tubes must be moved occasionally to achieve proper back focus, this operation is generally done by engineers during the basic alignment procedures of the cameras before the broadcast day. The back-focus alignment has to be done inside the camera, and it is a rather complicated and time-consuming operation. Fortunately, the color camera does not have as high a picture resolution (that is, a very sharp picture with fine detail) as the monochrome camera, and a slightly softer picture on a wide-angle shot is often not noticeable on a color home receiver. Ordinarily, you don't need to worry about back focus while the show is in progress. The zoom focus control on your panning handle should be sufficient for all focusing demands.

Like long-focal-length lenses, the zoom lens sets some limitations on how close the camera can get to an object and still remain in focus. The closest focusing distance for most zoom lenses lies between 3 and 4 feet for studio zoom lenses and approximately 6 feet for field zoom lenses. We will discuss this restriction more thoroughly in the section on the operational characteristics of zoom lenses.

## f-Stop

Similar to photographic film, the camera tube will operate properly only within a certain range of light intensity. If too little light falls on the camera tube, the picture quality suffers as much as if too much light strikes the tube surface. Since you will probably use the camera not only indoors but also outdoors on remote telecasts, you will have to adjust for the extreme difference in light levels. The lens diaphragm, or iris, is used to control the amount of light that enters the lens. The f-stops indicate the size of the lens (diaphragm) opening; f-stops usually range from $f/2.0$ to $f/22$ for I-O lenses ($f/1.4$ to $f/22$ for vidicon lenses). The lower the f-stop number, the wider the lens opening.

A lens is considered fast if a great amount of light can enter (low f-stop number); a lens is considered slow if the widest lens opening allows only a comparatively small amount of light to enter (higher f-stop number). Fast lenses, therefore, can be used under low light-level conditions. Slow lenses need more light to produce an acceptable picture. Long lenses are usually somewhat slower than short lenses.

The f-stops are set for two purposes: (1) to control the light level striking the tube and (2) to achieve a desired depth of field. It should be noted here that once a proper light level has been established, picture quality will be influenced only by a certain middle range of diaphragm openings. Anything below or above this middle range has no visible influence on the picture.

A large diaphragm opening (small f-stop number) will decrease the depth of field; a small diaphragm opening (high f-stop number) will increase the depth of field. The depth of field, however, is dependent on several factors, which will be discussed separately.

On older cameras, the f-stop is set after the studio has been properly lighted and the camera properly adjusted before the telecast. During the telecast, the f-stop remains untouched. Most newer cameras, however, have a remote iris control. The video-control engineer, or shader, can change the diaphragm openings of all turret lenses simultaneously from a remote position. Since most new cameras have very stable electronic characteristics, the remote iris operation has become the principal video control. The lens diaphragm is changed continually during the telecast in order to control and balance the light striking the camera tube.

Most newer monochrome and color cameras also have a filter wheel, which is located behind the lens and which holds several neutral-density and color filters. The neutral-density filter supplements the iris in cutting down excessive light, and the color filters correct the incoming light for the color responses of the various camera tubes.

## Depth of Field

If you place objects at different distances from the camera, some objects will be in focus and some out of focus. The area in which the objects are seen in focus is called "depth of field." A depth of field can be shallow or great. If the depth of field is shallow, only the object in the middleground may be in focus; the foreground and background will be out of focus. If the depth of field is great, all objects (fore-, middle-, and background) may be in focus.

If the depth of field is great, you will find it rather easy to keep the performer in focus, although he may move rapidly toward or away from your camera. If the depth of field is shallow, the performer will have to move very slowly toward or away from your camera in order to stay in focus.

The same rules apply, of course, when the camera moves. A great depth of field makes it easy for the cameraman to stay in focus while dollying. A shallow depth of field makes it extremely difficult for the cameraman to dolly without getting out of focus.

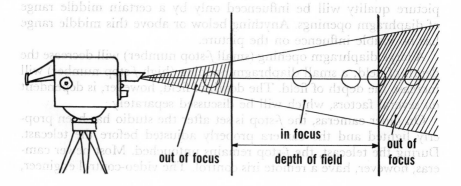

out of focus    depth of field    in focus    out of focus

It seems as though a very great depth of field would be the most desirable condition in television studio operation. A medium depth of field is often preferred, however, because the in-focus objects are set off against a slightly out-of-focus background. Thus, the object will be emphasized, and little attention will be drawn to busy background designs or the inevitable smudges on the television scenery. Foreground, middleground, and background will be better defined.

You can control the depth of field by coordinating three factors: (1) the focal length of the lens used, (2) the lens opening (*f*-stop), and (3) the distance between camera and object.

1. Short lenses have a great depth of field. Long lenses have a shallow depth of field. Since vidicon cameras use shorter lenses than I-O cameras, the depth of field for vidicon cameras is usually greater (assuming similar *f*-stops).

2. Large lens openings (small *f*-stop numbers) cause a shallow depth of field. Small lens openings cause a great depth of field. A low light level will necessitate the opening of the lens diaphragms, which will cause a decrease in the depth of field. More light permits you to "stop down" your lens (decrease the lens opening), which will increase the depth of field.

3. The farther away the object is from the camera, the greater the depth of field. The closer the object to the camera, the shallower the depth of field.

To take a close-up with a wide-angle lens, for instance, your distance from camera to object will be small; the initially large depth of field (wide-angle lens) will become quite shallow (distance from camera to object is small). If a similar close-up is taken with a long lens, the distance from object to camera may be comparatively great (great depth of field); the long focal length of the lens, however, will reduce the depth of field considerably.

With a zoom lens, the depth of field changes accordingly. When you are zoomed in, you have a shallow depth of field; when zoomed out, you have a larger depth of field.

In general, we can say that close-ups have a shallow depth of field, long shots a great depth of field.

Quite frequently, a shallow depth of field can work to the cameraman's and the director's advantage. Let us assume that you will have to take a quick close-up of a medium-sized object, such as a can of dog food. You don't have to bother to put up a special background for it so long as you take the close-up with a long lens. Anything behind the display will then be sufficiently out of focus, thus preventing undesirable distractions.

# TELEVISION LENSES

## Turret Studio Lenses

### "Old" I-O (35mm) Lenses

| Field of View | Focal Length inches mm | Appr. Horiz Angle of View | Maximum Lens Opening |
|---|---|---|---|
| Extremely Wide | 35 | 52° | f/2.0 |
| Wide | 50 | 34° | f/1.8 |
| Normal | 90 | 19° | f/3.5 |
| Narrow | 135 | 13° | f/3.0 |
| Narrow | 8½ | 8° | f/3.5 |
| Ext. Narrow | 13 | 5° | f/3.5 |

### "New" I-O (35mm) Lenses (Ortal)

| Focal Length inches | mm | Appr. Angle of View | Maximum Lens Opening |
|---|---|---|---|
| 1.4 | 35 | 51° | f/2.8 |
| 2 | 50 | 36° | f/2.0 |
| 3 | 75 | 24° | f/2.0 |
| 5 | 127 | 15° | f/2.8 |
| 8 | 203 | 9° | f/4.0 |
| 12½ | 318 | 6° | f/4.0 |

### Vidicon & Plumbicon (16mm) Lenses (Vidital)

| Focal Length inches | mm | Appr. Angle of View | Maximum Lens Opening |
|---|---|---|---|
| 0.47 | 12 | 56° | f/1.4 |
| ½ | 12.5 | 50° | f/1.4 |
| 0.8 | 20 | 35° | f/1.7 |
| 1 | 25 | 30° | f/1.4 |
| 1.8 | 30 | 24° | f/1.4 |
| 2 | 50 | 15° | f/1.4 |
| 3 | 75 | 10° | f/1.4 |
| 3.15 | 80 | 9° | f/1.6 |
| 4 | 100 | 7.5° | f/1.9 |

## Turret Field Lenses

### "Old" I-O (35mm) Lenses

| Field of View | Focal Length inches mm | Appr. Horiz Angle of View | Maximum Lens Opening |
|---|---|---|---|
| Normal Field | 15 | 4.5° | f/8 |
| Narrow Field | 17 | 4° | f/8 |
| Ext. Narrow Field | 25 | 2° | f/8 |

### "New" I-O (35mm) Lenses (Ortal)

| Focal Length inches | mm | Appr. Angle of View | Maximum Lens Opening |
|---|---|---|---|
| 16 | 406 | 4.5° | f/4 |
| 22 | 500 | 3° | f/5.6 |

### Vidicon & Plumbicon (16mm) Lenses (Vidital)

| Focal Length inches | mm | Appr. Angle of View | Maximum Lens Opening |
|---|---|---|---|
| 6 | 152 | 5° | f/1.8 |
| 12 | 300 | 2.5° | f/4.0 |

## Zoom Lenses

| | I-O Zoom (Verotal V) | | | Vidicon & Plumbicon Zoom (Angenieux 10 × 18) | | | "Old" Type Zoomar | |
|---|---|---|---|---|---|---|---|---|
| | Zoom Range 10:1 | Min Distance | Max Lens Opening | Zoom Range 10:1 | Min Distance | Max Lens Opening | Zoom Range | I-O Equivalent |
| Studio | 1.6-16  40-400 | 6 feet | f/4 | 0.70-7.1  18-180 | 3 feet | f/2.2 | 50mm-175mm | 1.4-14 inch |
| Studio Close-up Attachment | 1.6-16  40-400 | 3 feet | f/4 | 0.70-7.1 | 2 feet | f/2.2 | Field Zoomar | |
| Field Range Extender 1 | 2.4-24  60-600 | 6 feet | f/6 | 1.06-10.6  27-270 | 3 feet | f/3.3 | 3 inch-13 inches | 2.1-21 inch |
| Field Range Extender 2 | 3.2-32  80-800 | 6 feet | f/8 | 1.4-14  36-360 | 3 feet | f/4.4 | 5 inch-22 inches | 2.8-28 inch |
| Field Range Extender 3 | 4.8-48  120-1200 | 6 feet | f/12 | 2.1-21  54-540 | 3 feet | f/6.6 | | 4.2-42 inch |

This advantage also applies to unwanted foreground objects. In a baseball pick-up, the camera behind home plate may have to shoot through the fence wire. If you use a long lens, however, the fence wire will be so much out of focus that it becomes for all practical purposes invisible. The same principle works for shooting through bird cages, window screens, prison bars, etc.

One other example for the creative use of a shallow depth of field should be mentioned here. An interview show with TV writer-producer Rod Serling was begun by focusing the camera on the opening lines of *Patterns*, the play that helped Mr. Serling to become known. The opening paragraph of the play was not printed on a regular studio card, but was photographed onto a "cell," a piece of transparent cellulose acetate fastened to a frame. During the announcer's introduction, the camera slowly changed focus from the lettering on the cell to Mr. Serling, who was then seen through the acetate. Once the camera had focused on Mr. Serling, the lettering was completely out of focus and did not interfere at all with the picture of the writer, his typewriter, and his inevitable accessories of coffee cup and cigarettes. The closing of the show was handled in the same way, only in reverse.

A large depth of field is necessary if there is considerable movement of camera and/or subjects. If two objects are located at widely different distances from the camera, a great depth of field will enable you to keep both objects in focus simultaneously. Most outdoor telecasts, such as sports events and other types of remotes, require a large depth of field. Fortunately, there is usually enough light to stop down the lenses considerably, which, as we have seen, will help to increase the depth of field.

At this point you may find the chart on page 52 helpful. It classifies lenses according to turret lenses (fixed focal length) and zoom lenses (variable focal length), and into studio and field lenses. The older C-mount I-O lenses are shown in a separate column.

## PERFORMANCE CHARACTERISTICS OF LENSES

All production people directly involved in live telecasting, such as the director, cameramen, boom operator, floor crew, and talent, must know what a lens can and cannot do. Let us take a closer look at the two groups of television lenses—(1) studio and field turret lenses and (2) studio and field zoom lenses—to find out how they behave under normal conditions.

## Turret Lenses

Most lens turrets are equipped to hold four different lenses. Some turrets, however, can hold five lenses. The most common studio-lens complement consists of a wide-angle lens, a medium lens, and a narrow-angle lens. It is good practice to put the widest-angle lens on your turret opposite the longest lens. By doing so you will avoid having the long lens show in your wide-angle picture. The problem of a lens visible in the picture is sometimes called "cropping." If you use a normal lens complement, cropping is no problem, whatever the position of the lenses on the turret may be.

### Standard lens complement

The I-O lenses, which have proved the most flexible for studio use and are therefore combined most frequently on the turret, are (1) the 50mm lens—a wide-angle lens; (2) the 75mm or 90mm lens —the normal lens; and (3) the 127mm or 135mm lens. The normal "Ortal" lens turret is often referred to as the 2-3-5-inch turret (corresponding to the 50mm or 2-inch lens, the 75mm or 3-inch lens, and the 127mm or 5-inch lens).

Some stations include the 8-inch or 8½-inch lens in their normal lens complement. This lens enables you to get fast close-ups of objects that are located at a considerable distance from the camera.

### Studio turret lenses

*The 35mm lens.* The 35mm lens is the widest-angle television lens used. It should always be used when you want a wide field of view comparatively close to the camera. You can make a small studio look enormous simply by using the 35mm lens. The objects close to the camera will look quite large, while objects only a short distance away from the camera look comparatively small. The result is a somewhat forced perspective, which helps to increase the illusion of depth and distance. This distortion, however, will not always work for you. If you take a close-up of a face with this lens, you will notice that the nose, which is closest to the lens, is unusually large compared to the ears, which are farther away. An actor's hand, just slightly extended toward the 35mm lens, will become gigantic in comparison to the body and head of the actor. In a long shot, you may notice that the vertical lines of the background appear to be somewhat curved. This effect is called "barrel distortion," because the vertical lines look like the curved sides of a barrel.

Wide-angle lens distortion is frequently desirable, especially when something like the "long, low lines" of a new automobile are to be emphasized.

When you dolly with a 35mm lens, objects rapidly increase or decrease in size. The dollying speed, therefore, becomes greatly exaggerated. The dollying distance from an extreme long shot to a close-up is quite short. For several reasons, the 35mm lens is an excellent dolly lens: (1) rough or awkward camera movement is minimized by this extreme wide-angle lens; (2) the great depth of field aids the cameraman in keeping focus while dollying; (3) the wide angle of view makes it easy for the cameraman to frame even comparatively fast-moving objects.

*The 50mm (2-inch) lens.* The 50mm lens is the shortest lens of the standard lens complement. It is a wide-angle lens, which means that it gives a relatively large field of view.

The 50mm lens has three basic advantages: (1) it is an excellent dolly lens, (2) it will give you excellent close-ups of small objects, and (3) it is a fast lens.

1. If you have only one lens available and a great amount of dollying to do, the 50mm is the most practical lens. Similar to the 35mm lens, the 50mm lens de-emphasizes bumps and wobbles of the moving camera. The great depth of field of the lens helps you to keep in focus while dollying, with a minimum of focus adjustment. The only time you will have to be concerned about focus adjustment is when the distance from camera to object becomes fairly short. Since the dollying from a long shot to a close-up is relatively short with this lens, the dollying speed is exaggerated.

The relative size of objects is also exaggerated with the 50mm lens. Foreground objects look large, while background objects look small. This contrast aids in creating the illusion of space. The perspective appears slightly forced, although not as much as through a 35mm lens.

2. The 50mm lens allows you to take a close-up of an object as small as a postage stamp. Because of the short focal length, the image-orthicon tube can be racked far enough from the lens to maintain proper focus at close ranges. Longer-focal-length lenses cannot be focused at such close ranges from lens to object. Be sure to check carefully, however, on whether the camera can get physically close enough to the object. Sometimes a large dolly, or even the sunshade of the 8-inch lens, may prevent you from pushing the camera close enough to obtain the desired close-up. And again the camera may block out the necessary light.

3. The 50mm lens is the fastest television lens generally used—which means that it has a very low *f*-stop number. You can use this lens to get acceptable television pictures even under unfavorable lighting conditions.

The basic negative factors in using a 50mm lens are (1) distortion, (2) short distance of camera to object for close-ups, and (3) over-shooting.

1. Similar to the 35mm lens, a close-up with the 50mm lens distorts the object. A close-up of a washing machine, for instance, shows an obvious distortion, especially when the camera dollies in and looks down on the machine. You can minimize such distortions by placing the objects on an approximate level with the lens height.

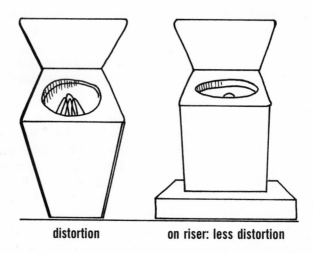

**distortion**          **on riser: less distortion**

2. When a performer demonstrates a small object, the camera will have to get quite close to the person in order to get the desired close-up of the object. This closeness especially bothers nonprofessional performers, such as guests, who frequently want to back away from the dangerously approaching camera. When the camera gets too close to a performer, the lighting engineer often complains about the potential danger of undesirable camera shadows.

3. If you use a 50mm lens in the studio, you will have to watch not to overshoot the scenery either on top or at the sides. The great depth of field of the 50mm lens will point up overshot areas clearly and embarrassingly.

*The 75mm (3-inch) lens.* The 75mm lens has almost entirely replaced the 90mm lens as the "normal" lens. "Normal" refers to the basic optical characteristics of the lens, which, when compared to human vision and optical experiences, appear to be the same. For example, when the camera is dollying in, you will see an object increase in size at about the same speed as that of the camera approaching the subject. Also, the picture as it appears on the television screen shows no visible distortion.

There are several advantages to the 75mm lens: (1) it is a good dolly lens, (2) the dolly speed is not exaggerated, (3) you can achieve a good close-up without bringing the camera too close to the object, (4) there is very little noticeable distortion, and (5) it is a fast lens.

It has virtually no disadvantages except that the step from the 75mm wide-angle lens to the 127mm (5-inch) narrow-angle lens is quite great.

*The 90mm lens.* The 90mm lens has very similar characteristics to those of the 75mm lens. It is still considered a "normal" lens. However, the 90mm lens exhibits some long-lens characteristics. For example, with this lens it is relatively difficult to dolly smoothly, and the camera has to travel a considerable distance before the object gets larger or smaller. Because the 75mm has proved to be more flexible than the 90mm lens, the 75mm is generally preferred.

Since television production is extremely complex and requires a high degree of coordination among many people, it is always desirable to standardize as many production procedures as possible. One method of standardization is to use a 75mm or 90mm lens on all easel cards. This method has several advantages: (1) you can quickly correct the framing without moving the camera too much in either direction; (2) you can dolly in on the easel card to pick out some detail without losing focus; (3) you will be far enough away from the easel to avoid camera shadows; and (4) the floorman can quickly place the easel at a standard distance from the camera, which again enables the cameraman to go from a live scene to the easel card with a minimum of effort and time.

*The 127mm (5-inch) and 135mm lenses.* The 127mm or 5-inch lens has almost the same characteristics as the 135mm lens, so we will discuss both lenses together.

The 5-inch lens is the most widely used narrow-angle lens on the standard television turret. With this lens, you can get tight close-ups without moving the camera too close to the subject. This advantage is especially desirable when the wide-angle views of other cameras or general studio traffic prevent you from shooting a particular object at close range.

The 5-inch lens is a telephoto lens, which means that it magnifies objects in the field of the lens' view. It enlarges not only the foreground objects, however, but also middle and background objects. These middle and background objects look rather large in comparison to foreground objects. Thus, an illusion is created that the distance between foreground, middleground, and background has decreased. This effect is in direct contrast to the effect of short-focal-length lenses, which seemingly increase relative distances.

The 5-inch lens is not a dolly lens. Although skilled cameramen may manage to dolly quite smoothly when using this lens, dollying should not be a standard practice. The enlargement of this long lens is great enough to emphasize rough or awkward camera movements quite noticeably.

The 5-inch lens is generally used for close-ups of persons in static interview shows and for objects that are fairly immobile, such as commercial properties.

The depth of field of this lens is rather limited—another factor that prevents excessive camera movement.

The 5-inch lens has an angle of view narrow enough to allow an opposite mounting of up to a 16-inch or even a 22-inch lens. It can also be used in conjunction with a studio zoom lens.

*The 203mm (8-inch) lens.* The 8-inch lens, or the 8½-inch lens for older cameras, is usually the longest lens used in normal small-studio operation. Its characteristics are very similar to those of the 5-inch lens. It is, however, a considerably longer lens, and its magnifying power makes movement of the camera impossible.

With the 8-inch lens, the distance between two objects seems greatly reduced. The depth of field is quite shallow and the widest lens opening is at best $f/3.9$, which makes the 8-inch lens comparatively slow. Excellent close-ups over relatively great studio distances, however, can be achieved.

Because of its shallow depth of field, this lens is sometimes used for close-ups of objects displayed away from the camera and sufficiently away from studio walls and scenery. If you focus on the display object, the background will, in general, be out of focus and thus will not distract from the display. If properly used, the 8-inch lens can help to solve many acute studio traffic problems.

### Field turret lenses

For the older cameras, the television field lenses included the 13-inch, the 15-inch, the 17-inch, and the 25-inch lenses. All these lenses have a bayonet mount, which is a C-mount adaptor to hold the long and bulky lenses.

Of all these field lenses, only the 13-inch lens has the regular lens diaphragm for setting $f$-stops. All other field lenses—the 15-inch, the 17-inch, and the 25-inch lens—have the so-called waterhouse stops

25-inch    17-inch    15-inch    13-inch    8½-inch

135mm      90mm       50mm       35mm

**Studio and field lenses**

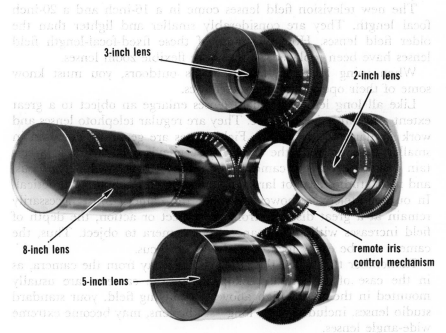

3-inch lens

2-inch lens

8-inch lens

remote iris
control mechanism

5-inch lens

**Normal lens complement for I-O cameras**

28mm     35mm     50mm     75mm     127mm
1.1-inch  1.38-inch  2-inch    3-inch     5-inch      8-inch  12½-inch  16-inch  22-inch

Ortal lenses (35mm format) by Taylor Hobson

(metal rings that are inserted by hand according to the desired lens stop).

The new television field lenses come in a 16-inch and a 20-inch focal length. They are considerably smaller and lighter than the older field lenses. However, most of these fixed-focal-length field lenses have been replaced by the more flexible zoom lenses.

When using long-focal-length lenses outdoors, you must know some of their operational characteristics.

Like all long lenses, the field lenses enlarge an object to a great extent and minimize distance. They are regular telephoto lenses and work similarly to binoculars. Field lenses are generally not used in small studios, because the object to be televised has to be at a certain distance from the camera before it can be brought into focus, and most studios are not large enough to make such lenses practical. In outdoor telecasts, however, where the camera must necessarily remain at a great distance from the object or action, the depth of field increases with the distance from camera to object. Thus, the camera can be easily focused and kept in focus.

Remember that when the object is far away from the camera, as in the case of a football pickup where the cameras are usually mounted in the stands high above the playing field, your standard studio lenses, including the "long" studio lens, may become extreme wide-angle lenses.

If you use the longer field lenses, such as the old 17-inch and especially the old 25-inch, wind may become a problem. A stiff breeze may shake the lens to such a degree that the greatly magnified vibrations become clearly visible on the television screen.

There are several extremely long field lenses available (up to a 40-inch lens), which, however, are of little importance to small station operation. Advanced writings on television optics give a good description of such special lenses for those who are interested.

## Zoom Lenses

Zoom lenses, like turret lenses, can also be divided into studio lenses and field lenses.

### Studio zoom lenses

The older Zoomar studio lenses have a zoom (focal-length) range of about 50mm to 180mm (7 inches). They are C-mount lenses and can be used with other turret lenses (90mm to 8½ inches). They are either manually or electrically operated. In the latter case, the Zoomar lens is called the "Electra-Zoom." The Electra-Zoom has to be mounted on a special turret plate, however.

Studio Zoomar lens

Most newer cameras, especially all new color cameras, use the larger and more capable Taylor Hobson, Angenieux, or similar type of zoom lens. They differ somewhat in their optical design from the old Zoomar lenses, and they differ greatly in their zoom operating controls.

The lens table on page 52 indicates the zoom ranges for the most common zoom lenses. The zoom capabilities of the Verotal V are of particular importance, because it is one of the most common I-O zoom lenses.

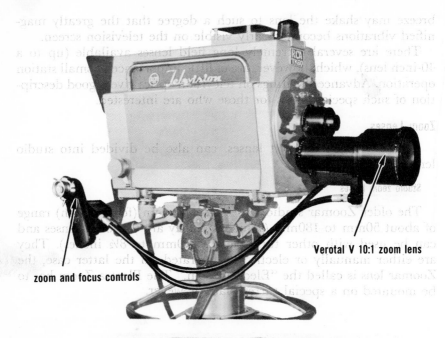

zoom and focus controls

Verotal V 10:1 zoom lens

Angenieux 10:1 zoom lens
with Zoomar control

The 10:1 zoom range from 1.6 inches to 16 inches (40mm to 400mm) makes the Verotal V an ideal studio zoom lens. It can get wider than the widest lens used on a turret (50mm), and it can get much tighter than the longest lens normally used (8 inches). To visualize the range of the Verotal V lens, imagine that you are standing 20 feet away from the camera. Zoomed out all the way, the lens will cover a field of view 16 feet wide; you will be able to move 8 feet to either side of the stationary camera and still remain in the camera's field of view. When the lens is zoomed in all the way, you had better not move within the narrow 1.6 feet field of view or you will wobble out of the picture.

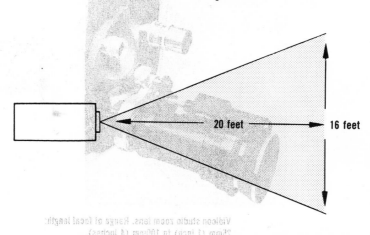

zoomed out: at 20 feet from the camera the field of view is 16 feet wide

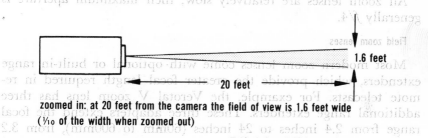

zoomed in: at 20 feet from the camera the field of view is 1.6 feet wide
(¹⁄₁₀ of the width when zoomed out)

Field of view of 10:1 zoom lens

The vidicon zoom lenses generally used for color cameras have a similar range in focal length and field of view, although the actual focal-length numbers are quite different from those of the I-O zoom format. But as the table indicates, the Angenieux 10:1 studio zoom lens ranges from 18mm to 180mm (0.7 inches to 7.1 inches), which is equivalent to an I-O lens range of 36mm to 360mm (1.4 inches to 14 inches).

Less expensive vidicon zoom lenses are also used on monochrome vidicon cameras, and they are adequate enough for simple studio shows.

Vidicon studio zoom lens. Range of focal length:
25mm (1 inch) to 100mm (4 inches).

All zoom lenses are relatively slow; their maximum aperture is generally $f/4$.

### Field zoom lenses

Most modern zoom lenses come with optional or built-in range extenders, which provide the greater focal length required in remote telecasts. For example, the Verotal V zoom lens has three additional range extenders. These three adapters extend the focal range from 2.4 inches to 24 inches (60mm to 600mm), from 3.2 inches to 32 inches (80mm to 800mm), and from 4.8 inches to 48 inches (120mm to 1200mm).

Of course, the longer the maximum focal length, the slower the speed of the lens. The $f/4$ of the normal zoom lens is reduced with the range extenders to $f/6$, $f/8$, and $f/12$, respectively. Fortunately, you will only use these extreme focal lengths outdoors where there is usually ample light available.

Vidicon and Plumbicon zoom lenses for color cameras have similar extension possibilities, as indicated in the lens table.

Normally, the range extender must be attached to the lens before a telecast. Some cameras, such as the TK-42, have built-in range extenders; you activate them simply by flipping a switch on the back of the camera. The extenders can be "switched" in or out even while the camera is on the air.

Special 16 : 1 zoom field lenses are also available; these lenses have little if any application in the studio. Despite the considerable cost, these lenses are sometimes preferred over the range extenders because they produce a clearer, sharper picture.

### Zoom operating controls

You can operate a zoom lens either by manual controls or by automatic, "servo" controls.

*Manual controls.* Some zoom lenses, especially the Zoomar lenses, are operated with a control rod that extends through the camera and turret handle at the back of the camera. With this rod you activate the zoom motion and the focus device simultaneously: to zoom in with a Studio Zoomar lens, you push the rod in. To zoom back, you pull the rod back. Focus adjustment at the control-rod knob is necessary only if the object that is "zoomed" moves toward or away from the camera.

Most of the zoom lenses used today have different controls, however. One of the most popular manual zoom controls is a small crank that is usually mounted on the right panning handle or on a special extender at the right of the camera. A small lever next to the crank enables you to select two turning ratios, slow or fast. The slow ratio is for normal zooming, the fast ratio for exceptionally fast zooms.

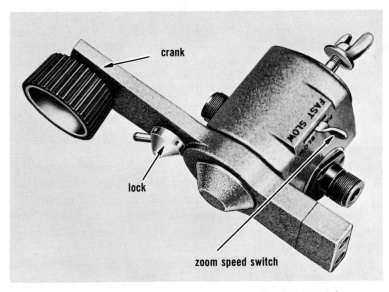

Manual zoom control

The focus control is a twist grip, very similar to a motorcycle handle. It is mounted on the left panning handle. Two turns are normally sufficient to achieve focus over the full zoom range.

focus twist grip

Manual focus control

The zoom and focus operations are transferred from the panning-handle controls to the lens by two cables that are strung along the outside of the camera.

Some attempts have been made to combine zoom and focus controls in one unit. As advantageous as this might seem (since it leaves one hand free for camera operation), the single control has not worked out very satisfactorily. Zoom and focus actions do not run parallel, especially when you are zooming in for a fairly tight shot. The simultaneous turning of the zoom control and the focus control at different rates can become unnecessarily difficult. The separate zoom and focus controls have proved much more manageable.

*Servo controls.* The servo lens controls do not activate the lens mechanism directly; rather, they signal a complex motor system that drives the zoom and focus mechanisms of the lens. In actual operation, both the zoom and the focus servo controls are quite similar to mechanical zoom controls.

The servo zoom control, like the mechanical zoom control, is normally mounted on the left panning handle. You zoom in and out by moving the thumb lever either right or left. The farther you move the lever from its original central position, the faster the zoom will be. A two-speed switch permits you to select a zoom speed four times as fast as the normal zoom rate. With the servo system, the zoom speed is automatically reduced as the zoom approaches either of the extreme zoom positions. This reduction prevents jerks and abrupt stops when you reach the end of the zoom range.

thumb zoom control

Servo zoom control

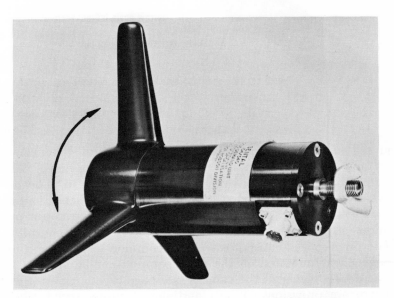

Servo focus control

There are several advantages to the servo system: (1) your zoom will always be perfectly steady and smooth, especially during extremely slow zooms; (2) the zoom control is easy to operate and allows you to concentrate more on other camera functions, such as panning, tilting, and focusing; (3) with the automatic zoom slowdown at extreme zooming positions, you will never get caught reaching the end of the zoom at full speed.

To make the zoom control even more flexible and precise, you can use a zoom preset system, called a "shot box," which can be also

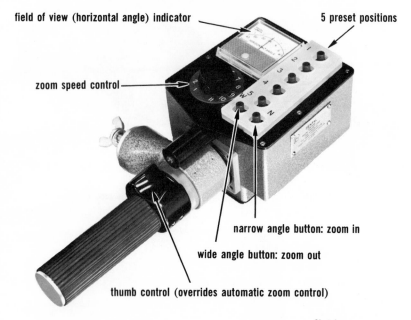

field of view (horizontal angle) indicator

5 preset positions

zoom speed control

narrow angle button: zoom in

wide angle button: zoom out

thumb control (overrides automatic zoom control)

Shot box

mounted on the left panning handle. With the shot box you can pre-select any of eleven zoom speeds and five zoom positions. "Wide" and "narrow" buttons activate the zooming out or in. The meter shows you at all times at what focal length the zoom lens is—that is, it gives you the angle of view. Of course, you can override the preset positions of the lens at any time with the servo thumb control.

The three-spoked capstan wheel is a common servo focus control. It is generally mounted on the right panning handle or on a short bar at the right rear of the camera (see page 67).

There are provisions for fast and slow focusing speeds and for compensating the turning of the focus control when the lens reaches long focal lengths. Remember, the tighter the shot, the smaller the depth of field. Consequently, when you zoom in for a tight shot, the focus becomes more critical as you get tighter, and you there-fore have to increase the turns of the focus control. The servo sys-tem can compensate for this change and keep the turning rate constant. Because of their experience with mechanical focus devices, however, most cameramen are already so used to the different turning ratios at close range that even with the servo system they prefer to compensate for the different close-range focus requirements themselves. The switch is, therefore, frequently left in the "uncompensated" position.

For similar reasons, the focus control unit, which provides for preselecting a certain focus, is not very popular. The preselected focus is useful only when the positions of the camera and subject are exactly the same in the show as in the rehearsal; and this rarely happens even in the most carefully worked out studio shows.

### Operational characteristics of zoom lenses

The zoom lens seems to be the ideal television lens. It has a large 10 : 1 variable-focal-length range, which is greater than any normal turret provides, and it has a servo system that makes zoom operations relatively easy. Indeed, all newer color cameras and several models of monochrome cameras have provisions for zoom lenses (or, at best, one fixed-focal-length lens) only.

Unfortunately, however, a zoom lens is not without serious disadvantages.

1. As mentioned previously, zoom lenses are relatively slow (and thus need more light than faster turret lenses).

2. A zoom lens has many more lens elements than a fixed-focal-length lens. Even under ideal conditions, the zoom-lens picture always looks slightly less defined and crisp than the turret-lens picture.

3. If the lens is not kept in top condition, the lens elements will sometimes stick, which makes a smooth zoom impossible. If you try to zoom in on an object with a "sticky" zoom lens, the object will appear to be jumping toward the television screen in great leaps. This happens especially when you operate the zoom lens manually.

4. The minimum distance between camera and object is particularly annoying if you want to take extreme close-ups of very small objects. You cannot get close enough for a close-up that fills the entire screen. Close-up adapters reduce this problem somewhat, but then your zoom range has been reduced throughout the entire show. Also, if your performer walks too close to your camera, you will no longer be able to keep him in focus. (In one television show, studio zoom lenses were used to cover an indoor rodeo. The cameras were located close to the performing arena behind a low protective fence. The show's master of ceremonies stood in the middle of the arena, commenting on the different happenings. Every once in a

while, however, a mean horse or bull would chase the M.C. behind the protective fence. Although this amused the cowboys considerably, it thoroughly annoyed the cameramen who could no longer keep the M.C. in focus; the distance between the M.C. and the cameras had become too short.)

Because of this minimum-distance requirement, intentional wide-angle lens distortions are often impossible to achieve properly with the zoom lens, even if you zoom out to a very short focal length.

5. Frequent repositioning of the zoom lens in relation to a particular object may cause a severe focus problem. Every time a zoom camera is repositioned, you will have to readjust the focus so that the picture will remain in good focus during the zooming action. Quick changes of camera positions followed by fast zooms are therefore not desirable. Even an experienced cameraman generally needs some time to set his zoom before he can operate effectively from his new position.

6. Although this point is not necessarily a disadvantage, you should keep in mind that a zoom looks different from a dolly. If you dolly in for a close-up with a wide-angle lens, the object in front will become larger, while the background will remain relatively small. If you zoom in, however, the foreground and the background will be magnified simultaneously—there will be no obvious perspective change.

There are a few potential dangers when using a zoom lens; they are not inherent in the zoom lens itself but instead are caused by the operator. Precisely because zooming has become relatively easy to do, there is a great temptation to overuse it. Directors as well as cameramen who misunderstand what visual interest in television means are often inclined to zoom in and out vigorously and indiscriminately on a lecturer, for example, just to keep up the viewer's interest. But rather than maintaining the viewer's interest, a constant zooming motion on the screen usually distracts it. Also, zooms are often used when dollies would be much more appropriate and aesthetically effective.

One word of caution about fast zooms: they may very well create a good and impressive dramatic effect; more frequently, however, a fast zoom seems to make the object jump right out of the television screen. Continuous fast zooming (in or out) is apt to make even the steadiest television viewer somewhat seasick.

For remote television pickups, in restricted studio space, and for color cameras, of course, zoom lenses have become an essential tool in television production. If you have only one zoom camera available on a three- or four-camera remote telecast, always place your zoom camera first so that you can set it up in the most advantageous field position. Also, it is a good idea to have your most able cameraman operate the zoom camera, since this will be the camera most frequently used during the telecast.

## SUMMARY

There are two basic types of television lenses: (1) fixed-focal-length lenses, or turret lenses, on which you cannot change the angle of view, and (2) variable-focal-length lenses, or zoom lenses, which allow a continuous changing of the angle of view.

Important optical characteristics of television lenses are (1) focal length or zoom range, (2) focus, (3) $f$/stop, and (4) depth of field.

The turret lenses come in two lens types: the 16mm-film type and the 35mm-film type. All image-orthicon lenses use 35mm type; most vidicon, Plumbicon, and color cameras use the 16mm type. However, some of these cameras can also operate with 35mm lenses.

With the exception of the TK-42 camera, which has a lens turret, all color cameras have zoom lenses.

As with turret lenses, which are grouped into studio and field lenses, the zoom lenses vary in zoom range for studio and field use. Some zoom lenses come equipped with a range extender, which increases the zoom range.

Zoom lenses can be operated either by manual zoom and focus controls or by motor-driven servo controls.

In general, zoom lenses are slower (larger minimum diaphragm opening) than turret lenses.

## EXERCISES

1. Are dolly lenses short or long lenses? Why?
2. What is a variable-focal-length lens?
3. What do you accomplish by turning the focus knob?
4. What is the difference between image-orthicon lenses and vidicon lenses?
5. What are the differences between a zoom and a dolly?
6. What are the advantages of using a zoom lens instead of the normal lens complement? What are the disadvantages?
7. What is the relationship between $f$-stop number and diaphragm opening?

8. Define depth of field.
9. How can you increase the depth of field?
10. What lens of your normal turret would you use to get a very tight close-up of a small object? Why?

# 3

## Audio

Experts in the field of communication estimate that as much as 65 per cent of human intelligence is transmitted among people by sound. Although the term *tele-vision* indicates a strong emphasis on the transmission of pictures, *tele-audio,* the sound part of television, plays a vital part in the television communication process. We may even wonder sometimes whether the picture portion or the sound portion of television is more important for getting ideas across. At one time or another, you may have experienced a temporary interruption of the picture transmission right in the middle of a fascinating program you were watching. As long as you could hear the audio portion, you were still able to follow the story more or less accurately. But have you ever noticed how difficult it is to follow a program when the sound portion is temporarily interrupted? The relative importance of audio and video is not the major argument of this discussion, however. The point to remember is that television audio is one of the most vital television production factors.

Good television audio is very difficult to achieve. In radio, the announcer or actor is mostly "on mike," which means that he is moderately close to the microphone at all times. The distance from sound source to microphone varies little; a good audio level can be easily maintained. All extraneous noises are kept out of the immediate vicinity of the live radio microphone. Only planned and intended sounds are picked up and amplified.

(In television operation, the audio situation is quite different. First, contrary to radio, the sound source in television is often in motion. Television actors and performers may move rapidly around the studio while speaking. Second, the performer usually speaks to the camera or to someone else, but rarely speaks directly to the microphone. Third, many television shows require the microphone to be kept out of the camera picture. The microphone will thus have to be raised or lowered to correspond to the position of the camera and the lenses used. This in turn causes a frequent and sometimes extreme change of distance from sound source to microphone. Fourth, in the construction of television studios, acoustics are usually considered last, if at all. The noise level during a telecast is always high. Production and engineering crews are constantly moving about on the hard-surfaced studio floor. They are pushing heavy camera and microphone dollies, changing scenery, getting performers into the proper positions, and talking, more or less softly, through their intercommunications system.)

In order to combat these audio hazards, an ideal microphone would have to be (1) light and mobile to follow performers quickly and easily; (2) able to pick up the desired sounds from comparatively great distances without any loss of audio quality; (3) highly directional— that is, very sensitive to desired sounds and insensitive to all extraneous noises; and (4) rugged enough for both studio and outdoor use.

Unfortunately, no one microphone has all these characteristics. To satisfy specific television audio requirements, existing radio microphones have been specially adapted and new microphones developed. All three general types of microphones—(1) ribbon microphones, (2) dynamic microphones, and (3) condenser microphones—are used in television operations. Although all three types work on different electronic principles, their common purpose is to pick up sound vibrations and to convert them into electrical energy. How good or how bad a specific microphone is depends not only on its electronic characteristics but also on where and how it is used. Therefore, television microphones are usually classified according to the way in which they are used. There are nine types of television microphones: (1) boom microphones, (2) hand microphones, (3) lavaliere and lapel microphones, (4) desk microphones, (5) stand microphones, (6) hanging microphones, (7) concealed microphones, (8) wireless (FM) microphones, and (9) "long-distance" microphones.

In the following discussion, we will divide television microphones into two general groups—mobile and stationary.

## MOBILE MICROPHONES

The mobile microphones include (1) boom microphones, (2) hand microphones, (3) lavaliere and lapel microphones, (4) wireless or FM microphones, and (5) long-distance microphones.

### Boom Microphones

#### The big boom

The most flexible television studio microphone is one that is suspended on a special microphone boom. The boom facilitates rapid and smooth movement of the microphone from one spot to another anywhere in the studio. This freedom of movement makes it easy to keep the microphone out of the television picture. You can simultaneously extend and retract the microphone, pan it horizontally, tilt it vertically, and rotate it at the end of the boom to allow for directional sound pickup. During all these operations you can freely move the boom assembly from one place in the studio to another. Thus, you can follow sound sources over relatively great distances without interrupting the audio pickup because of rapidly moving cameras.

The most widely used large booms are the Mole-Richardson boom and the Fisher boom. Two minor limitations of the Mole-Richardson boom are the restricted panning radius and the tricycle steering mechanism. You cannot pan the boom more than 180 degrees without stepping off the comparatively small platform. The whole boom assembly will have to be moved to allow a full-circle boom swing. The one-wheel steering mechanism limits quick and easy maneuverability. You can move the boom only backwards and forwards, straight or in turns, according to the position of the steering wheel. You cannot move it sideways.

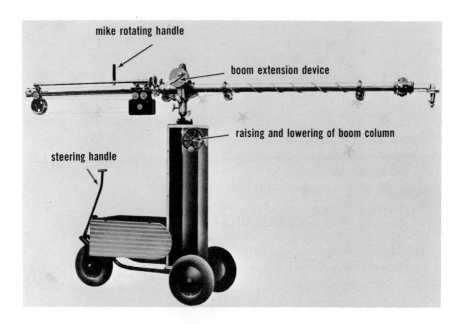

mike rotating handle

boom extension device

raising and lowering of boom column

steering handle

Both limitations can be easily overcome by rather simple platform adjustments, however. Several local stations have built their own platform devices, which allow flexibility in horizontal panning and in boom repositioning (see the photograph on page 77). The boom is mounted on a triangular base with three swivel casters. Since all three casters can swivel freely, the boom can be moved in any direction without delay. A round platform enables the operator to pan the boom a full 360 degrees without running the danger of falling off.

The Fisher boom incorporates these adjustments in its design. In comparison with the Mole-Richardson boom, the Fisher boom assembly (see page 78) is lighter, allows a 360-degree pan, can be moved in any direction without delay, and even has a small stool attached to it. The stool is greatly appreciated by the boom operator, who may have to work for two or three hours under hot studio lights.

There are two major disadvantages in using a big boom in small studios and small station operations. (1) It needs two men for proper boom manipulation: (a) a boom operator who works the microphone boom and (b) a boom platform operator who helps to reposition the boom assembly whenever necessary. (2) It takes up valuable floor space, which, in a small studio, may cut down considerably the maneuverability of the cameras. If the studio is large enough, however, you can place the big boom in the center of the performing areas, allowing the boom to cover two or three performing areas with-

out having to reposition the boom dolly. In this case, the cameras can work either in front or to one side of the boom.

### The medium boom

In a studio with severe space limitations, you may prefer a medium boom to the bigger and bulkier Mole-Richardson. The medium, or giraffe, boom can do almost anything the big boom can do with the exception of extension and retraction. This, however, can be easily compensated for by pushing the boom closer to the sound source or by pulling it back.

There are other advantages of the giraffe over the big boom. (1) The medium boom requires only one operator, who can also handle the relocation of the boom. (2) The medium boom does not take up as much studio space as the big boom. (3) The microphone tilting

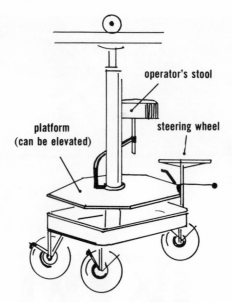

operator's stool

platform
(can be elevated)                        steering wheel

Fisher microphone boom base

and rotation devices are mechanically simpler than those of the big boom—they require less maintenance and are less inclined to become inoperative during a telecast. (4) The medium boom can, because of its low height and narrow wheel base, be easily moved from one studio to another through narrow doorways or hallways. It can also be quickly disassembled and taken to remote locations, if necessary.

Some disadvantages of the giraffe, however, deprive it of being the ideal microphone boom in television production. (1) Because of the considerable weight of the microphone, the extension of the light boom is limited in length. This relatively short boom requires the boom operator to stand close to the sound source, which not only tends to increase the general noise level but also may prevent the camera from getting extreme wide shots; the boom operator and microphone may very well get into camera range. (2) The boom is relatively low, another danger of getting the microphone into the picture. (3) Contrary to the big boom, where audio and earphone cables are counterweighted from the ceiling, the microphone and earphone cables for the medium boom are usually on the floor. These cables may hamper quick relocations of the medium boom, especially in dollying in or out. (4) Because of its lightness, the boom is subject to shock and vibrations. The microphone attached to the

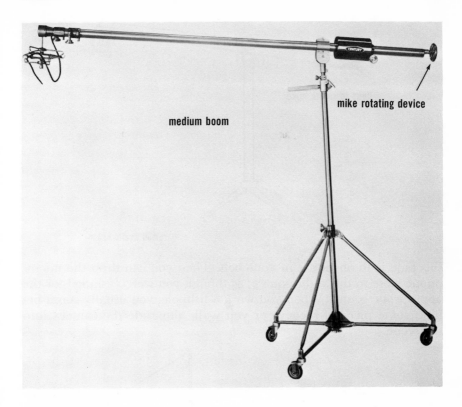

mike rotating device

medium boom

medium boom is more exposed to physical shock than the micro-phone of the smoothly operating Mole-Richardson or Fisher booms.

### The small boom

The small boom (see page 80) is simply a small giraffe. It has the same characteristics as the medium boom. The boom extension, how-ever, is shorter and the swivel-caster base smaller than those of the medium boom. The small boom is most advantageous in extremely limited space, such as kitchen studios or small set areas. It is often used as a supplementary boom.

### The fishpole boom

In certain production situations, even the small giraffe boom is not flexible enough for a quick and accurate audio pickup. What you can use then is an extremely simple yet very effective device: a hand-held aluminum or bamboo pole to which a microphone is at-tached. As "boom operator" you hold this fishpole device into the scene for brief periods of audio pickup. One of the best ways to hold

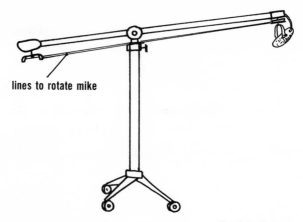

lines to rotate mike

**Small giraffe boom**

this pole is to anchor it in your belt. Then you can drop the microphone close to the audio source, as though you were "fishing" for the appropriate sound. When you work a fishpole, you usually stand behind some piece of scenery or you walk alongside the camera into the scene.

**"Fishpole" microphone technique**

The advantages of this fishpole technique are obvious: (1) the microphone is extremely flexible; it can swing easily up and down and sideways; (2) the fishpole is easy to operate and needs only one person per microphone; and (3) the fishpole takes up very little space.

### Types of boom microphones — long distance ; Shot gun mike

A good boom microphone should have the ability to pick up sound over a relatively great distance without too much distortion or loss of sound presence. Also, the boom microphone should be rugged enough to withstand jolts and to resist abrupt climatic changes.

Most modern television microphone research is directed toward the development of rugged, high-quality dynamic or ribbon microphones.

The microphone that ideally fulfills all these pickup requirements has still not been developed. However, several available microphones have proved extremely useful as boom microphones. These are (1) the Electro-Voice 642, (2) the RCA BK-5A, (3) the Shure SM 5, (4) the Electro-Voice 666, and (5) the RCA 77-DX.

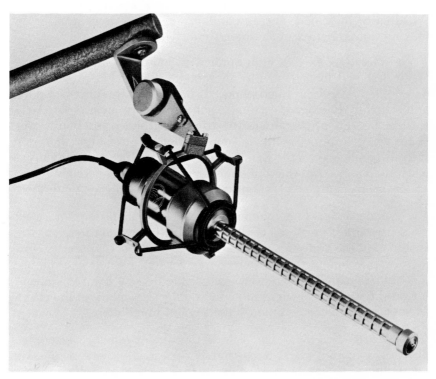

**Electro-Voice 642**

*The Electro-Voice 642.* This ultradirectional dynamic microphone with an extremely narrow pickup pattern has become one of the most widely used television boom microphones. Although quite heavy and bulky for a boom microphone, the E-V 642 picks up sound with rather good presence over a comparatively great distance. This quality is, of course, especially desirable in situations where the microphone must necessarily remain fairly far away from the sound source. The narrow pickup pattern helps in shutting out extraneous noises that would be picked up, at least partially, by a microphone with a wider pattern. A windscreen covers the microphone assembly and permits rapid boom swings and even outdoor use without picking up annoying wind blasts.

This microphone has several disadvantages. (1) The very directional pickup pattern makes constant "aiming" of the microphone essential. (2) Although the pickup pattern is extremely narrow, the sharp pickup beam does not necessarily stop at the sound source, but extends frequently beyond the source, picking up extraneous noises just as clearly. (3) The frequency response is somewhat limited; the 642 needs very good studio acoustics to work at full efficiency. (4) As already indicated, the microphone is rather long and heavy, making manipulation of the boom somewhat difficult.

*The RCA BK-5A.* This high-quality ribbon microphone, also especially designed for use on the microphone boom, has proved to be an excellent television microphone. It has a good frequency response and a highly directional cardioid, or heartshaped, pickup pattern. It is rugged and relatively insensitive to physical shock and blasts, especially when equipped with its good (optional) blast filter. It is considerably lighter than the Electro-Voice 642, another great advantage when used as a boom microphone. This relatively light-weight microphone is especially good when used on a medium or a small boom.

*The Shure SM 5.* This dynamic microphone has pickup characteristics very similar to those of the BK-5A. It has a good frequency response to music and voice and has an amazingly good presence. However, despite an integral windscreen that covers the whole microphone, it is quite sensitive and not as rugged as the BK-5A. Even so, depending on the studio acoustics, the sound quality is sometimes thought to be superior to other commonly used boom microphones.

*The Electro-Voice 666.* The E-V 666 is an extremely rugged, all-purpose dynamic microphone that is occasionally used as a boom microphone. It has been specifically designed to operate under a great variety of pickup conditions. It can be used indoors and outdoors. There are several apparent advantages of using this micro-

RCA BK-5A

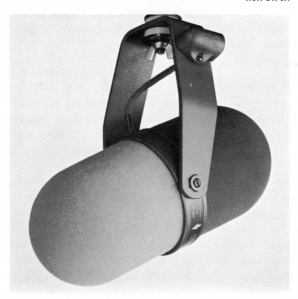

Shure SM 5

phone on the television boom: (1) it can withstand extreme temperature changes and physical shock; (2) with a rubber windscreen, it is relatively insensitive to unwanted wind noise; and (3) its cardioid pattern is fairly directional.

Electro-Voice 666

Its major disadvantage is that it lacks quality, especially when used on a boom fairly far from the sound source. The somewhat limited frequency response tends to accentuate room rumble, especially in small studios. Also, when the microphone is relatively far away from the sound source, it lacks presence.

*The RCA 77-DX.* This "classic" radio microphone is still occasionally used as a television boom microphone. Far from being a perfect boom microphone, the RCA 77-DX nevertheless fulfills one important audio function: it has an excellent sound-pickup quality, with a fine low- and high-frequency response. Its variable, cardioid pickup pattern is frequently directional enough for close sound pickup. However, there are several disadvantages that severely limit its use as a television boom microphone: (1) as a ribbon microphone, it is extremely sensitive to physical shock; (2) it is large and fairly heavy; (3) its pickup pattern is not narrow enough to shut out many of the extraneous noises in a television studio; (4) if the sound source is relatively far away from this microphone, a considerable loss of presence becomes inevitable; and (5) it is very sensitive to wind, which pretty nearly rules out any rapid boom movement as long as a constant audio level has to be maintained during the boom swings.

**RCA 77-DX**

### Operational techniques of boom microphones

In smaller television stations, booms are operated quite frequently by production people rather than by engineers, so you should know a few basic boom-microphone techniques.

There are many books on how to drive an automobile, but we only really learn how to drive through actual practice. Practice and experience are also necessary for the operation of a boom microphone or, for that matter, any other television equipment. There are, however, some basic rules that will make your learning process shorter and easier and that will help you avoid time- and energy-consuming mistakes.

As a television boom operator, you are responsible for keeping the microphone as close as possible to the sound source without getting the microphone into camera picture range. Doing this involves a great amount of coordination and anticipation. Simultaneously you must (1) keep the microphone in front of the sound source, (2) watch the audio balance in case there is more than one sound source, (3) listen to the director's signals, (4) watch the movement of cameras and lenses that are used, (5) watch for undesirable boom shadows, and (6) anticipate as much as possible the movements of the television performers. Not an easy task, indeed! Let's examine these tasks in detail.

1. Sometimes an unskilled boom operator keeps the microphone directly over the head of the performer. Yet the performer speaks with his mouth and not with the top of his head. The microphone should always be kept *in front* of the sound source. Doing so requires good judgment of distance and quick reactions. It also involves complete cooperation with the performer. A good performer will always be conscious of the microphone boom without letting anyone know. He can help both the boom operator and the audio engineer to a great extent. A slight movement of the performer can mean a complicated boom operation. Even though the performer merely turns his head from left to right while talking, for instance, you will have to pan the boom horizontally several feet and rotate the microphone in order to keep it in front of the sound source. A single stooping down of the television performer while talking involves a great vertical movement of the boom. Vertical movements are usually difficult to manipulate quickly, especially when the boom is racked out as far as it will go.

If the performer turns to a blackboard while talking, you will have to rack the boom out in front of him and rotate the microphone around so that its live side is pointing toward the sound source. This procedure requires smooth, fast coordination. Usually, by the time you have racked the boom into its proper position, the performer will have turned around again to speak to the camera. The same fast boom movement is now necessary in reverse. In the above-mentioned example, it would be more practical to place the microphone to the side and compromise pickup quality. Much better results can, of course, be achieved if the performer talks only when he faces the camera and not while his back is turned.

2. Watch the audio balance. If you have to cover more than one sound source with a single boom, place the microphone between the sound sources so that an adequate balance can be achieved. Boom operator and audio engineer will have to cooperate in maintaining this balance. In general, always favor the weaker voice. This you can do by rotating the live side of the microphone toward the weaker sound source. Once you have found a proper balance, leave the microphone in this position, if possible, even though the stronger voice may do most of the talking. The rotating of the microphone toward whoever is talking is a satisfactory device if properly handled. However, it requires constant microphone movement and volume adjustment,

which should be avoided whenever possible. If the show has not been rehearsed and you are not familiar with the voice quality of a studio guest, for instance, a safe practice is to favor the guest. The professional performer will almost always have a stronger voice than the nonprofessional guest.

When there are three or more sound sources, you may have to move the microphone to the specific person talking; this is not an easy job, especially if the sequence of the persons speaking has not been predetermined. Again the talent can help by cooperating closely. A practical example might help to explain this problem.

*Situation:* There are two major audio areas: (1) a group of ten high school students covered by a mobile big-boom microphone, and (2) a political personality covered by a fixed medium-boom microphone opposite the student group. The students direct random questions at the politician.

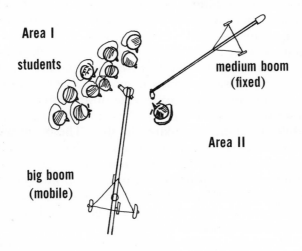

*Problem:* The big-boom operator must anticipate which student will ask the next question so that he can place the boom microphone properly before the question is asked.

*Two possible solutions:* (a) The *sequence* of students asking questions is predetermined, or (b) the students asking questions *identify* themselves by raising their arms. The personality being interviewed can then point out a particular student he wishes to hear. This gives the boom operator a chance to place the boom properly before the student speaks.

3. Listen to the director's signals. The director's signals and camera instructions are equally important for the boom operator and the

cameraman. By listening to the director's camera instructions, the boom operator will be kept informed about such problems as camera movement, the nature of shots, lenses used, movement of performers, general studio traffic, and relocation of the boom.

As a boom operator, you will probably wear telephone headsets with "split audio"—one earphone will carry the director's signals and the other will be hooked up with the program audio. Sometimes boom operators prefer the regular one-ear telephone talkback headset, which leaves one ear free. The director's signals can be picked up more accurately on the one-ear headset, since only the intercommunication signals are carried. Proper audio balance is achieved by listening to the actual sound sources. In case of traffic and severe boom shadow problems, the boom operator can talk to director, audio engineer, and cameramen over the intercommunication line.

4. Watch cameras and lenses used. The use of a boom means, in general, that the microphone must be kept out of the picture. Camera position and lenses used will determine how close the microphone can get to the sound source.

If the camera is set up for a wide shot, you must necessarily raise the boom so that it will be out of the camera picture. If the camera is using a close-up lens, however, you may be able to bring the boom fairly close to the sound source. In case of an extreme long shot to establish a set or scene, the director should advise the performer not to speak while the camera is taking the shot. The boom will have to be so far up, away from the sound source, that even a bad audio pickup is impossible under these circumstances.

You will have to learn just how far up a boom must be to stay out of the camera picture. If the show is rehearsed, you can watch the studio monitor and see how close you can get the microphone to the sound source before the boom dips into the picture. Make sure, however, that you explain to the audio engineer and your director that you are merely testing how close you can bring the microphone to the sound source, and that you will certainly keep the boom out of the picture once the show is on the air. A good cameraman can help you with this type of rehearsal by motioning to you whenever the microphone begins to dip into his viewfinder picture.

Once you are on the air, and the microphone happens to get into the picture despite all your precautions, it is sometimes better to retract the boom slightly than to raise the microphone out of the picture. By retracting the boom, you will pull the mike out of the camera's view and at the same time will stay in front of the sound source rather than on top.

In an unrehearsed show, always keep the mike well above the

sound source, especially when close-ups and long shots follow each other rapidly.

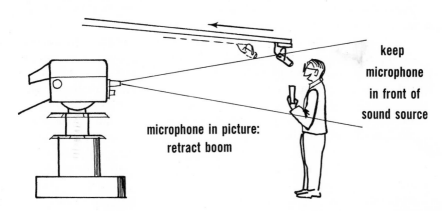

microphone in picture: retract boom

keep microphone in front of sound source

5. Watch shadows. Even the best lighting engineer cannot eliminate boom shadows; he can only throw the shadows into places where they are ordinarily not seen. It is up to the skill of the boom operator to keep the shadows out of the picture. That is not an easy task, especially when the show is unrehearsed. It may happen, for instance, that you have to move the microphone into a position that prevents good audio pickup, just to avoid big boom shadows on the face of the performer. You must quickly decide whether you should sacrifice good audio quality for good pictures. Quite frequently you will hear the director call, "Watch that boom shadow!" and then after you have corrected the microphone placement in order to eliminate the shadow the audio engineer will yell, "Get that mike closer to the guy, I can't hear a thing!" A good boom operator must then find a spot that will satisfy both parties sufficiently.

Since avoiding boom shadows can cause serious audio problems, you should check for shadows before the show. While specific set areas are lighted, swing the boom into these areas and look for undesirable shadows. Your lighting engineer will be happy to cooperate with you on this problem.

If you cannot avoid a boom shadow or if you discover it when the camera is already on the air, do not try to move the microphone quickly. Everyone will then be sure to see the shadow travel across the screen. Rather, try to move the shadow slowly out of the picture. Sometimes it may even be better just to keep the microphone and its shadow as steady as possible until a relief shot permits you to move the microphone into a more advantageous position.

6. Anticipate movements of performers. As a good boom operator,

you should never get too involved in what the performers are saying or in any other aspect of the show. It may distract you from your job as boom operator. But you should always anticipate their movements. If the performer is sitting, you will have to raise the boom just as he is about to rise. You should have your boom ready for panning just when he is going to make his cross into another set area. You will also have to rotate the mike just ahead of his actual turn. You should remember all the rehearsed boom swings and be ready for them just a split second before the actual move. That way you can avoid fast boom swings, which always bring about some undesirable wind noise, regardless of the windscreen you might have on your microphone. Also, the danger of hitting something with the microphone or with the boom itself is greatly increased by sudden and frantic boom swings.

Horizontal and vertical locking of the boom during an ad-lib show is also dangerous. If the performer rises unexpectedly, he may already be out of the chair before your boom is unlocked. This can be quite embarrassing for both of you, especially when he bumps his head on the locked microphone.

The locking mechanisms on the boom are usually intended for a fixed boom position, which means a positioning over a particular area in which the sound source may move only slightly, if at all. A locked boom does not need a boom operator.

### Hand Microphones

Television hand microphones do not need a special operator and are usually carried by the performer. Because hand microphones are "handled" so much, they must be very rugged and insensitive to physical shock. Often they are taken outside on remote locations during rain, snow, and summer heat, so they must also be immune to extreme temperature changes. For these reasons, rugged dynamic microphones are used.

Additionally, hand microphones should be small and slim enough to be handled easily and should not look obtrusive when held by the performer. Since hand microphones are often used outdoors and therefore close to the mouth, they must be fairly insensitive to explosive breath "pops." Above all, they must have good quality, since they are often used by singers. As with boom microphones, manufacturers are constantly trying to fulfill all these requirements with one microphone. Consequently, new hand-microphone models appear frequently on the market. However, the differences among the various models are not great enough to influence basic production techniques. We will therefore discuss only a few representative models.

### Types of hand microphones

The most common types of hand microphones are (1) the Electro-Voice 655C; (2) the Shure SM 58, (3) the Electro-Voice 635A, and (4) the Shure SM 60.

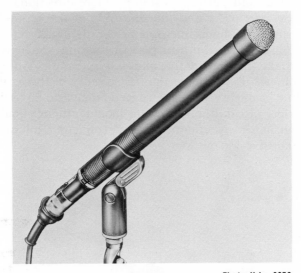

Electro-Voice 665C

Shure SM 58

The *Electro-Voice 665C* and the *Shure SM 58* are both rather rugged and fairly large. They are designed for outdoor work where the announcer works very close to the microphone. Both microphones have a "pop" filter to eliminate unwanted speech noises. The 665C has an omnidirectional (all-directional) pickup pattern; the SM 58, with its rather wide cardioid pattern, is slightly more directional.

The *Electro-Voice 635A* and the *Shure SM 60* are representative of the many "slim-line" hand microphones available. Both microphones are fairly rugged, have built-in pop filters, and are light and slim enough to make them attractive and easy to handle. Although these two microphones do not have the best quality of those available in the "slim-line" category, they are rugged enough to be used outdoors under a variety of conditions. Similar-looking, higher-quality microphones, such as the Neumann KM 63 condenser microphone, are much too sensitive for outdoor use.

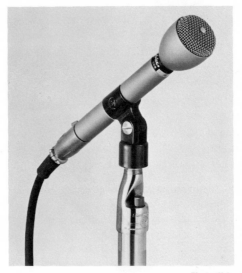

Electro-Voice 635A

With few exceptions (such as the Shure SM 58), the hand microphones are omnidirectional. This pickup pattern is quite desirable, since it allows the hand microphones to be worked from any direction without noticeable frequency discrimination.

### Use of hand microphones

*Outdoor use.* The hand microphone is used for a great variety of programming. Most obviously, it is used for telecasts in remote loca-

Shure SM 60

tions. The hand microphone is always seen on camera. It can therefore be held as close to the sound source as is desirable. Since the performer holds the hand microphone himself, he takes care of audio balance simply by pointing the microphone toward a specific sound source. Even amidst surrounding noise, such as in a factory or in the middle of a cheering crowd, he achieves good audio pickup by holding the microphone close to whomever is speaking.

*Studio use.* The use of hand microphones in the studio eliminates all worries about undesirable boom shadows or sudden appearances of boom microphones in the television picture. There is no boom to cast shadows, and the microphone is in the picture all the time. The great advantage of using a hand microphone in the studio is that it makes a special boom operator unnecessary, thereby saving manpower and, ultimately, money—an important factor in any production consideration.

The hand microphone is used extensively in audience participation shows. The performer can talk to anyone in the audience simply by walking up to certain people with the hand microphone and picking up their answers as he sees fit.

The hand microphone, however, is not without severe disadvantages:

1. The quality of a hand microphone is not as good as that of a sensitive boom microphone.

2. Since almost all hand microphones are omnidirectional, they can pick up unwanted sounds from all directions, especially when the performer is in an "off-mike" position.

3. The performer must take care of the microphone cable, dragging it across the studio floor between cameras and around scenery; there is always the danger that the cable will get caught someplace, stopping the performer from moving any farther without losing his hand microphone. Cables are a constant menace to the freely traveling cameras. If many microphone cables are strung across the floor, the camera may have to roll over several of these cables in order to get quickly into proper shooting position.

4. Since the hand microphone has to be carried by the performer, one of his hands will always be tied up. Some skilled performers wedge the hand microphone under one of their arms so that they will have both hands available to demonstrate a commercial product. This particular technique is not desirable, however, because the microphone is usually too far from the sound source for good audio pickup. Rubbing and banging noises are easily picked up this way.

5. The unskilled performer may consider the hand microphone as an effective prop, swinging it wildly through the air in order to make a point. This practice, of course, also impairs good audio pickup.

6. The performer may hold the microphone too close to his mouth, thereby transmitting more speech noises than messages.

### Lavaliere and Lapel Microphones

Lavaliere microphones (or neck microphones, as they are sometimes called) were developed especially for television operation. These small, unobtrusive microphones are usually hung on a neckcord close to the chest, leaving both hands free for demonstration. Lavaliere microphones can also be held by hand, in which case they are handled just like regular hand microphones. Lavaliere microphones are excellent wherever microphone concealment, individual mobility, or free movement of hands is required.

There are several types of lavaliere microphones on the market. The most widely used are the RCA BK-6B, the Electro-Voice 649A, and the very small RCA BK-12A.

Although there are some differences in ruggedness and frequency response among the various lavaliere microphones, the differences are, in general, not distinct enough to warrant a lengthy discussion. Generally, the wearing techniques and the advantages and disadvantages of using lavaliere microphones are common to all types mentioned. All lavaliere microphones have an omnidirectional pickup pattern.

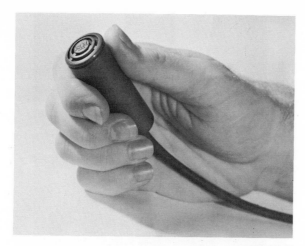

RCA BK-6B

Electro-Voice 649A

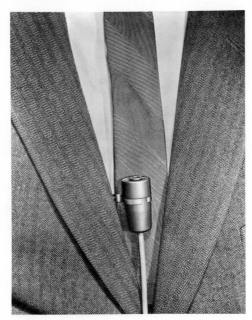

RCA BK-12A

### Wearing techniques

The small size of the lavaliere microphone is important, since it is intended to be more or less concealed. The audience is usually not aware of the microphone (at least the performer likes to think so). Some performers hide the microphone under a tie or a high-buttoned jacket, or, if a woman, underneath the blouse or dress. Complete concealment, however, reduces audio quality considerably. Burying the microphone beneath layers of clothing produces the same effect as good soundproofing material in the studio. The sound, if it manages to penetrate the unwanted "filter" at all, comes out extremely muffled. A dress or blouse of light material or a tie is about all that should be worn over the microphone. Even then, clothes rubbing against the microphone can produce disturbing crackling noises. Much better sound quality will be obtained if the microphone is worn on top of the clothing.

Always fasten the microphone to the neckcord securely to keep the microphone in place, even if there is a heavy pull from the microphone cable. Make sure that no tie clasps, large buttons, jewelry, or similar objects can rub against the microphone. Also, avoid hitting the microphone with any objects you may be demonstrating on camera.

mike open          mike concealed

Wearing techniques

### Some advantages and disadvantages

The advantages of the lavaliere microphone are many. (1) In contrast to a boom microphone, it can be used in even the most cramped studio locations. (2) The performer wears the microphone himself; no special microphone operator is necessary. (3) The performer does not have to worry about proper handling of the microphone, because it is securely fastened to his chest; his hands are free. (4) Since the distance from sound source to microphone remains relatively unchanged, the sound quality and sound intensity remain fairly even; thus the job of the audio engineer in the audio booth is considerably easier. (5) The performer can move quickly and easily without having to worry about being followed by a boom. (6) There are no boom shadow problems. (7) A flexible microphone cable allows fairly unrestricted movement within the studio.

Again, there are some disadvantages to this type of microphone. (1) The general microphone quality rule—the smaller the mike, the lower the sound quality—unfortunately applies to the lavaliere microphone. Although lavaliere microphones are used for voice pickup only, lack of frequency response is quite noticeable, especially when the performer is switched from the lavaliere microphone to a high-quality boom microphone. (2) The lavaliere microphone has a non-directional pickup pattern, which is a disadvantage since it is worn at a distance from the sound source. (3) The microphone can be used for one sound source only—that of the particular wearer. Even for a simple interview, two microphones will have to be used. (4) Although the microphone cable allows considerable mobility, it still may cause considerable restriction of the performer's movements. When two or more performers are "wired" with lapel microphones, movements are even more restricted. Crossing the cables usually results in a tangle.

Nevertheless, lavaliere microphones are excellent audio pickup devices, especially in view of the lack of manpower and space in small studio operation. The lavaliere microphone can be used extensively for one-man newscasts, interviews, commercial announcements, and other one-man performances. Extremely limited space may necessitate the use of several lavaliere microphones.

Lapel microphones are similar to the lavaliere microphones. They are smaller than the lavaliere mikes, however, and are often worn as a "lapel button."

## Wireless or FM Microphones

The ideal television microphone would be a small, high-quality lavaliere microphone without a cable—a wireless microphone. Constant efforts are being made to develop a wireless microphone that would satisfy the broadcast industry's operational and electronical requirements.

The most widely used wireless microphones are the Vega-Mike*, the Budelman microphone, and the Sony CR-6.

*Vega-Mike is a registered trademark by Vega Electronics Corporation.

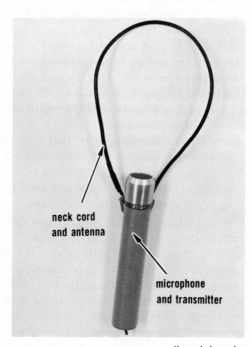

neck cord
and antenna

microphone
and transmitter

Vega wireless microphone

Vega wireless microphone receiving station

All wireless microphones work according to a basic FM-transmission principle. The performer wears or holds a medium-sized microphone. This microphone is connected to a small pocket transmitter whose sending antenna is either worn around the waist or pinned along the trousers or skirt of the performer. The most flexible wireless microphones are entirely self-contained. Such a mike is the Vega-Mike, which has its transmitter built into the microphone itself. The sending antenna either sticks out of the microphone or serves as the neck cord by which the microphone is worn. A special receiving station with one or several antennae can be located as far as 1,000 feet from the microphone, although most stations operate most satisfactorily at a distance not exceeding 500 feet. This receiving station amplifies the signal and sends it to the master audio mixer. Since the signal transmission from the microphone to the receiving station represents, in fact, a miniature FM broadcast, you will need an FCC license for operating wireless microphones.

Despite the obvious advantages of wireless microphones, their operation has been restricted to some highly specific production tasks. Most often, wireless microphones are used in restricted remote locations. Less frequently, they are employed in studio productions. One television network used nothing but wireless microphones in the production of a daily soap opera with considerable success. In small station operations, however, wireless microphones are rarely used, for several reasons. (1) Wireless microphones are quite expensive. Considering that you will need one microphone per sound source, the cost factor becomes a real issue for most day-to-day television operations. (2) Several qualified engineers are needed to operate the equipment effectively. (3) Problems in transmission still occur. (4) The audio quality as transmitted by the wireless system is somewhat below that of a good boom microphone.

## Long-Distance Microphones

The basic problem in television audio is to pick up sound adequately over a comparatively great distance. This problem becomes especially apparent in televising remote events. In sports telecasts, for example, it is fairly easy to get a close look at far-away action through long lenses, but it is quite difficult to accompany such pictures with adequate sound.

Three basic "long-distance" microphone techniques have, therefore, been developed: (1) the strategic placement of microphones in the field; (2) the operation of ultradirectional microphones; and (3) the parabolic-reflector microphone technique.

### Field microphones

Whenever the sound occurs in stable and fairly predictable areas, rugged microphones, such as the E-V 666, are placed directly into the field and aimed in the general direction of the anticipated sound source. Microphone cables are strung back to the remote control center, which is usually located in the remote truck.

This method sounds simple, but it is difficult to employ. First, you need several microphones to cover even a fairly restricted area. Second, the many cables have to be strung over a wide area and long distance, thereby causing not only traffic problems but audio problems. The many cables use up valuable inputs on the audio board—imputs that might have to be used for other, more critical audio purposes. Field microphones, which remain stationary, are used only when the installation is fairly permanent.

### Ultradirectional microphones

The usual long-distance sound pickup, especially when the sound source is moving in a rather unpredictable way, is accomplished by using ultradirectional microphones. There are two basic techniques: (1) the "shotgun-microphone" technique, and (2) the "camera-microphone" technique.

*Shotgun microphones,* sometimes referred to as "machine-gun" microphones, are highly directional microphones, such as the E-V 643, and can pick up sounds over a relatively great distance. The shotgun microphone is a rugged, omnidirectional microphone with tubes, ranging from 2 inches to 5 feet in length, bundled tightly together at the microphone diaphragm. The tubes make the omnidirectional microphone highly unidirectional. The long-barreled shotgun microphone is aimed at the distant sound source and follows that sound source much as a gun follows a moving target. Unfortunately, the microphone is quite heavy. It must rest on a special pedestal that permits simultaneous tilting and panning. Despite its ultradirectional features, the audio pickup is adequate at best and is generally used only when quality is the least important factor in the sound transmission.

Electro-Voice 643 "machine-gun" microphone

A simplified version of the shotgun principle is the *"camera-microphone"* technique. In this operation, highly directional microphones, such as the E-V 642, are mounted directly in front of the key cam-

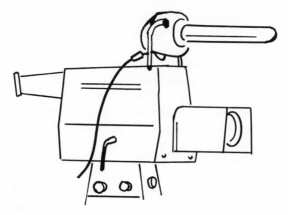

Electro-Voice 642 as "camera mike"

eras. The cameramen thus aim not only the lenses but also the camera-attached microphones in the direction of the action.

### Parabolic-reflector microphones

The parabolic reflector is one of the earliest devices developed for picking up sound over relatively great distances. Instead of the long barrels of the shotgun microphone, a parabolic disc is used to catch and focus the distant sound waves and to direct them into an ordinary microphone, which is placed in the focal point of the parabolic disc.

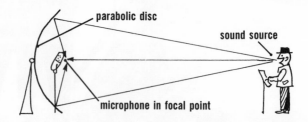

Unfortunately, depending on the size and material of the disc, only certain frequencies of the sound can be picked up. Since high and low frequencies react quite differently from each other, however, the over-all sound quality is not satisfactory. So far, parabolic-reflector pickups have been used only for broadcasting crowd effects, band music originating across a football stadium, and other sounds that provide atmosphere rather than specific information. Of course, there is ample room for experimentation in this area of long-distance sound pickup.

## STATIONARY MICROPHONES

Although most television microphones are mobile because the sound source is generally in motion, stationary microphones are also needed in television operation.

Stationary microphones are always used when the sound source remains fairly immobile. They are grouped into (1) desk microphones, (2) stand microphones, (3) hanging microphones, and (4) hidden microphones.

### Desk Microphones

Desk microphones are, as implied in the name, usually put on tables or desks. They are widely used in panel shows, public hearings, news shows, and all other shows where the performer is working from behind a desk, table, or lectern. In general, any television microphone can be used as a desk microphone, provided that suitable microphone stands are available. Most hand microphones are commonly used as desk microphones, since these microphones all come with optional desk stands. The desk mikes most frequently used are

Shure SM 56 Unidyne microphone

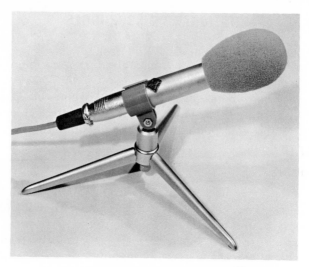

Neumann U 64

RCA BK-IA

(1) the E-V 635A, 655C, or 666; (2) the RCA BK-1A, (3) the Shure SM 56 or 57 (the Unidyne III), and other, higher-quality models, such as the Neumann U 64.

The RCA 77-DX is still used occasionally as a desk microphone. Its bulky appearance and its sensitivity to physical shock, however, tend to outweigh its fine pickup qualities.

*Placement for one performer.* Placing a desk microphone for one performer can present several problems. Since the performer is not only heard but *seen*, microphone placement is influenced by the camera picture, by the camera-conscious performer, and by other television equipment with which the television performer may have to work.

Consider desk-mike placement for a newscaster, for example. Because of various television equipment, the performer may talk in three different directions: (1) he may read the news script, looking down on the desk; (2) he may look up to face the camera; or (3) he may turn sideways during a film narration and look into an offside monitor. The news narration, delivered in three different directions, will have to be picked up adequately by one microphone.

If you place the microphone directly in front of the newscaster, you will (1) obstruct the camera's view of the newscaster and (2) neglect the audio pickup when he turns toward the monitor. To compensate for these factors, you should place the microphone somewhat

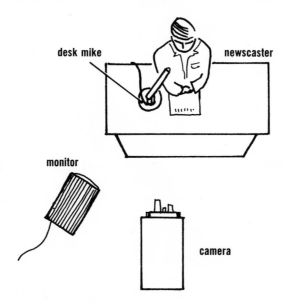

to the monitor side of the newscaster. The tilting angle of the microphone is usually determined by the voice quality of the performer. A good rule is to point the microphone toward the collarbone of the performer, approximately two or three feet away.

*Placement for two or more performers.* A proper audio pickup for two or more performers on a panel discussion, for instance, becomes difficult if the panel members face in different directions for their comments. Assume that there are five panel members seated in a row, all facing downstage, with the moderator in the middle and two panel members on each side. In general, the panel members will direct their

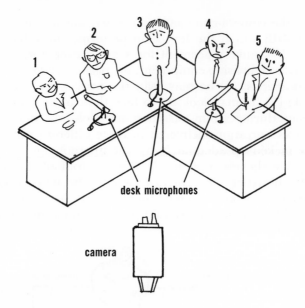

desk microphones

camera

comments to the moderator. At times, however, they may turn and address members of the panel who are seated at the extreme left or right of the table. You will have to provide for a satisfactory voice pickup at all times. This you could probably accomplish by placing a microphone between panel members 1 and 2 (counting from camera left to right), one microphone in front of the moderator, and a microphone between panel members 4 and 5. It is important to have the panel members sit as close together as possible, an advantage not only for good audio pickup but also for good camera work. All microphones must be of the same type. If different types of microphones are used, differences in audio quality become noticeable and distracting.

When two people are sitting opposite each other across a desk or a table, both persons will have to be "miked" separately.

In general, the final indicator of how many microphones are needed and where they should be placed is always the actual audio heard on the control room speaker. If one microphone is sufficient for good audio, then only one should be used.

Another problem, which is not too serious but which nevertheless exists, is the proper concealment and placement of microphone cables. Most often the cables are not just dropped in front of the desk or table but are carefully strung to the upstage side of the camera. Special news or panel desks sometimes have holes through which the cables can be dropped to the floor without being strung across desk or table. Masking tape is sometimes used to cover exposed microphone cables on the studio floor.

## Stand Microphones

Stand microphones are used whenever the sound source is immobile and when the type of program permits microphones to be seen.

High-quality microphones are placed on stands that can be vertically adjusted to a desired height. Since no attempt is made to conceal the microphones, large, high-quality microphones are generally used.

The sound pickup of an instrumental group, for example, is normally accomplished with several stand microphones. The microphones are placed in front of individual instruments or groups of instruments so as to assure maximum audio control during the sound mixing. The type of microphones used depends on such a variety of factors that any specific suggestions would only be misleading. For example, studio acoustics, the type and combination of instruments used, and the aesthetic quality of the "sound" finally desired all play an important part in the choice and placement of microphones. However, in music pickup, the RCA 77-DX is often used for the pickup of woodwinds, violins, or basses. European condenser microphones, such as the Neumann U 67 or various Sennheiser models, enjoy great popularity among music-recording engineers. Of course, the more rugged dynamic microphones (Shure SM 56 and 57, E-V 666) are also often used as stand microphones.

Stand microphones are also employed for guests and performers, such as an M.C., who remain standing.

The placement of stand microphones is governed by sound factors rather than by picture requirements. Whenever possible, however, the stand microphone should be placed so that it does not interfere too much with either camera movement or camera picture. In televising a piano concerto, a close-up of the pianist's hands is more important than a full view of an RCA 77-DX microphone standing in front of the piano, in spite of the all-important audio considerations.

Many factors influence the placement and types of microphones used, but the diagram on page 108 should give you some idea of what a typical microphone setup looks like for a small instrumental group consisting of piano, drums, saxophone, and bass.

## Hanging Microphones

Hanging microphones are used whenever a boom microphone cannot be used. Lack of space may make big-boom operation impossible, or one big-boom microphone may be insufficient for a large audio pickup area.

You can hang rugged dynamic microphones by their individual microphone cables from the overhead lighting grid so that they are

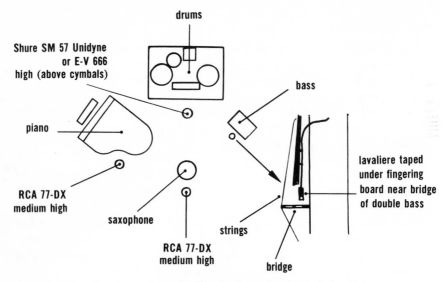

drums

Shure SM 57 Unidyne
or E-V 666
high (above cymbals)

bass

piano

lavaliere taped
under fingering
board near bridge
of double bass

RCA 77-DX
medium high

saxophone

strings

RCA 77-DX
medium high

bridge

Possible microphone set-up for standard musical group

out of camera range. Hanging microphones are not flexible. The sound source, in order to be picked up properly, must be fairly stationary. Hanging microphones can be used for stationary sound pickups, such as panel discussions and any other type of show where the sound source remains immobile at the time of sound pickup and where the showing of microphones on the screen is undesirable. These microphones are frequently used in dramatic presentations, where the action is carefully blocked so that the actors will be, ideally, in one particular spot for a particular speech. The actor will have to make sure to speak or sing only within the "audio pool" of the non-directional hanging microphone. Similar to a spotlight pool, where the actor is seen only so long as he moves within the limited area of the light pool, the actor is heard only if he speaks within the limited range of the audio pool.

In general, the audio quality of the hanging microphone is not very good. The sound source is relatively far away from the microphone. The sound waves do not always hit the microphone directly; at times they are picked up as reverberations.

If hanging microphones are placed near a hardwall set, or even worse, between two hard-surfaced scenery walls, the set may act as an echo chamber and distort the audio considerably. Sometimes even standing waves may be produced by the hardwall scenery, again an undesirable audio effect.

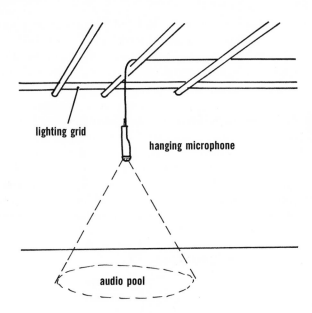

lighting grid

hanging microphone

audio pool

As a general rule, hanging microphones should never be placed too close to scenery. Avoiding close scenery is not always easy, especially since hanging microphones are used primarily when complex scenery prevents the use of boom microphones.

The successful use of hanging microphones depends to a great extent on the acoustical excellence of the television studio. Some small studios are very "live," which means that every sound is greatly reflected by the studio walls and ceiling. It is extremely difficult to achieve a proper sound pickup with hanging microphones in "live" studios.

Hanging microphones have several advantages. (1) No undesirable shadows are cast by these stationary microphones; full dramatic lighting can be employed with no consideration to boom shadows. (2) Hanging microphones do not need special boom operators. (3) These microphones are kept out of the camera's pictures. (4) There are no microphone cables on the floor, since the microphones are suspended from the ceiling by their own cables.

Some disadvantages are (1) relatively poor pickup quality, (2) limited performance radius, and (3) limited flexibility.

### Hidden Microphones

In the early days of television production, hidden microphones were quite fashionable. Television engineers could make use of several ingenious ideas, such as hiding small microphones in flower tufts, telephone dials, and desk drawers, behind commercial props, name plates, and curtains, and in many other places. The results of hidden-microphone audio pickup were not always satisfactory. First of all, the microphone cable presented a problem. Not only the microphone but also the cable had to be properly hidden. This was often time-consuming. Specific hiding places, such as desk drawers, quite frequently acted as sound chambers and produced a "boomy" audio quality. The sound source was often outside the audio pool of the concealed microphone, and the pickup could not always be compensated for by the audio engineer in the control booth.

Today, hidden microphones are sparingly used. Sometimes in dramatic productions a microphone may be hidden behind a curtain or some other object if a long speech will be delivered in its immediate

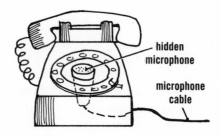

vicinity. This practice demands exact blocking and keeping within the blocking for good audio pickup. Audio engineers for the "Person to Person" remotes used hidden microphones in strategic places around the visited homes, strictly as a precautionary measure in case the mobile wireless microphones went out of order. Sometimes a small microphone is attached directly to an object for a special sound effect, such as a creaking rocking chair. Such mikes are then called "contact mikes."

## SOUND PERSPECTIVE

Sound perspective means that sound intensity and sound presence must be in proper relationship with the picture. When we see a close-up of a speaker, we expect to hear a louder and "closer" voice. In an extreme long shot showing us the speaker at a distance, we expect the voice to come from a distance, too. If the intensity and quality of the sound are the same for both shots, the pictures lose their credibility.

In some network shows, frequency and volume filters are coupled with the camera-switching panel. If the close-up camera is punched

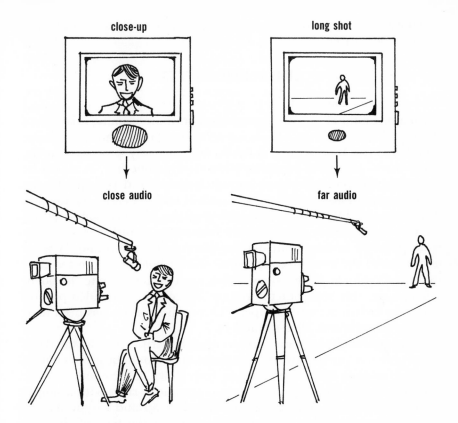

close-up long shot

close audio far audio

up (put on the air), the sound pickup is normal. If the wide-shot camera is punched up, the filter comes into effect and reduces quality and volume so that the sound appears to come from a distance. This technique, however, is effective only if ample rehearsal time is available so that camera and audio perspective can be worked out in great detail. We all can imagine how embarrassing and distracting a reversal of audio perspective could be.

The video-switcher–audio-filter hookup is now usually used for telephone filter effects in well-rehearsed dramas.

In smaller operations, audio perspective can be achieved by good cooperation between audio man and boom operator. The boom operator brings in the boom a little closer on a close-up and the audio man increases the audio to a slight degree. In a long shot, the reverse procedure takes place. These methods are usually sufficient for a believable audio perspective in smaller studios. Extreme wide shots are not possible in the small studio, so the audio change does not have to be very radical. Usually, the natural off-mike quality that is inevitable during an extreme long shot is enough to make audio perspective believable.

## LIVE SOUND EFFECTS

Manual live sound effects in television are not common. Most of the major sound effects are prerecorded or, more usually, taken from the sound effects library. There are a few exceptions, however. Some sounds can be more easily, quickly, and precisely produced in the studio itself. Gunshots on camera are always done live. It would be very hard for the audio man to match sound and picture exactly, since the sound lasts only a split second. It is much easier for the performer to use blank cartridges and produce his own sound effect. Off-camera gunshots, however, are frequently recorded, since there is no problem in synchronizing the picture and the sound. A word of caution to the gunslingers, however. Never hold your gun too close to the microphone. In one show, a shot went off too close to the boom microphone and blew out the ribbon altogether. The video portion had to be continued with a super: "Our audio portion has been temporarily interrupted. Please stand by."

For gunshots that are not written into the script, such as the demonstration of a quick draw, the audio engineer should be given enough warning so that he can prepare to turn down his volume control.

Other live sound effects may include telephone rings with a simple mobile bell battery unit, gongs, and other small and easy-to-handle sound instruments that require little effort on the part of the production crew. They may make the audio engineer's job a lot easier. Footsteps and opening and closing of doors are normally done live, too.

### Filters and Chambers

The most frequently used special live audio effects in television are the frequency filter, which reduces sounds purposely to familiar low-quality sounds like telephone voices and small radio sounds, and the echo chamber. Sometimes the audio engineer feeds the telephone directly into the audio board, or he places a microphone close to the telephone receiver. In the absence of an echo chamber, small stations often use an electronic echo device that works on a tape-delay basis. Echo devices are useful in "sweetening" music—that is, giving it a more fluid, alive sound than you would ordinarily get from a soundproof recording studio. The echo effect is quite similar to that of the sustaining pedal on a piano. If used properly, it is a fine asset; if used too often, it can ruin the best musical efforts.

## RECORDED SOUND

Recorded sound is used in television operation in a great variety of ways. Background music for film and live performances and recorded sound effects are the most commonly used recorded sound. Prerecorded commercials are sometimes played over specific video sequences.

Recorded sound can be reproduced from five television sources: (1) records, (2) electrical transcriptions (records intended for broadcast use only), (3) audio tape, (4) video tape, and (5) film. Records and audio tape are only indirectly coupled with the picture portion; that is, they are not mechanically synchronized with the picture. The audio portion of video tape and film is directly recorded on these media. The sound is thus mechanically synchronized with the picture. We will discuss video tape and film sound in Chapter 8.

### Records and Electrical Transcriptions

Records, including electrical transcriptions, are still the most frequently used recorded sound in television operation. For short segments, the standard records are increasingly being replaced with the more efficient cartridge-tape or "Cue-matic"-disc* operation. However, we can safely assume that standard records will be used for some time to come and that audio control rooms will still have to be equipped with a minimum of two turntables for smooth operation.

While one turntable is in operation, the next record can be cued up on the second turntable. A two-turntable operation also permits cross-fades, which could not otherwise be achieved.

Turntables have provisions to play all speeds—78, 45, 33⅓ rpm (revolutions per minute)—and all record sizes—6½, 7, 10, 12, and 16 inches in diameter. A special attachment is necessary for the wide-hole 45 rpm commercial records.

Different types of records also require different styli. Turntable tone arms are therefore equipped with interchangeable cartridges. Although you will seldom if ever use a 78 rpm record, you should have a cartridge with a 78 record needle available. Be sure to use the 78 cartridge on 78 records only, since its large stylus would ruin any long-playing record immediately.

You may also find different cartridges used for mono and stereo records. With a stereo cartridge, you can play stereo as well as mono long-playing records. But you must not play stereo records with a

---

*"Cue-matic" is a trademark of Ampex Corporation.

mono cartridge. Most tone arms now have a stereo cartridge, which can handle any record except 78s.

During all record-spinning operations, be sure to check for the proper speed of the turntables and the proper cartridge.

The Cue-matic (Ampex AG-100) audio-disc system is a highly efficient one. The Cue-matic system uses an 11¾ inch magnetic disc called a Cue-mat. The disc is so flexible that you can bend or practically fold it without doing any damage to it. The operation of the Cue-matic system is extremely simple and fast. All you do is insert the disc into a slot and wait for a signal light, which tells you that the disc has cued itself up. Depending on how you place the disc in the slot, this cuing procedure will take anywhere from less than one-half second to five seconds. After the disc is cued, you simply press a button and the disc will play virtually instantaneously, having reached stable speed within one-tenth of a second. Compared to standard records, the Cue-mat's maximum playing time of 3 minutes and 45 seconds is rather short. Most announcements and audio inserts in television, however, rarely go beyond this maximum playing time.

For more information on audio control, see the several good books available, particularly on turntable and audio-console operations.

### Audio Tape Recorders

The audio tape recorder is used frequently for the playback of pre-recorded sound portions. A very efficient type of tape recorder, the tape cartridge, is being used increasingly in place of records.

The *tape cartridge system* is used for short announcements, musical bridges, news inserts, and other types of brief informational material. The tape cartridge system consists of a small machine that can hold and play back several (often ten or more) short audio tapes, either individually or simultaneously. All you do is plug in a cartridge and press the appropriate button. Similar to the Cue-matic, the tape plays back immediately (within a fraction of a second) without any annoying wows or pauses. The cartridge system threads the tape, cues it up, and rewinds it automatically. The only disadvantage of the cartridge system is that the playing time of the individual cartridges is rather brief (a maximum of four minutes).

Longer recordings or playbacks must be done with the conventional *tape recorder*. Often, audio tape is used to record audio material worth saving. All newscasts, political speeches, religious broadcasts, and editorials are usually tape recorded for reference purposes.

Generally, remote start and stop controls for the tape recorder are located on or near the audio control board.

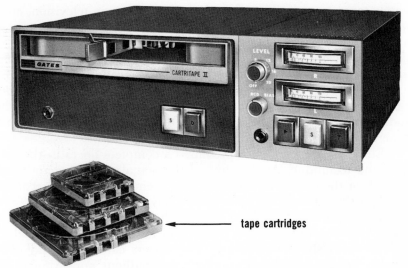

tape cartridges

Gates Cartritape II system

## Telephone Beeper Recording

Federal law forbids recording telephone conversations for any purpose without special authorization from the telephone company and from all parties involved. All telephone conversations intended for broadcasting must first be legally recorded. The telephone company supplies broadcasting institutions with a recording "beeper," a beep that recurs at a specific frequency. This beeper must be superimposed on the telephone conversation.

The party or parties hooked up on the telephone line hear this beeper quite clearly; it is the necessary indication that the conversation is being broadcast or recorded. The home viewer, however, often does not hear the beeper, since it is electronically suppressed by the station transmitting the telephone messages.

A special telephone tape recorder usually records the message and plays it back for on-the-air transmission with a delay of three to seven seconds. The seven-second delay gives the audio engineer a chance to edit out any comments that are thought to be in bad taste.

Be sure to check beeper hookup with switchboard operators and master control room. Always have the person on the other end of the line agree verbally to the intended broadcast. Record the agreement.

## Audio Prerecording and Live Video

Nobody is surprised to find that in motion pictures much of the sound track is recorded individually and later matched with the separately taken picture. There is quite a controversy in television, however, concerning the validity of prerecording sound portions that are later matched to the video portion of the telecast.

In many cases, prerecorded audio could improve television programming. There are two reasons for this assumption. (1) The audio portion could be recorded under strictly controlled recording-studio conditions. (2) With prerecording, bulky audio equipment in the studio would become unnecessary. Lighting engineers, director, and cameramen would have full artistic freedom.

A European network once presented a complete opera in the prerecording technique. At the time of the actual telecast, actors substituted for the singers by synchronizing their lips to the prerecorded audio portion. The actors were free to pay full attention to the acting, unrestricted by the strain of difficult passages and arias.

The prerecording of sound portions in television musical productions is obviously an advantage. The singers can dance and twirl through the set with breath-taking speed without appearing to be affected at all by the physical labor; they can go right into their next songs.

The prerecording method is widely used in smaller stations for presenting guest singers, for instance. A record of the singer's number is played through the studio speaker and the guest singer merely mouths the words to the song. The advantages of this method are obvious. (1) The audio quality is always excellent. (2) The singer can be accompanied by a full, well-rehearsed orchestra, a luxury that most small stations could hardly afford for a two- or three-minute song. (3) Prerecording allows the performer full freedom, and the imagination of the director has no limits, since there are no restricting audio problems to worry about.

The prerecording method, however, is not without drawbacks. Technically, lip- and action-synchronization to the prerecorded audio must be flawless or the over-all effect of the presentation will lack authenticity. Aesthetically, prerecording removes the viewer just one more step from the actual event. Hence, the energy and apparent spontaneity of the event is often sacrificed. Pro and con arguments concerning the aesthetic validity of prerecording will not be attempted here. But possible arguments of this nature must be taken into consideration before a producer blindly starts prerecording all possible program material.

Prerecording audio portions and then combining them with prerecorded video portions does not present particular aesthetic or ethical arguments, since everything is recorded.

## SUMMARY

Television audio is a major part of television production. In general, good television audio is difficult to achieve. Varying distances from moving sound sources to microphones and the requirements of the camera to keep boom microphones and their shadows out of picture range influence audio quality considerably. Inevitable studio noises add to audio problems.

There are two types of television microphones: (1) mobile microphones and (2) stationary microphones.

Mobile microphones include (1) boom microphones, (2) hand microphones, (3) lavaliere microphones, (4) wireless microphones, and (5) long-distance microphones.

Stationary microphones include (1) desk microphones, (2) stand microphones, (3) hanging microphones, and (4) hidden microphones.

Recorded sound is widely used in television operation, especially music and sound effects records and special prerecorded audio portions on electrical transcriptions or audio tape.

The following table lists the type, pickup pattern, characteristics, and use of the most commonly used television microphones.

| Type | Pickup Pattern | Characteristics | Uses |
|------|---------------|-----------------|------|
| E-V 642 | Cardioid, extremely directional | Dynamic, fairly rugged, large, excellent presence | Studio boom, outdoor use; long-distance remote pickups |
| RCA BK-5A | Cardioid, directional | Ribbon, fairly rugged, good-to-excellent quality | Studio boom, stand mike |
| Shure SM 5 | Cardioid, directional | Dynamic, excellent quality, somewhat sensitive | Studio boom |
| RCA 77-DX | Cardioid (multiple) | Ribbon, sensitive to shock, large, excellent quality | Studio boom, desk, stand mike; excellent music pickup |
| E-V 666 | Directional, condensed cardioid | Dynamic, rugged, medium size, good quality | Studio boom, desk, stand, hanging mike; possible outdoor use; hand mike if necessary |

| Type | Pickup Pattern | Characteristics | Uses |
|------|----------------|-----------------|------|
| E-V 655C | Omnidirectional | Dynamic, rugged, comparatively small, medium quality | Excellent hand, desk, stand mike; excellent outdoor use |
| Shure SM 58 | Cardioid | Dynamic with built-in windscreen and pop filter, good quality | Hand, desk, stand mike; excellent outdoor use |
| E-V 635A | Omnidirectional | Dynamic, built-in pop filter, small, good quality, rugged | Hand, desk mike; excellent outdoor use |
| RCA BK-1A | Omnidirectional | Dynamic, fairly rugged, small but bulky, medium quality | Desk and hand mike; fair outdoor use |
| Shure SM 57 (Unidyne) | Cardioid | Dynamic, rugged, good quality, prevents low-frequency "boominess" | Excellent all-purpose mike for hand, desk, or stand use; excellent for rhythm pickup |
| Neumann U 67 | Cardioid, variable | Condenser, very sensitive, superior quality | Mostly boom-mounted for critical audio recordings; indoor use only |
| E-V 649A | Omnidirectional | Dynamic, fairly rugged, extremely small, fair quality | Lavaliere, hand mike |
| RCA BK-6B | Omnidirectional | Dynamic, rugged, rather small, fair to poor quality | Lavaliere, hand mike |
| RCA BK-12A | Omnidirectional | Dynamic, extremely small, rugged, fair to poor quality | Lavaliere |

## EXERCISES

1. What is the pickup pattern of television hand microphones?
2. Why would it be impractical to use an RCA 77-DX microphone for a remote outdoor telecast?
3. In television drama, television microphones are usually concealed from the home viewer. Why? How can this be achieved?

4. What would be the chief advantage of using a small microphone on the television boom? Why, then, aren't small microphones used?

5. You are to conduct a television interview on the flight deck of an aircraft carrier. What type of television microphone would you use? Why?

6. Your morning show format calls for three sets: (1) the host-demonstration area, (2) an interview area, and (3) a piano-vocalist area. They are arranged from camera left to camera right in the studio. The host will be moving in and out of each area in no particular order. What microphone arrangements would you specify?

7. Your guest singer tells you that he thinks he won't be able to sing because of a severe cold. He tells you, however, that you may be able to use his recording of the scheduled song. How could you ensure his appearance?

8. A great celebrity has agreed to be interviewed by a group of ladies from the local women's club. The women will all be seated in a row of chairs, and the guest will be standing in front of the chairs. What audio pickup would you suggest?

9. Because of traffic and light problems, your boom is in such a position that one of the performers has his back to the microphone while speaking to another performer facing it. Where would you place your microphone? Why?

10. Your newscast format calls for two newscasters, a man and a woman. They will have to move around to different set areas, such as the news desk, the weather desk, and the interview area. The studio space, however, is limited. Lighting equipment is scarce. There is a possibility that the newscasters will have to interview important guests from time to time. What types of microphones would you select? How and where would you use them? Why?

# 4

# Lighting

*cc. 12' from back light to subject*
*cc. 24' from spot to subject*

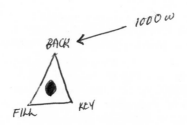

Television lighting techniques are greatly influenced by the monochrome or color camera. First, the camera needs a certain amount of light to produce an acceptable electronic picture. Second, the lighting instruments must be placed so that the camera will be able to move freely through the set without televising the lighting instruments.

We have already seen that lighting affects microphone boom placement. In the same way, the boom influences lighting techniques. Undesirable boom shadows can become a major production problem unless the lighting is specifically adjusted to the freely moving microphone boom.

Television lighting must also fulfill some aesthetic requirements. Locale, time, mood, and the style of a television play are all expressed to a great extent by proper lighting.

Always keep in mind that television lighting is not intended to please the observer in the studio; it must please the *camera* and, ultimately, the television viewer. The quality of studio lighting should always be judged by the picture as it appears on the control room monitor.

## SPECIFIC LIGHTING OBJECTIVES

The obvious purpose of television lighting is to illuminate what the camera sees. If the camera is to see well, a certain amount of over-all light is necessary. This light is called *base light*. Also, the contrast between the brightest highlight and the darkest shadow must be kept within certain limits. The *technical* lighting objectives, then, are (1) to provide enough base light and (2) to limit the contrast between highlight and shadow so that the camera and its electronic accessories can produce acceptable pictures. We will discuss technical lighting objectives more thoroughly in the section on the techniques of television lighting.

The *nontechnical* lighting objectives are (1) to indicate form and dimensions, (2) to create an illusion of reality or nonreality, and (3) to indicate mood.

### Indicating Form and Dimensions

Since the television screen has only two dimensions, height and width, the third dimension, depth, must be created by illusion. A proper control of light and shadow is essential for the clear revelation of three-dimensional objects, their position in space and time, and their relation to each other. Selective lighting also emphasizes the important and de-emphasizes the unimportant, thereby aiding picture composition. Lighting can also help to reveal the nature of an object. Through emphasis of the textural characteristics of an object, lighting can show whether a surface is rough, smooth, shiny, even, or uneven. *Two main dimensions — height & depth width — Experimentation is the key*

### Creating the Illusion of Reality and Nonreality

Lighting helps to achieve an illusion of reality. It aids in setting a *specific* time and place. Long shadows suggest late afternoon; harsh, bright light helps to establish a sun-flooded outdoor scene.

Illogical or special-effects lighting can effectively create the impression of nonreality.

### Indicating Mood

Lighting is one of the chief means of creating an appropriate mood. Various psychological effects, such as gaiety, mystery, excitement, or gloom, can be achieved through proper lighting techniques. For instance, lighting from below the eye level can create a mysterious mood; excessive lighting from the back tends to glamorize a fashion model.

One television production element, such as lighting, is hardly enough to create a complete illusion, of course. In general, you will need a combination of all elements to achieve a desired effect.

## LIGHTING INSTRUMENTS

All television lighting employs two types of illumination: (1) directional light and (2) diffused light.

*Directional light* illuminates only a relatively small area with a very distinct light beam. It produces clearly defined light and shadow areas. Comes from a spotlight

*Diffused light* illuminates a relatively large area with an indistinct light beam. It produces soft, undefined light and shadow areas.

The choice of directional or diffused lighting, or a combination of both, depends on the scene to be lighted and on the specific lighting objective.

All television lighting employs two types of lighting instruments: (1) spotlights, which are directional light sources, and (2) floodlights, which are diffused light sources. It also employs three types of light-producing elements: (1) the incandescent bulb, which is the familiar light bulb used in the home, (2) the quartz-iodine bulb, which is a very small tubular light "bulb" that produces an extremely bright beam, and (3) the fluorescent tube, which is still occasionally used for specific diffused light requirements in monochrome television.

### Quartz Instruments

By now, quartz-iodine lights are used extensively in television, either replacing the traditional incandescent lights altogether or serving as important additional light sources. Because the traditional incandescent instruments allow more directional control than the quartz instruments, a mixture of both instruments is often preferred by lighting technicians.

The types, application, and operation of quartz lights are very similar to those of incandescent instruments. However, there are some important performance characteristics unique to quartz lights.

*Most lighting used is 1000 w*
*3½ Times color To – monochrome lighting*

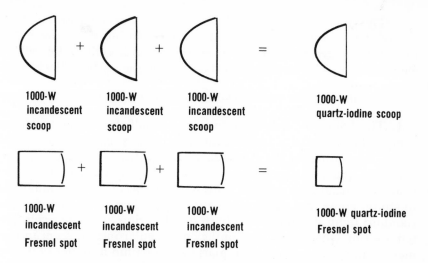

1000-W
incandescent
scoop

+

1000-W
incandescent
scoop

+

1000-W
incandescent
scoop

=

1000-W
quartz-iodine scoop

1000-W
incandescent
Fresnel spot

+

1000-W
incandescent
Fresnel spot

+

1000-W
incandescent
Fresnel spot

=

1000-W quartz-iodine
Fresnel spot

1. The illumination efficiency of quartz lamps is extremely high. Under ideal conditions, a 1,000-watt quartz floodlight (scoop) provides the same illumination (in foot candles) as at least three 1,000-watt incandescent scoops. This light output does not decrease with age. Incandescent light bulbs gradually blacken with carbon and do decrease in light output. *I= 3½*

2. The size and weight of quartz lights are less than those of equivalent incandescent instruments. The quartz-iodine light bulb is quite small and therefore requires a less bulky housing than the large incandescent bulbs.

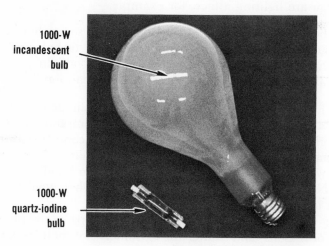

1000-W
incandescent
bulb

1000-W
quartz-iodine
bulb

Quartz bulb and incandescent bulb

3. The color temperature (which we will discuss later in this chapter) of the quartz light remains unchanged during the entire life of the bulb—a great advantage over the incandescent bulbs, which change their color temperature because of the carbon blackening.

Unfortunately, the quartz instrument is not without disadvantages.

1. The life of the quartz lamp is about half that of the incandescent bulb. The quartz lamp is rated for a maximum of 150 to 500 hours, depending on the size and type of instrument used.

2. The quartz instruments get extremely hot and also radiate more heat than incandescent lights. This heat can become rather annoying to studio crews and performers, and it is rather destructive to such standard light attachments as barn doors, scrims, and color gels. Often a scrim, which lasts for months on a regular incandescent instrument, will be burned up by a quartz lamp within a matter of weeks. Heat filters, which can be put in front of the quartz instrument to cut down the heat output, also change the color temperature, so they are rarely used.

3. Most seriously, the quartz light beam is very difficult to control accurately. Although the spreading and narrowing of the beam is possible, it cannot be shaped as precisely as the incandescent light beam. With quartz light, the narrowed beam still has very soft edges and an abundance of spill. Also, when the spotlight is pinned to a narrow beam, the light tends to concentrate on the rim of the beam, leaving a "blind" or dark spot in the middle of whatever happens to be lighted. This blind spot is especially noticeable and annoying when you are lighting a face, for example.

For these reasons, many lighting experts are somewhat hesitant to use quartz lights exclusively. Some lighting technicians will use quartz lights only for diffused illumination (floodlights).

Operationally, quartz lamps demand extra caution in these areas:

1. When you put in or exchange a quartz light bulb, try not to handle the bulb excessively. Its chemical composition causes the quartz glass to deteriorate when it comes into contact with the skin.

2. Since the instruments get very hot when in operation, you should wear thick asbestos gloves whenever you handle a hot instrument. Never neglect personal safety, even when you are terribly pressed for time.

3. As with incandescent lamps, quartz lamps can explode (for a variety of reasons) and shatter the extremely hot molten quartz glass into the studio. Although they explode very infrequently, you should

take some precaution against this potential danger. Some stations insist on putting protective scrims or wire-mesh screens in front of all quartz instruments that have no lenses, such as floodlights. Scrims will cut down the light output somewhat and will have to be replaced frequently because of heat deterioration, but the increased safety is well worth these minor inconveniences.

## Spotlights

There are three types of regular spotlights and two types of special spotlights. The regular spotlights are (1) the Fresnel spotlight, (2) the ellipsoidal spotlight, and (3) the internal-reflector spotlight. The special spotlights are (1) the follow spot and (2) the beam spot projector.

### The Fresnel spotlight

The Fresnel spotlight, which derives its name from the Fresnel lens, is the most widely used spotlight in television lighting. It is comparatively light and very flexible, it has a high light output, and its spot-focusing device allows easy adjustment of the light beam. The spotlight can be spread to a wide, flooded beam, or it can be pinned to a sharp, clearly defined beam. To spread a spotlight beam, push the lightbulb-reflector unit *toward* the lens. To pin the beam, pull the bulb-reflector unit *away* from the lens. The normal range of the incandescent Fresnel spotlight is 150–5,000 watts. Quartz Fresnel spotlights range in size from 400 to 2,000 watts.

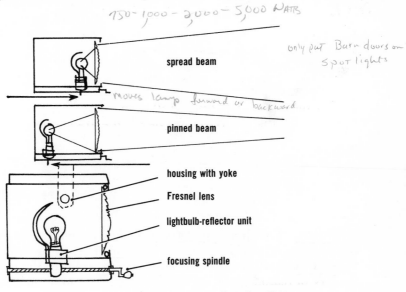

spread beam

pinned beam

housing with yoke

Fresnel lens

lightbulb-reflector unit

focusing spindle

Fresnel spotlight

Incandescent Fresnel spotlight

Quartz Fresnel spotlight

The size of the lighting instrument used depends on several factors: (1) the type of camera used and the sensitivity of the camera pickup tube or tubes, (2) the studio ceiling height, and (3) the reflectance of scenery and costumes.

As we saw in Chapter 1, monochrome I-O cameras need the least amount of light to operate properly, vidicon and Plumbicon monochrome cameras about twice as much light as the image-orthicon cameras, and color cameras about three times as much as the standard monochrome I-O. *[handwritten: 3-1]*

Light intensity grows when the light source is moved toward the lighted object. Therefore, low-ceiling studios require smaller lighting instruments than high-ceiling studios. Since most small studios have low ceilings (16 feet or below), medium or low intensity lighting instruments are sufficient. Also, smaller lamps radiate less heat, an important consideration in small studio operation.

Highly reflectant scenery and costumes need, of course, less light than dark, light-absorbing studio decor.

For these reasons it is difficult to say with accuracy what size of lighting instruments should be used. Generally, 1,000- and 2,000-watt incandescent or quartz instruments are used in most studios, along with 5,000-watt incandescent spotlights wherever color is used. For maximum lighting control, most lighting technicians prefer to operate with fewer but larger spotlights.

### The ellipsoidal spotlight *[handwritten: (pattern light) - "globo light"]*

The incandescent ellipsoidal spotlight has an intense directional beam. A high-power lamp is reflected by an ellipsoidal reflector and projected through a powerful plano-convex or Fresnel lens. The light beam can be trimmed and shaped by metal shutters, located behind

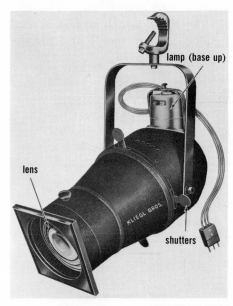

lamp (base up)

lens

KLIEGL BROS.

shutters

**Ellipsoidal spotlight**

*[handwritten: must be close to get focus effect]*

*[handwritten: Kleigl + Century - sell the most Fresnal]*

**Quartz ellipsoidal spotlight**

the lens in the second focal point of the ellipsoidal reflector. The ellipsoidal spotlight is used whenever sharp "pools of light" are required. It can also serve as a projection spot. In place of shutters, a thin metal cutout, called cucalorus, or kookie (sometimes mislabeled "gobo") is inserted behind the lens and projected as a shadow pattern on cycloramas or scenery.

The quartz ellipsoidal spotlight has the same characteristics except that its beam is not so sharp and controllable as its incandescent counterpart. The ellipsoidal spotlight is a special effects light and is rarely used in normal television studio lighting. The incandescent ellipsoidal spotlight ranges in size from 500 to 3,000 watts, and the quartz models range from 400 to 2,000 watts. The normal size for medium studio use is 1,000 watts for incandescent and 650 watts for quartz lights. Ellipsoidal spotlights are sometimes called Leko lights.

### The internal-reflector spotlight

The internal-reflector spotlight is frequently used as an auxiliary lighting instrument. It is lightweight, comparatively cheap, and extremely flexible. The reflector is inside the lightbulb, which eliminates housing, lens, and external reflector. The internal-reflector bulb is usually screwed into a socket with a clip spring. This clip spring enables the small spotlight to be fastened quickly to such equipment as flats, ground rows, microphone stands, camera tripods, and easels. In television jargon they are usually called "cliplights." The two most widely used cliplights are (1) the R-40, which throws a relatively soft beam of light, hence called a "soft spot," and (2) the

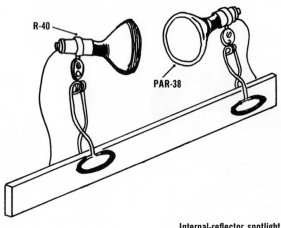

Internal-reflector spotlight

PAR-38, which throws a relatively sharp beam of light, hence called a "hard spot."

The photo spots which give off an extremely bright beam of light have been largely replaced by the more expensive, yet ultimately more efficient "sun guns." These highly portable, 1,000-watt quartz lights can be hand-held or, like cliplights, fastened to flats, door frames, and other convenient objects. Sun guns are used extensively

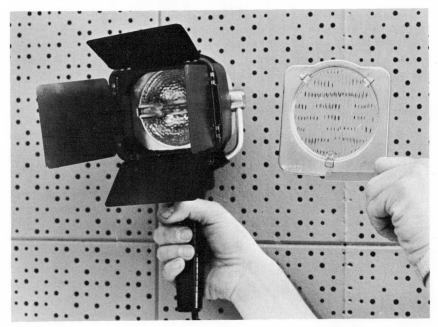

Sun gun

on remote telecasts from schools, churches, and hospitals, where heavy equipment cannot be installed. The sun gun has a high- and low-position switch. Whenever the lights are not needed, the lamp is switched to the low position in order to preserve the 12-hour lamp life. It is available with either a floodlight or a spotlight beam.

### Special spotlights

The *follow spot* is a powerful special effects spotlight. It is primarily used as a spotlight to simulate theatre stage effects. Through several special effects attachments, the follow spot operator simultaneously spreads, pins, and shapes the beam while following the action. The follow spot is generally of little use in small station operation. Its

Follow spot

range is 2,000 to 3,000 watts for incandescent instruments and 1,000 to 2,000 watts for quartz instruments.

The *beam spot projector* is used when an intense shaft of light has to be projected over a considerable distance. Two reflectors (rather than a lens) reinforce and project the light from a powerful lamp. The light shaft is not adjustable.

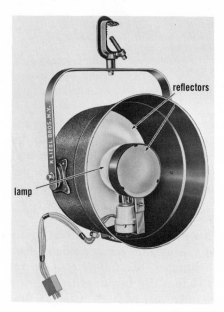

Beam spot projector

1000-Watt quartz "punch scoop," similar to the beam spot projector

"Super Beam-1000," functioning like a beam spot projector

In monochrome television, the practical use of the beam spot projector is limited to special effects, such as beams of sunlight or special shafts of light for dramatic or decorative purposes. In small studios, a medium-sized ellipsoidal spotlight is more useful for these or similar effects, especially since its beam can be adjusted. The beam spot projector's range is 1,000 to 2,000 watts.

For color productions, however, the beam spot is a very useful instrument. It is extremely bright yet not too harsh, and thus it serves quite well as a key light (the principal directional light source).

## Floodlights

Floodlights are designed to produce a great amount of highly diffused light. Despite this diffusion, the light must still be controllable to a certain extent to avoid excessive spillover into other set areas. Although floodlights play an important yet secondary role in monochrome television, they are essential for color television. For floodlighting, quartz instruments are especially suitable and popular.

There are five basic types of floodlights: (1) the scoop, (2) the pan or broad, (3) the floodlight or flood-clip bank, (4) strip lights or cyc lights, and (5) the fluorescent bank.

### The scoop

The *scoop*, or *bucket*, is named after the peculiar scoop-like shape of its reflector. The scoop, like most other floodlights, has no lens.

The incandescent scoop most frequently used is an 18-inch scoop with a 1,500- or 2,000-watt bulb.

15-inch scoop

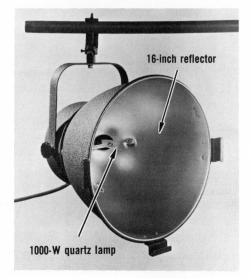

16-inch reflector

1000-W quartz lamp

Scoop floodlight                                                    Quartz scoop floodlight

Quartz scoops are considerably smaller and much more efficient. The 12-inch scoop with a 500-watt quartz lamp delivers almost as much light as the 1,500-watt incandescent scoop. The 16-inch quartz scoop with 1,000 watts of power is the more popular floodlight for color operation.

In larger studios, *punch-scoops* are sometimes used. These 12-inch, 1,000-watt quartz instruments, which have a more directional light beam, are generally applied when shadow areas have to be brightened from longer-than-normal distances.

In color television, the usual combination of two scoops in one location is often not enough, especially when incandescent instruments are used. In this case, some stations resort to a "scoop-cluster" arrangement, which means that up to four scoops are all hung closely together for a highly efficient light source. Of course most circuits cannot handle such combined wattage; the scoops must therefore be plugged into at least two separate circuits. Quartz clusters, however, rarely exceed two instruments, which a normal circuit can usually tolerate.

### The pan or broad

The *pan*, or *broad* (from "broadside"), is a floodlight instrument whose reflector looks like a deep baking pan. It is extensively used in the motion picture industry, and has now been adopted by television studios because of the urgent demands of color television for increased light levels. There are several very efficient quartz broads on the market; they come in various shapes and sizes of anywhere from 400 to 1,000 watts.

1000-W quartz broad with barn doors

*diffused light*

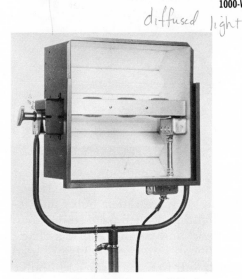

1000-W quartz "Soft-Lite" similar to quartz broad

Quartz "Mini-Lite" with four-way barn doors

The pan light is not as controllable as the scoop light and is there-fore not, or only very rarely, used in monochrome television lighting. In color television, however, the broad is very useful in providing additional base light.

The Kliegl "Nook" light and the ColorTran Mini-Lite are similar to a broad, yet much smaller. They are designed for use in cramped quarters, especially when more light is needed than sun guns or clip lights can deliver.

### The floodlight bank

The *floodlight* or *flood-clip bank* consists of a series of soft internal-reflector spots mounted in strips or series of strips. As with the broad, the light source covers a large area, causing shadows to be extremely soft. The flood-clip bank does not have the power or the long range of regular scoops or broads. For small studio operation, however, flood-clip banks can do most of the necessary fill lighting. The dis-

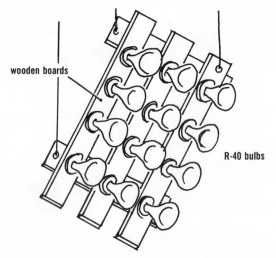

wooden boards

R-40 bulbs

Flood clip bank

advantage of flood-clip banks is that they are rather bulky and in-flexible. But they are useful for fill-lighting of such fixed studio areas as permanent news and weather desks and commercial sets. Their range depends on the number of 150-watt soft-spot R-40 lamps used at one time (usually twelve). Quartz soft-light banks are less bulky and more efficient, so they are preferred for color operations.

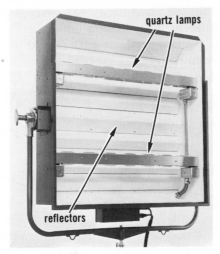

4000-W Soft-Lite (fill light similar to flood-clip bank)

Mini-Brutes quartz flood-lamp banks

### Strip lights

*Strip lights,* often called *cyc lights,* are similar to the border or cyc lights of the theatre. Rows of six to eight lamps are usually mounted in a long box-like reflector housing. Some of the more expensive models come equipped with individual reflectors.

In color television, the eight-light, 500-watt quartz strip light is a highly useful instrument. Like theatre borderlights, it has glass color frames for each of the lamp-reflectors, thus enabling you to light the cyclorama in different colors.

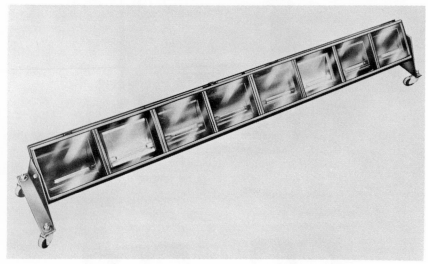

Quartz cyc strip light

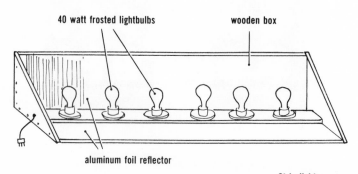

40 watt frosted lightbulbs          wooden box

aluminum foil reflector

Strip lights

"Homemade" versions of the strip light are often quite adequate for monochrome lighting purposes. A simple wooden box lined with aluminum foil will, in most cases, be a more than sufficient reflector. Any size household bulb, or any internal-reflector spotlight up to 150 watts, can be used. However, ordinary 40-watt frosted lightbulbs are recommended for small studios, since they produce a more diffused light than the relatively expensive soft-spot internal-reflector bulbs.

Strip lights can be used as floodlights suspended from the studio ceiling, or they can be placed on the studio floor to separate ground rows from the cyclorama or pillars and other set pieces from the background. They are also extensively used for silhouette lighting effects.

### The fluorescent bank

The *fluorescent bank* consists of four to six fluorescent tubes mounted in a flat, box-like reflector. These fluorescent banks were widely used for fill lights in the early days of television, and they seemed to be the ideal solution for television lighting problems. Since the light spread is broad, it is virtually shadowless. It is a cool light, which keeps the studio temperature down, a particular advantage in small studios. Despite these advantages, however, fluorescent banks are rarely used in modern television lighting, for several reasons: (1) the reflector box is bulky and inflexible; (2) it is difficult to maintain; (3) light intensity is very hard to control—in some cases impossible; (4) directional control is virtually impossible, so that spill light into other set areas is unavoidable; (5) fluorescent banks may develop annoying hums and flickers and may cause electronic interference; and (6) fluorescent light is a "cold" light—that is, it has an entirely different color temperature from incandescent or quartz lights and is therefore unusable in color television.

## LIGHTING CONTROL EQUIPMENT

Television operation, especially on the local level, necessitates extremely flexible lighting equipment, for several reasons. (1) Constantly moving television cameras and microphone booms make any permanent lighting setup on the studio floor impossible. (2) In small studio operation a minimum of lighting equipment is available; the equipment must therefore be flexible enough to light adequately every corner of the studio. (3) There is rarely enough time or manpower to design and execute a lighting plan properly for each television production. The lighting setup must be flexible enough to allow one man to change the studio lighting with speed and a minimum of effort.

The necessary control and flexibility of lighting equipment is achieved primarily by two methods: (1) directional control and (2) intensity control.

## Directional Controls

Directional controls for television lighting include (1) basic mounting devices, (2) basic hanging devices, (3) mounting devices for floor lights, and (4) beam controls.

### Basic mounting devices

Basic mounting devices for lighting instruments are usually attached to the studio ceiling. They include pipe grids, counterweight battens, mobile rails, and power rails.

*Pipe grids.* Ordinary pipe lighting grids provide the most common and economical light suspension method. A lighting grid consists of rather heavy pipe (1½ to 2 inches in diameter) strung either parallel or crosswise and mounted from 10 to 18 feet above the studio floor, depending on ceiling height. The lighting instruments are either mounted directly on this lighting grid or suspended from the grid by special vertically adjustable hanging devices.

*Counterweight battens.* A counterweight rope system allows the parallel pipes to be lowered and raised to any desirable position. Lighting instruments can thus be hung and adjusted without the use of bulky ladders. In small studios, however, the studio floor is rarely sufficiently cleared of cameras, microphone booms, and scenery to allow the individual battens to be lowered to convenient working height. In this case, accurate final adjustments must be made either from the studio floor with a lighting hook or from the ladder after the battens have been raised to the proper position.

*The Mobilrail.* Similar to curtain rods, the Mobilrail (trademark of the Century Lighting Company) works on the principle of roller couplings. Crossbeams of the lighting grid, as well as individual lighting instruments, can be moved freely from one end of the studio to the other simply by pushing them with a lighting pole. Mobilrails have not been too popular in local studio operation, mainly because of the high installation cost.

*The power rail.* Similar to the Mobilrail principle, the power rail enables lighting instruments to be moved laterally along power-carrying crossbeams. The power feed is uninterrupted while lighting instruments are being moved. The power rail, however, imposes severe restrictions on the flexibility of lighting instruments. For instance, hanging positions are limited and vertical adjustments of lights are rather difficult. High installation and maintenance costs make the power rail rather impractical for small station operation.

*The Kliegtrack.* Kliegl Brothers have developed a single track system that is especially valuable for low-ceiling operations. The track is attached directly to the ceiling, and lighting fixtures are then hung in any position along the track. The principle is similar to that of curtains that are hooked to and moved along an ordinary curtain rod.

This method has two advantages: (1) virtually no space is lost between the lighting instruments and the studio ceiling; and (2) the instruments are clamped in with a simple spring fastener, which is both quick and safe; no tools are needed.

The biggest disadvantage of the Kliegtrack system is its cost, which is considerably higher than that of the ordinary pipe grid system.

### Basic hanging devices

Basic light-instrument hanging devices include (1) the "C" clamp, (2) the sliding rod, (3) the individual telescope and wire-winch method, and (4) the pantograph. The "C" clamp is merely a fastening device. The sliding rod and pantograph are lowering and raising devices for the lighting instruments.

*The "C" clamp.* The simplest and cheapest light-mounting device is the "C" clamp. A large bolt keeps the light securely fastened to the grid pipe. Through constant turning and tilting of the light instrument, "C" clamp bolts are sometimes loosened, but you can easily guard against falling light instruments by periodic checks of

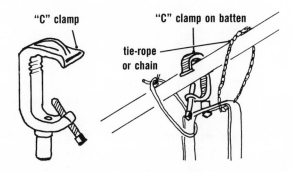

"C" clamp                    "C" clamp on batten

tie-rope
or chain

the "C" clamp bolts. It is always a good idea to chain or lash the light unit to its support. If the "C" clamp slips off accidentally, the line will keep the light temporarily suspended. Be sure the chain is long enough so that you can still freely aim the instrument into any direction.

*The sliding rod.* One of the simplest devices for lowering or raising the light instrument is the sliding rod. A rod to which the light instrument is attached can be pushed up and down through a metal sleeve, which is clamped to the lighting grid. The rod can be securely set anywhere within a six-foot extension limit. The major disadvantage of the sliding rod is that it has to be adjusted from the grid. This requires bulky ladders for each adjustment and is usually a tiresome and extremely time-consuming job.

*The individual telescope and wire winch.* This is one of the most flexible (and most expensive) hanging devices. Each individual lighting instrument or instrument cluster is hung on a motor-driven telescope pole, which extends and retracts like the legs on a regular camera tripod. The individual instruments can also be lowered and raised with electrically powered wire winches. The great advantage of this hanging device is that the lowering and raising of the individual instruments can be operated from a central control board. Also, since each instrument is suspended individually, the hanging pattern is extremely flexible and the lights can usually be dropped as far down as necessary, even when the studio is crowded with complex scenery and production equipment. So far, the high cost of such an installation has prevented such facilities from being installed in small and medium-sized studios.

*The pantograph.* A much less expensive yet highly flexible hanging device for individual lighting instruments is the pantograph. A panto-

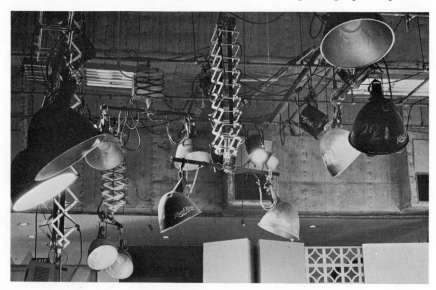

graph is a counterbalanced hanger that can be adjusted quickly and easily from the studio floor to any height within its more than sufficient 12-feet range. Depending on the weight of the lighting instruments, one or two sets of springs can be adjusted for perfect counterbalancing. Some of the heavier pantographs have four powerful springs, which can easily counterbalance a 21-inch studio monitor, for instance. Modern pantographs have a small pipe extension that permits the mounting of two separate lighting instruments on one pantograph. In most small studios, where the ceiling height rarely exceeds 18 feet, you can quickly and easily pull the lighting instrument down almost to floor level, make the necessary lighting adjustments, and push the instrument back to the desired position, all in a matter of seconds.

### Mounting devices for floor lights

Floor lights are usually mounted on vertical roller-caster stands. A three-wheel base allows quick repositioning of the light unit. The stands are vertically adjustable to a height of 4 to 6 feet, or, as in some larger models, 5 to 8 feet. Such lighting stands can hold any type of lighting instrument—scoops, spots, strip lights, four-tube fluorescent banks, or any type of special effects instruments. The roller-caster stands can also be adapted to stands for studio easels or similar floor equipment that has to be flexible and mobile.

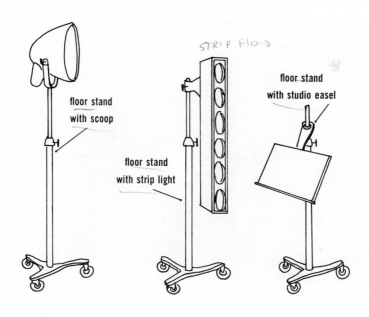

floor stand with scoop

STRIP FLOOD

floor stand with strip light

floor stand with studio easel

### Beam controls

Lighting instrument beam controls are usually attached to the instrument itself. There are three types of spotlight beam controls: (1) the Fresnel spot-focusing device, (2) the ellipsoidal shutter device, and (3) the Fresnel spot barn doors. The Fresnel spot-focusing device and the ellipsoidal shutters have already been explained in the discussion of individual lighting instruments.

*Barn doors* are adjustable metal flaps hinged to the front of the spotlight instrument. The spotlight beam can be narrowed or widened by positioning the flaps. In small studios, where different sets

Two-way barn door

Four-way barn door

are necessarily close together, spill light can become a major problem. If each spotlight is equipped with barn doors, however, the hazard is greatly reduced. You can frequently eliminate a boom shadow by partially closing a barn door and thus blocking the light from striking the microphone boom.

There are two-way and four-way barn doors.

In order to prevent the barn doors from sliding out of their holders accidentally, you should chain all barn doors to the instruments. Also, barn doors often get very hot, especially when used on quartz instruments. Be sure to wear your asbestos gloves whenever you adjust barn doors while the instrument is turned on.

## Intensity Controls

### Dimmers          BASic with Patch Board Cable

Light intensity can be most accurately and smoothly controlled by dimmers. There are three basic kinds of dimmers: (1) the resistance dimmer, (2) the transformer dimmer, and (3) the electronic dimmer. Although these dimmers work on different principles, they all enable the dimmer operator gradually to increase or decrease the voltage going to the light, and therefore its intensity. According to need, one or several of the lights can be dimmed down and others simultaneously brought up to full intensity.

Dimmers have become an indispensable production tool even in small station operations. Highly improved cameras and monitors, and an increased aesthetic awareness by television personnel as well as viewers, have inadvertently led to more refined lighting techniques.

Most often, dimmers are used to balance the over-all lighting. For example, if you find one instrument to be unnecessarily bright and another not bright enough, you bring down the intensity of one instrument and bring up the intensity of the other.

Dimmers are also the ideal tool for special effects, such as silhouette lighting and the quick appearance or disappearance of specific set areas in the studio.

In the early days of color television, the necessity for dimmers was frequently questioned, since dimming a light affects its color temperature and with it the color of the lighted scene. A drastic color change on a face, for example, would not only be displeasing to the average viewer but would probably prompt him to readjust the color on his home receiver. Therefore, the lights on faces are almost never dimmed, or only to a very slight degree. We will discuss this practice further in the section on television lighting techniques. However, dimmers are often used to great advantage on the rest of the lighting. Dimmers can play an important part in achieving particular color moods. And since color television demands generally more lighting instruments than does monochrome television, more dimmers rather than fewer are needed for good color lighting.

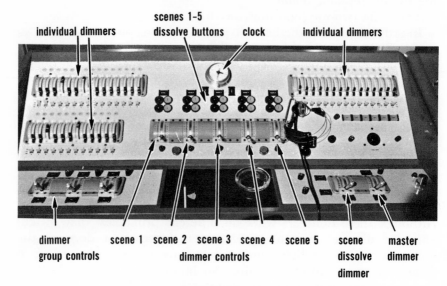

Large 42 dimmer control board (Studio 1, San Francisco State College)

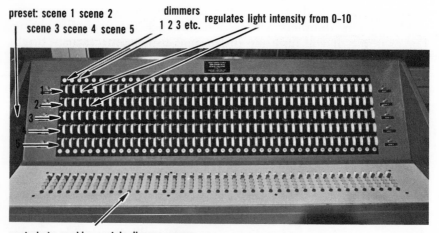

Large 42 dimmer 5-scene preset board (Studio 1, San Francisco State College)

Although dimmers are technically complicated, their basic principle and operation are quite simple. A dimmer works like a throttle: if you want more light, you push the dimmer lever up, thus sending more current to the lamp. If you pull the lever down, you decrease the current and therefore the intensity of the lamp. Since the number of dimmers used is necessarily limited because of their size, several instruments are patched into one dimmer control, causing them all to increase or decrease their intensity simultaneously.

More complex dimmer boards have a preset control that stores the dimming requirements of several scenes simultaneously. At the appropriate time, you can then activate the stored lighting setup at your regular dimmer control board.

### The patchboard

The lighting patchboard is a great aid in the general lighting control system. Resembling an oversized telephone switchboard, it has a terminal for each lighting instrument and major wall outlet in the studio. Short patchcords connect lights to either switches or dimmers. Depending on the capacity of the individual dimmers (two to eight kilowatts or more), you can hook several lighting instruments to each dimmer.

The patchboard should be big enough to accommodate a majority of the outlets on the light battens. Ordinarily, the batten outlets are numbered, and the patchboard plugs are numbered to correspond. For example, if you want to patch instrument No. 5 (a spotlight

dimmer connections          patchcords connected to lighting instruments

circuit breakers

Large lighting patchboard (379 patches; 42 dimmers) (Studio 1, San Francisco State College)

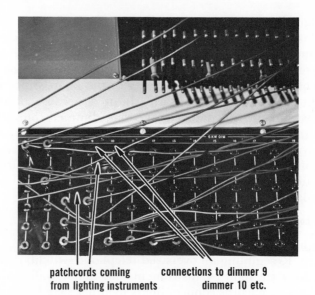

patchcords coming         connections to dimmer 9
from lighting instruments        dimmer 10 etc.

Large lighting patchboard (close-up)

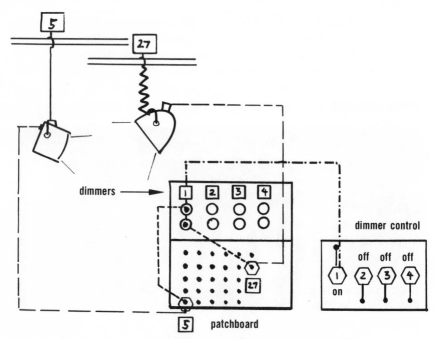

Spot no. 5 and flood no. 27 patched into dimmer no. 1 and controlled with dimmer no. 1

plugged into the No. 5 batten outlet) and instrument No. 27 (a scoop plugged into the No. 27 batten outlet at the other end of the studio) into dimmer No. 1, you simply take patchcords 5 and 27 and plug them into the receptacles under dimmer 1. When you now bring dimmer 1 up, lights 5 and 27 will simultaneously get brighter.

Each patchboard should have a number of nondim terminals to feed the lighting instruments that do not have to be dimmed.

Quite frequently you will find it necessary to hang more lights in the studio than your circuits can handle. When this happens, the patchboard may act as a guard against overloading the circuits. No matter how many lighting instruments are installed in the studio, you can operate no more than the number of available patchboard plugs.

Other intensity controls are scrims and metal screens that are put in front of lighting instruments. Especially when a light on a face is too "hot" (intense), a stainless steel scrim is inserted in front of the Fresnel lens; it reduces the intensity to some extent without changing any other light characteristics.

## DEFINITIONS OF LIGHTING TERMS

In spite of almost heroic efforts by numerous production experts (such as Rudy Bretz, Edward Stasheff, and writers in *The Journal of the Society of Motion Picture and Television Engineers*) to standardize lighting terminology, great confusion still prevails among production personnel about the proper definitions of lighting terms. The nomenclature of lighting instruments may even differ from one television plant to another.

The following definitions of lighting terms are, therefore, intended not to add to the general confusion but to support previous efforts in the standardization of lighting jargon.*

BASE LIGHT is an extremely diffused, over-all illumination in the studio, coming from no one particular source of light. A certain amount of base light is necessary for the technical acceptability of a television picture.

KEY LIGHT is the apparent principal source of directional illumination falling upon a subject or an area.

BACK LIGHT is directional illumination coming substantially from behind the subject.

---

*Lighting definitions are partially adapted from a reprint of *The Journal of the Society of Motion Picture and Television Engineers,* Vol. 64, No. 2 (February 1955), p. 87.

FILL LIGHT is a generally diffused light to reduce shadow or contrast range. Fill light can be directional if the area to be "filled in" is rather limited.

BACKGROUND LIGHT is a separate illumination of the background or set. It does not include lights provided for the performers or performing area.

SIDE LIGHT is a directional light that illuminates the front side of a subject, usually opposite the key light.

KICKER LIGHT is a directional illumination from the back, off to one side of the subject, usually from a low angle.

CAMERA LIGHT is a small spotlight mounted on top of the television camera. The directional front illumination is used for additional fill, eye sparkle, or as principal light source for objects located in dark corners of the studio.

## TECHNIQUES OF TELEVISION LIGHTING

In small stations, lack of proper equipment, space, time, and manpower influence lighting techniques and usually limit lighting possibilities to a considerable extent. These limitations, however, do not mean that good and creative television lighting is impossible. On the contrary, some limitations will call for great ingenuity on the part of the lighting man.

Since there are usually many solutions to one problem, a universal lighting recipe that works for every possible lighting situation cannot and should not be given here. An attempt is made, however, to list some basic lighting principles, which can be easily adapted to specific television lighting problems.

Although the basic lighting principles are the same for color and monochrome cameras, there are many important differences between color and monochrome lighting. These differences lie especially in (1) the operating light level, (2) the contrast between light and shadow, and (3) the "color" of the light itself, called color temperature.

### Operating Light Level: The Base Light

#### Signal-to-noise ratio

The television camera needs a certain amount of light to operate properly. Every television picture has a certain amount of "picture noise," generated by the mere movements of electrons. We have all seen the rain- or snow-like effect on a television set that is not properly tuned in on a particular station. If tuned in carefully, however, the strong signal will virtually drown out the video noise and the picture will appear clear of any snow-like picture noise.

The same problem occurs in television lighting. If the studio light level falls below the operating level of the camera tube, the noise will outweigh the picture signal; the picture will appear unclear and full of "snow" interference. This is usually called a poor signal-to-noise ratio. In a good signal-to-noise ratio, sufficient light produces an electronic image strong enough to make the picture noise no longer apparent.

### Base-light levels

*GE monochrome Plumbicon*

Many an argument has been raised concerning an adequate minimum base-light level. In general, the following base-light levels have proved most satisfactory for ordinary television productions:

| | |
|---|---|
| I-O monochrome camera: | 75 to 100 ft-c (foot-candles) |
| Vidicon camera: | 200 to 250 ft-c |
| Plumbicon camera: | 75 to 100 ft-c *monochrome* |
| Color camera: | 285 to 500 ft-c |

This generalization indicates that the vidicon camera needs roughly *twice* as much light, and the color camera *three times* as much light, as the standard I-O monochrome camera. Base-light levels, however, can vary greatly from these figures. Excellent pictures have been produced with a base-light level as low as 30 ft-c and, of course, with much higher base-light levels. The minimum base-light level always depends on the highest and lowest amount of light actually striking the camera tube. Thus, lens openings and lighting contrasts have considerable influence on the base-light level.

Because the vidicon camera is subject to "lag," it needs fairly high base-light levels in order to produce high-quality, lag-free pictures. The color camera, with its three tubes for the chrominance channel and its luminance channel, needs even more light. You will remember from our discussion of the color camera that the light that enters its zoom lens has to travel through a complex optical system before it is converted into electrical energy. The inevitable loss of light through this system demands rather high initial light levels.

*Lens openings.* When the base-light level is low, the lens opening must be large to allow the necessary amount of light to strike the camera pickup tube. High base-light levels call for small lens openings to keep excessive light from striking the camera tube.

But you will remember that the depth of field decreases with wide lens openings. Therefore, if you need a great depth of field, you must operate within a small lens opening and a high base-light level. Remember also that the vidicon camera uses 16mm film lenses. The $f$-stop–focal-length relationship is different from that of the I-O 35mm-lens system.

### Base lighting versus model lighting

In former television lighting techniques, an even light level was established by turning on diffused light sources throughout the television studio. Although technically acceptable, this lighting looks flat and makes everything else look flat. It gives no feeling of depth, has no sparkle, and lacks expressiveness.

Later, television lighting experts established a sufficient base-light level first and then superimposed specific modeling lights. This lighting technique, still used extensively in television studios, definitely adds some depth, character, and sparkle to all visible show elements.

Modern monochrome television lighting employs spotlights almost exclusively as modeling light sources, with carefully added fill light (which may be spotlights, too) to reduce harsh shadow contrasts. The spill and reflection of these lights from floor and scenery establish quite incidentally the necessary base-light level. No special consideration is given to the base light as such. This technique seems to create the most plastic, exciting, and expressive television lighting so far achieved.

Since color cameras demand a fairly high base-light level and rather "light" transparent shadows, this monochrome lighting technique is not adequate for color. Fill light figures as prominently in color lighting as does directional modeling light. Considerably more floodlights are therefore used in color lighting than in monochrome lighting.

## Contrast

The color camera has trouble reproducing shadow areas. If the shadows are too dense, detail will be almost totally lost, and the colors of the shadow areas will look unnatural and distorted. Such color distortion becomes quite noticeable on the television receiver with its relatively small over-all screen area and its great color intensity.

### Shadows

Contrary to lighting for monochrome television, where deep shadows are often needed to give a scene its proper dimension and character, you must lighten most shadows when working in color. Often a considerable amount of additional fill light, called "holy factor," is needed to make the dense shadows transparent. This lightening of shadows is especially important on performers' faces. Be careful, however, not to eliminate the shadows altogether; otherwise you may end up with a picture that looks much too flat, especially on a black-and-white receiver.

### Contrast ratio

Besides the problem of getting the shadows too dark, you have a problem of getting the light areas too bright. Apart from a few sparkling highlights, the brightest area in your picture should be only 20 times lighter than the darkest area. This rather limited brightness range is often expressed as a *contrast ratio* of 20:1. If you exceed this ratio of 20:1 and make the whites or light colors, say, 40 times brighter than the darkest area, the white areas will lose all detail and begin to "bloom"—that is, to glow as though they were actually emitting light themselves.

### Reference white and reference black

The strict adherence to the 20:1 contrast ratio, however, still does not guarantee a properly balanced color picture. If you start out with a "black" (any color of your darkest area) that is fairly bright, your "white" (the brightest area in your picture) may be much too bright for the system to handle adequately, although this light color is only 20 times brighter than your black. Or conversely, you might have as your brightest spot a rather dark color, which would make any other color that is 20 times darker much too "black." When this happens, an unattentive or insensitive video control operator might electronically "pull the whites" down to a manageable level, thereby destroying the middle and lower brightness ranges in your picture, or "stretch the blacks," thereby causing the lighter colors and picture areas to lose detail and to bloom. This problem is not restricted to color television. Monochrome pictures behave in a similar way except that the brightness range is somewhat extended.

To achieve a properly balanced color picture, you need to establish reference points for the darkest and lightest areas in your scene. These points are called "reference black" and "reference white." You can establish them simply by finding the colors that reflect the least light and the most light. Theoretically, absolute black would reflect nothing; you would have a reflectance of zero per cent. Pure white would reflect all the light; you would have a reflectance of 100 per cent. In practice, of course, there is no color material that absorbs or reflects all the light falling on it, nor is there any camera system that would accurately respond to these extreme values. The actual light reflectance lies somewhere near these absolute values.

For color television, the reference black should not go below 3 per cent reflectance and the reference white not beyond 60 per cent (which is in accordance with the contrast ratio: the white is 20 times lighter than the black).

An example may help to relate these concepts for you. Let us assume that you are asked to establish reference white and reference black in a scene in which a performer wearing a white shirt and a medium-gray suit stands in front of a dark blue background. For convenience's sake, let us also assume that the key and fill lights falling on the performer total 400 ft-c. You measure this light intensity by pointing a foot-candle meter into the lights from the performer's position. This way you are reading the _incident_ light, which in our example is at a level of 400 ft-c. Most foot-candle meters are _incident_ light meters.

Incident light reading: toward the light

In order to measure the _reflected_ light, you must use a reflected-light meter (most common photographic light meters can measure reflected light) and point it close to the lighted object, such as the

Reflected light reading: toward the subject (not toward the lights)

performer's white shirt. If the color of the shirt is an off-white, and if you have lighted the subject properly, your meter might read 240 ft-c, the ideal 60 per cent reflection of your original 400 ft-c falling on the subject. You have now established your white reference point. You then measure the darkest spot in your picture, probably the dark blue background. If this background happens to reflect 12 ft-c, which is the lower three per cent limit of the 400 ft-c of main illumination, you have established your black reference.

### Skin tones

The only reference you have for adjusting the color scheme on your home receiver is the performers' skin tones. Obviously, the skin tones should be reproduced as faithfully and as naturally as possible. Besides make-up, lighting is one of the chief controlling factors in this task. One of the ways of preserving the natural skin tone is to light all performing areas as evenly as possible. Even if the performer is to walk from a light scene to a dark scene, such as from a brightly lighted livingroom to a moonlit balcony, the face of the performer should be kept as evenly lighted as possible. The difference between livingroom and balcony lighting must be achieved primarily through careful background lighting. Avoid extreme shadows on faces, since dense shadows take on their own color, which is often quite unnatural in relation to skin tones. Try to keep all unwanted color reflections from clothing and scenery away from the performer's face. Also, never use colored lights (lights that have color gels in front of them) on a performer, as useful as you may find these lights for background lighting. Ideally, skin tones should have a light reflectance of about 35 per cent.

## Color Temperature

Whereas the monochrome camera is relatively insensitive to color temperature, the color camera is greatly affected by it. You can observe the change of color temperature by carefully watching a light being dimmed. When the lamp is undimmed, you see a bright, white light that looks similar to the sun at high noon. But when the lamp is greatly dimmed down, the light begins to take on a reddish tinge, similar to the red sun at sunset. This color change is expressed in a scale of Kelvin degrees; the degrees stand for actual temperature degrees, because incandescent and quartz lamps get whiter, even bluer, as the filament gets hotter. If a quartz scoop, for example, has a color temperature of 3,200 degrees K when turned up full, the "color" of its light corresponds to that of a theoretical, totally light-absorbing filament, called "black body," which is heated from its normal absolute zero degree temperature to 3,200 degrees centigrade. As soon as you dim this scoop, its color temperature begins to decrease, causing the color of the light to change accordingly. While this change of color temperature can hardly be noticed simply by looking at the light (especially when the dimming occurs in the upper ranges), the color camera reports this change readily by producing a distinct color tint over the whole picture. Especially in the lower ranges of light intensity, the orange glow of the low color temperature shows up quite prominently. This color change is, of course, very distracting when it occurs on performers' faces. On the other hand, this effect is often useful for background lighting.*

Many lighting experts maintain that lights illuminating performers and performing areas should never be dimmed. However, practice has shown that you can dim these lights by a good 200 degrees K, especially in the upper intensity ranges, before the color change becomes too noticeable on the monitor. However, you should dim the performing lights only if you have to balance your over-all lighting. Dimming the lights on performers while the show is in progress is almost never done, nor is it recommended.

Generally, the illumination for color television is kept within a 3,000 to 3,400 degrees K range; 3,000 and 3,200 degrees K seem to be the preferred color temperatures. Most lighting instruments are available in the 3,200 degrees K category. Of course, as with the contrast range, the criterion for the ideal color temperature is not necessarily the Kelvin meter but how the picture looks on the monitor.

---

*The current edition of *The American Cinematographer Manual* contains more information on color temperatures and filters.

Some people get so involved in reflectance percentages, color temperatures, and all sorts of ratios that they forget entirely the most important final criteria for television lighting—criteria that are aesthetic rather than technical. A critical look at the color and monochrome monitors is often more telling about the quality of your lighting than are readings of a variety of meters and scopes. If the picture looks "good"—that is, if it looks as you have intended it to look—your lighting is correct. As in all artistic endeavors, the technical aspects should become an aid rather than a hindrance to your creative expression. In television lighting, as in all other aspects of television production, your major guide is still your aesthetic sensitivity and, above all, common sense.

## The Photographic Principle

Television is one of the photographic arts. As such, photographic lighting principles apply to television lighting.

The basic television lighting setup for monochrome as well as color productions consists of three main light sources: (1) key light, (2) back light, and (3) fill light.

In order to demonstrate the interrelationships of these three light sources, let's use a light-colored cube as our lighting object.

### Key light

The key light is the principal source of illumination. It is usually placed above and in front of the subject. If you move the key light a little to one or the other side of the cube, you will discover that the key light is even more form-revealing; three sides of the cube are then made visible by the key light.

Since the key light is the motivating source of light, it must be directional light. Fresnel spotlights, medium spread, are used for key illumination.

### Back light

Now put a second spotlight directly behind the cube, above the back wall of the set. This back light brightens up the top of the cube and separates it a little more from the back wall. The position of the cube now becomes important. If it is too close to the background wall, the back light will no longer reach the top of the cube. You may be able to hit the cube partly with back light by tilting the lighting instrument all the way down. Such a steep angle, however, will cause a bright, undesirable top light. In general, lighting angles of 45 degrees are considered ideal for normal lighting situations. For this reason, performing areas should never be placed too

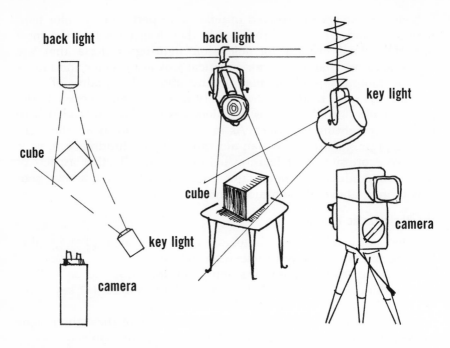

close to the scenery. Furniture used by the performers, such as tables, chairs, and sofas, should always be moved out into the middle of the performing areas, away from the walls. This will also help to prevent the performers' shadows falling sharply on the walls of the set and the reflection of the set colors falling on the performers' faces and clothing.

### Fill light

After the key light and back light have been turned on, you will notice that the side of the cube away from the key illumination is unnaturally dark and quite indistinguishable. You must now try to lighten up this dark side without erasing the shadow effect altogether, which would eliminate the modeling effect of the key light. You can "fill in" some of the dark shadow areas by placing a floodlight—a scoop—in front of the cube or a little to the side, opposite the key light source. In order to soften this fill light, you can place a special spun-glass diffuser, a so-called scrim, in front of the scoop.

If the fill light spills into too many other areas, you will have to use a Fresnel spot instead of a scoop. In this case, you must adjust the spotlight for a maximum spread beam (bulb-reflector unit pushed toward the lens), which will make the light a little softer and eliminate the danger of washing out the shadow altogether. The use of

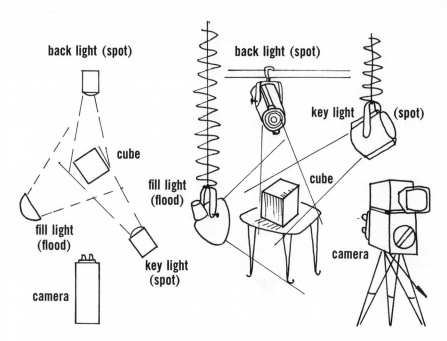

back light (spot)

back light (spot)

key light (spot)

cube

fill light (flood)

cube

fill light (flood)

key light (spot)

camera

camera

controlled fill light (spread spots) is especially important for small station operation, where spill light into other set areas can create major problems.

With the key, back, and fill lights in these positions, the cube should be properly lighted now.

### Different key-light effects

If you replace the cube with a plaster bust, preferably one with deep-set eyes and hollow cheeks, you can observe the importance of

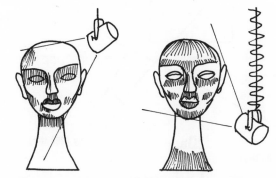

key light above eye level    key light below eye level

a proper key-light positioning. If you place the key light too high, large dark shadows will unfavorably emphasize the deep-set eyes and hollow cheeks of the model. If you place the key light below eye level, unrealistic highlights and shadows will produce a ghostly and mysterious effect. Obviously, the vertical positioning of the key light is extremely important. Those Fresnel spots that are used mostly for key lighting should be made very flexible (contrary to the general television lighting practice) and suspended on pantographs.

### Key-light to back-light ratio

On the plaster bust you can also observe the effect of the back light. A back light that is too intense will cause a rather unnatural halo effect. If the back light is not bright enough, however, the plaster model will blend too much into the background. A back light equally or slightly more intense than the key light seems to be most desirable. In general, light objects need less back light than dark objects. A television performer with blond hair and a light

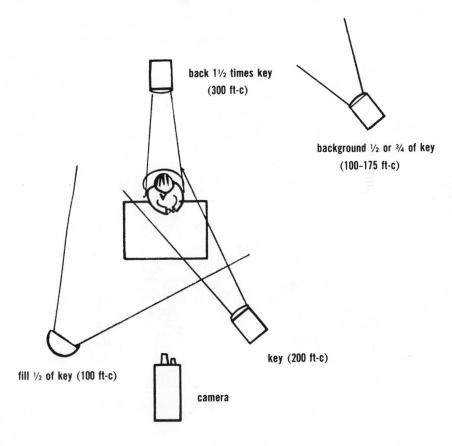

back 1½ times key
(300 ft-c)

background ½ or ¾ of key
(100–175 ft-c)

key (200 ft-c)

fill ½ of key (100 ft-c)

camera

suit will need less back light than a dark-haired performer in a dark suit.

Intensity ratios among the key, back, and fill lights depend entirely on your particular lighting objective. A simple, typical lighting setup employing the photographic principle might have the following ratios: (1) a key light of a specific intensity (let us assume we are lighting a newscaster for a color production: 200 ft-c.); (2) a back light with 1½ times the intensity of the key light (300 ft-c.); (3) a fill light one half the intensity of the key (100 ft-c.); and (4) a background illumination of one half to three quarters the intensity of the key light (100–175 ft-c). This combination of light intensities should give you a base-light illumination of approximately 285 to 300 ft-c.

Generally, dimmers help immensely in achieving the appropriate balance among the various light sources. Be careful, however, not to dim too heavily the light that falls on performers when you are working in color.

### Filling in eye shadows

By looking at the plaster model, you will see that one of your main lighting problems will be the softening of eye shadows. Deep eye shadows can be softened only if the fill light strikes the subject at a rather low angle. All scoops should be mounted on pantographs so that they can be pulled down, if low angle fill light is desired. Some lighting men point the scoops toward the light-reflecting studio floor. The reflected, highly diffused light will thus strike the subject from an extremely low angle, filling in all shadow areas that could never have been reached by overhead lighting.

If you need additional fill light in limited areas, a small 150-watt baby spotlight, the "inky-dinky," which is mounted on top of the

dimmer for
camera light

camera light

camera, can be turned on. In order to prevent obvious intensity variations when this camera moves in and out, a small resistance dimmer is mounted on the camera and hooked up with the inky-dinky. The cameraman can then adjust light intensity while dollying in or out. In color productions, this method of fill lighting is rather dangerous, however, since the dimming changes color temperatures.

### Boom shadows

Now that you have lighted the plaster bust fairly adequately, try to simulate the microphone boom operation. By moving an ordinary broomstick in front of the plaster model, you will notice "boom" shadows whenever the broomstick passes through a spotlight beam. A more diffused fill light usually casts soft, less-defined shadows. You might think that to eliminate undesirable boom shadows you should use only floodlights for television lighting, or else you should wash out hard boom shadows with additional fill lights. Both methods, however, result in flat lighting. You should try to hide boom shadows rather than eliminate them. Careful positioning of the key light and other directional light sources, plus full cooperation from the boom operator, can throw boom shadows into areas that will not be picked up by the television camera. Also, as pointed out before, a partial blocking of a directional light beam by the use of barn doors may frequently help to eliminate some of the boom-shadow problems.

The easy way out, of course, is not to use the boom microphone but to rely on the more economical hand, desk, and lavaliere microphones. The nature of the show, however, may make their use not always possible or desirable.

### Application of the photographic principle for continuous action

The basic photographic lighting principle of key, back, and fill light can be multiplied and used for every individual set or performing area. All adjacent performance areas should be lighted so that the lighted areas overlap. This will give the performer even lighting as he moves from one area to the other. When there are many set areas, however, the usually limited number of available lighting instruments will not be sufficient. The lighting man will then have to position his lighting instruments so that one lighting instrument can serve two or sometimes even three different functions. In reverse-angle shooting, for instance, the key light for one performer may become the back light for another, and vice versa. Another key light may also be utilized as directional fill in one of the adjacent set areas. This lighting technique requires exact

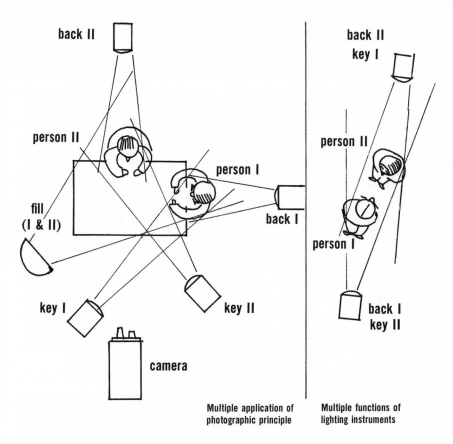

back II

back II
key I

person II

person I

fill
(I & II)

back I

key I

key II

camera

person II

person I

back I
key II

Multiple application of
photographic principle

Multiple functions of
lighting instruments

positions for set pieces, such as tables and chairs, and clearly defined performing areas. Directors who, at the last minute, decide to change blocking or reposition furniture after the show has been lighted are not very popular with television lighting men.

## Additional Light Sources

Several additional light sources are used in connection with the basic photographic lighting setup. The major additional light sources are (1) the background or set light, (2) the side light, (3) the kicker light, and (4) the camera light.

### Background light

The most important additional light source is the background light or, as it is sometimes called, the set light.

The function of the background light is to illuminate background that is not a direct part of the principal performing areas. The background light can accentuate the folds of a background drapery, for instance, or project a slice of light across an otherwise dull-looking cyc background. Special cucalorus (kookie) projections are also part of background lighting.

The background light frequently goes beyond its mere supporting role to become a major production element. It often emphasizes, better than any other light source, the mood of the show, the locale, or the time of the day. Short, steep shadows, for instance, may indicate high noon or early afternoon; long, low shadows on the background may suggest late afternoon or evening.

The background light, like any other light source used, should be barn-doored off on the upper portion of the set and concentrated in the middle and lower parts of the scenery. The reasons for this lighting practice are simple. First, most indoor lighting is designed to illuminate low working areas rather than upper portions of walls. Second, the performer's head will be more pleasingly contrasted against a dark background. Too much light on the upper portions of the background usually turns faces dark. On the other hand, furniture and medium- to dark-colored clothing are nicely set off from the lighted lower portions of the set. Third, as mentioned previously, barn-dooring down the upper portions of the set helps to eliminate some of the undesirable boom shadows.

### The side light

A side light is sometimes used in place of or in addition to the fill light. The side light is usually placed directly to the side of the subject. Fresnel spotlights are generally used for side lights, which then act as directional fill lights. The side light helps to reduce harsh shadow areas; it also acts as additional modeling light, providing some additional highlights.

### The camera light or eye light

As mentioned previously, the camera light is either a small 150-watt Fresnel spotlight or an internal-reflector cliplight, mounted on the camera. It is used whenever additional light is needed. Quite frequently you will have to put studio easels in corners that are not properly lighted. The small spotlight on top of the camera can adequately provide the necessary illumination for a proper pickup of the easel card. More often, however, the camera light is used for additional fill light on television performers. It is very effective in lightening up the inevitable eye shadows, and it supplies some sparkle to eyes and clothes. Small dimmers mounted next to the focusing knob are desirable so that light intensity can be controlled while dollying in or out.

### The kicker light

An additional back light that is not placed directly behind the subject but is positioned somewhat off to one side is called a kicker light

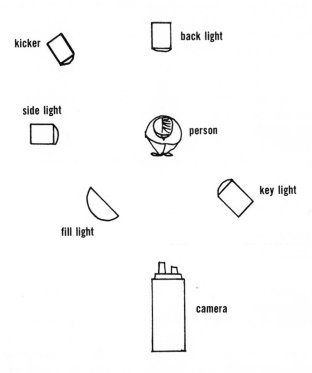

or side back light. Its purpose is to add special highlights, mostly for dramatic effects. Since only a relatively small area is illuminated by the kicker, pinned spotlights are used.

## Special Lighting Techniques

We should now look at three special lighting techniques that are quite often used: (1) cameo lighting, (2) rear screen lighting, and (3) color background lighting.

### Cameo lighting

Certain television shows, especially those of a dramatic nature, are sometimes staged in the middle of a seemingly empty studio against a black background. This lighting technique, where only the performers are highlighted against a dark background, is commonly known as cameo lighting. All cameo lighting is highly directional and is generally achieved entirely with spotlights. Background areas are carefully shielded with black draperies from any kind of distracting spill light. Technically, cameo lighting is extremely difficult to handle. For I-O cameras, the cameo lighting contrast range is unusually high, the base-light level almost always too low. Vidicon cameras can absorb a much greater contrast range, but they need more light on the performers. Such a great amount of light concentrated on a comparatively small area is likely to wash out actors' features. For color cameras, the shadows are usually too dark, the contrast ratio too extreme and the base-light intensity not sufficient.

From an aesthetic point of view, however, cameo lighting is quite expressive. It is a dramatic lighting technique and should be used only for shows of dramatic character.

No background scenery is necessary in cameo lighting and, generally, only a few set pieces are used. Full emphasis is put on performers.

Limbo lighting is very similar to cameo lighting, except that in limbo lighting the background is always light.

### Lighting the rear screen performance area

The intensity of a rear screen projection depends, like any ordinary slide projector, on the power of the projector. But even the most powerful home slide projector will produce pictures of poor quality if you turn on the lights or open the curtains and allow sunlight to flood the room. Similarly, any light that falls on the rear screen projection damages the picture partially or fully. Lighting in the close vicinity of the rear screen, therefore, must be highly directional. You can use only spotlights with barn doors carefully adjusted so that no spill light will hit the rear screen. You must also move performers and lighted set pieces at least six feet away from the rear screen. Since the lighting area in front of the rear screen is confined, the performer is restricted in his movements. In general, only stationary action is possible. Under no circumstances should the performer try to walk back to the rear screen. He will turn black immediately, since no light can approach the screen.

If the rear screen slide is bright, the performer's face may appear black. Additional light will be needed to brighten up his face, which, in turn, will increase spill light problems. As you can see, rear screen lighting is anything but easy.

When several sets are lighted in addition to the rear screen, spill light and the high amount of base light may cloud the rear screen projection. This cloudiness occurs most often in small studios, where the sets are necessarily close together. The only solution is to separate

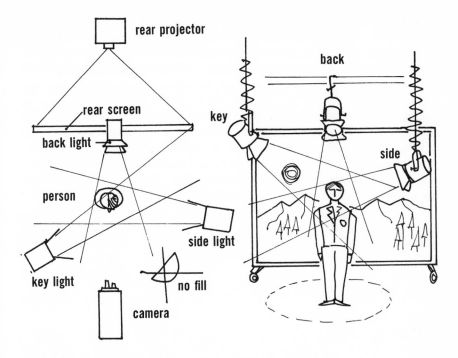

performing areas as much as possible and to keep them on opposite sides of the studio so that the set lighting is directed away from the rear screen. If the spill light problem becomes too great, a photo mural may have to be substituted for the light-sensitive rear projection.

### Color background lighting

In color television lighting, color gels called "cinemoids" are sometimes used for coloring background scenery. Depending on what color you want, specific color gels are inserted into the background spotlights. Remember, however, that color gels should never be used for lighting performance areas.

## Lighting Techniques for Remote Telecasts

Obviously, careful studio lighting can rarely be achieved on remote locations. Fortunately, remote telecasts rarely demand aesthetic lighting effects; they need only a basic functional light level so that the camera can see. In most remote locations, the available power is quite limited and generally insufficient for large lighting setups. Some compromises will have to be made. A maximum amount of light has to be produced with a minimum of lighting instruments. Quartz scoops and sun guns are preferred to the Fresnel spots. If you use sun guns or photo cliplights, you should unplug the whole lighting setup after each rehearsal in order to preserve the very limited life span of these lighting instruments for the on-the-air performance. You will need a great number of extension cords and multiple-outlet plugs for a remote lighting setup.

On most remote telecasts, the camera will inevitably have to look through a door toward one or several windows. Shutters and curtains will have to be drawn to combat excessive back light, which turns performers into black, unfavorable-looking silhouettes. In these situations, you should use pole-cats (see pages 176–177) for supporting back lights.

## SUMMARY

In all television lighting, the photographic lighting principle of key light, back light, and fill light is used. Additional lighting sources, especially background light and side light, are used to enhance the over-all lighting effect.

In general, vidicon cameras need twice as much light as the monochrome I-O or Plumbicon camera; color cameras need three times as much light. Approximate base-light levels are set at 100 foot-candles for the monochrome I-O and Plumbicon cameras, 200 ft-c for the vidicon camera, and 300 ft-c for the color camera. Base-light levels may vary considerably, depending on the general contrast range and on individual lens openings.

Fresnel spotlights are the most useful instruments in television lighting. Scoops are used for fill light. On remote telecasts, quartz scoops may become the principal light sources.

In lighting for color television, dense shadow areas should be made transparent with fill light, and extremely bright areas should be toned down. Color temperature is an important factor in color lighting, since it affects the "tint" of the over-all scene. Faces and other skin tones should be lighted as evenly as possible; very little, if any, dimming should be done with lights used for performers or performing areas.

Since operation time and manpower are at a premium in television, close attention must be paid to the original placement of the lighting instruments.

Follow three steps to simplify lighting operations:

1. Divide the studio into several major performance areas.

2. Hang all lights so that they can serve multiple functions. This procedure will help to illuminate adequately all performance areas.

3. Have all lights flexible enough to allow quick and easy lighting changes. Minor light changes should be possible simply by rotating and tilting the light instrument, rather than by repositioning it on the grid.

Once the lights are hung in strategically useful places, routine shows should be put into those performance areas that can be lighted most quickly and easily.

The following table of lighting instruments applies to a small to medium-size studio in which monochrome I-O or color cameras are used.

| Light Source | Type | Size (mono-chrome) (color) (watts) | | Position | Effect |
|---|---|---|---|---|---|
| Key | Fresnel spot | 1,000–1,500 | 2,000 | (45 degrees) | Principal source. |
| | Quartz Fresnel | 1,000 | 1,000–2,000 | Side and above. | Reveals basic form. |
| | | | | Below eye level. | Creates a mood of mystery. |
| | | | | Far above eye level. | Emphasizes eye shadows and features. |
| Back | Fresnel spot | 750–1,000 | 1,000–2,000 | (45 degrees) Behind and above. | Separates figure from background, highlights hair and shoulders. |
| | Quartz Fresnel | 400–1,000 | 1,000–2,000 | | |
| Fill | 18-inch scoop | 1,500 | 1,500 | Low front or front side. | Softens shadows. |
| | Quartz scoop | 500 | 1,000 | | |
| | Quartz broad | 500 | 1,000 | | |
| | Fresnel spot | 1,000 | 1,000–2,000 | Low front or side (spread). | Softens shadows in a specific area. |
| | Quartz Fresnel | 500 | 1,000 | | |

| Light Source | Type | Size (mono-chrome) (watts) | (color) | Position | Effect |
|---|---|---|---|---|---|
| Back-ground | Fresnel spot | 1,000 | 1,000–2,000 | Varies with scenery. | Livens back-ground, sets mood. |
| | Quartz Fresnel | 500 | 1,000 | | |
| | Cyc lights incandescent or quartz with glass color frames | 300 | 500 | | |
| Side | Fresnel spot | 1,000 | 1,000 | Side of sub-ject opposite key. | Supplies direc-tional fill, addi-tional modeling. |
| | Quartz Fresnel | 500 | 1,000 | | |
| Kicker | Fresnel spot | 1,000 | 1,000–2,000 | Side back. | Supplies modeling highlights. |
| | Quartz Fresnel | 500 | 1,000 | | |
| Camera | Fresnel spot or R-40 | 150 | 150 | On camera. | Serves as addi-tional fill and modeling; principal source for easel cards, etc. |

## EXERCISES

1. Define "reference black" and "reference white."
2. What is the normal contrast range in color lighting and the accept-able reflectance limits?
3. While taking a final look at your lighting setup in the control room monitor, you discover that the ground rows blend into the background cyc. What do you do?
4. Your director complains about a small but clearly visible black spot behind an archway. Your overhead lighting equipment does not reach that particular dark corner. What do you do?
5. You have used all available lighting instruments for lighting your major performing areas. Your director informs you that he will need some light on the studio card in the far corner of the studio. What do you suggest?

6. Your lighting plan for a rear projection scene shows Fresnel spotlights for key and back, an ellipsoidal spot for background, and scoops for fill light. Do you agree with the plan? If so, why? If not, why not?

7. What are the advantages and disadvantages of wide lens openings in connection with studio lighting?

8. Your director asks you to do some cameo lighting for his color dance show. What are your reactions? Why?

9. What is the difference between incident and reflected light readings?

10. What is color temperature?

# 5

## Scenery and Properties

All television scenery is designed for the television camera. Size, texture, color, and location of sets, as well as all the set dressings, are specifically adapted to what the television camera can see. Certain sections of the set are usually more important than its total impression. A television set does not have to be continuous. One part of it —the entrance to a house, for instance—may be in one corner of the studio, while the other part—the hallway—may be located in the opposite part of the studio. Location depends on the sequence of events and on the director's camera placement. Television scenery must allow primarily for (1) optimum camera angles, including camera and microphone boom movement, (2) good, functional lighting, and (3) maximum action of the performers. Always remember that television scenery, like any scenery, is intended primarily to support the performance, not to dominate it; television scenery should help to create the necessary environment for a show.

Since the television camera may look at a set both at close range and at a distance, television scenery must be detailed enough to appear realistic yet plain enough to prevent overladen, cluttered, "busy" pictures.

Most of the television scenery for small station operation should be designed and constructed so that one man can set up (assemble) and strike (disassemble) all required studio sets. Setup and strike should take a minimum amount of time. Once the scenery is struck, it should take up very little storage space. All properties must be flexible and durable enough to allow a great variety of applications. All scenery and properties should be painted in a color scale that reproduces equally well on color and monochrome monitors. And most of the scenery pieces must be interchangeable, requiring little or no modification.

## TYPES OF SCENERY

We can divide television scenery into four groups: (1) standard set units, or stock scenery, (2) special set units, (3) hanging units, and (4) set pieces.

### Standard Set Units

All stock scenery is interchangeable and thus requires uniformity in major dimensions, in construction methods and materials, in the method of joining the flats, and in color and texture.

Stock scenery consists of softwall flats and hardwall flats. Softwall flats are wooden frames covered with muslin or canvas; hardwall flats are wooden frames covered with various types of fiberboard, such as masonite.

All stock scenery should have a uniform height. There are two basic units in small station operations: (1) the 10-foot unit, and (2) the 8-foot unit.

*Ten-foot units.* The height of most television scenery is 10 feet. This height is great enough to prevent the camera from overshooting too easily, yet it is low enough so that the sets can be lighted without bringing in the lights at too steep an angle.

*Eight-foot units.* Many small stations have a low-ceiling problem. In this case, 8-foot scenery is adequate. Overshooting on long shots, however, may become a serious problem.

A combination of 10-foot and 8-foot units is the most desirable solution in small station operation. For instance, quite frequently an 8-foot flat is all you will need to back a commercial display. The following dimensions of width are the same for 8- and 10-foot unit scenery.

*Softwall unit scenery* consists of single flats, twofolds (or books), and threefolds.

*Single flats.* 1-foot single, 18-inch single, 2-foot single, 3-foot single, 4-foot single, 5-foot single, 5-foot 9-inch single, and 6-foot single. (The width limitation of 5 feet 9 inches is an old carryover from the theatre. The railroad companies could store nothing wider than 5 feet 9 inches in their boxcars.) Single flats can be made even wider than 6 feet, if the situation requires it.

*Twofolds.* Two 4-foot singles hinged together make a 4-foot twofold; two 5-foot singles hinged together make a 5-foot twofold; and two 5-foot 9-inch or 6-foot singles hinged together make a 6-foot twofold.

*Threefolds.* Three 4-foot singles hinged together make a 4-foot threefold: three 5-foot singles hinged together make a 5-foot threefold.

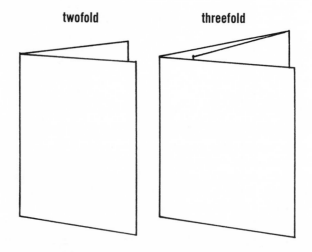

**twofold**                    **threefold**

*Hardwall unit scenery* usually consists only of single flats that are bolted or pin-hinged together according to need. Although hardwall scenery can be built in any width, the most common unit dimensions of hardwall flats are 2, 3, 4, 5, and 6 feet in width.

### Construction of Flats

Although you may never intend to become an expert stage carpenter, you should at least have a working knowledge of some basic scenery construction methods. Any of the better known stage craft books, such as Sol Cornberg and E. L. Gebauer, *A Stage Crew Handbook,* and Burris-Meyer and Cole, *Scenery for the Theatre,* will give you excellent information on scene construction. Only the basic methods of building television scenery will be pointed out here.

Flats consist of (1) the frame, (2) the covering, and (3) the hardware.

### The softwall frame

The softwall frame consists of 1 × 3 lumber that is glued and supported by corner blocks and keystones. Corner blocks and keystones are either screwed in (No. 9 woodscrews) or nailed in with clout nails. If you nail the joints with clout nails, you must first lay the flat on a hard-surfaced floor. When the clout nails are driven through the flat, the hard surface bends them back into the wood frame, which locks cornerblocks and keystones solidly to the frame. Joints made with

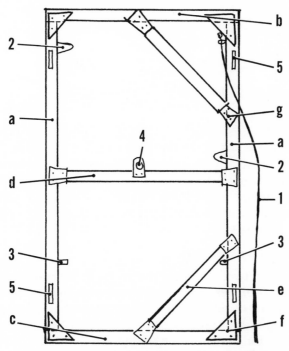

Frame: a) stiles, b) top rail, c) bottom rail, d) toggle rail, e) corner braces, f) corner block, g) keystone.

Hardware: 1) lashline, 2) lash cleats, 3) tie-off cleats, 4) brace cleat or pin hinge, 5) blocks or stop-cleats.

woodscrews are a little more expensive and somewhat slower, but they are also more durable.

### Covering softwall flats

Softwall flats are usually covered with relatively inexpensive un-bleached muslin. The covering process is the same as that for theatre scenery. First, tack one continuous piece of muslin along the stiles and rails, close to the inside edge. Then glue the muslin to the flat frame (except on the corner braces and the toggle rail). You will find that modern, white, water-soluble plastic glue will work much better than the old ground glue, which had to be preheated in a steam bath before it became applicable.

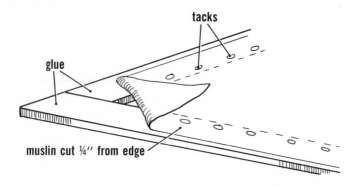

The next step is sizing the flat. The simplest way is to thin out the plastic glue with an ample amount of water and then brush the solution liberally all over the flat surface. The muslin will then stretch tightly over the flat frame. Don't forget to flameproof all scenic material. There are several good commercial flame-proofing agents on the market, and they can be mixed in and applied with the size water.

### Constructing twofolds and threefolds

To construct a twofold, hinge two single frames together with three 2-inch backflap hinges. The whole twofold is then covered with one continuous piece of muslin.

Before hinging the third flap to a twofold for the construction of a threefold, insert a 1½-inch-wide batten. This batten will allow you to close the threefold properly without putting too much strain on hinges or frames. The threefold, too, is covered with one continuous strip of muslin.

Always put two or three metal gliders into each bottom rail. They aid greatly in pushing the flats along the smooth studio floor.

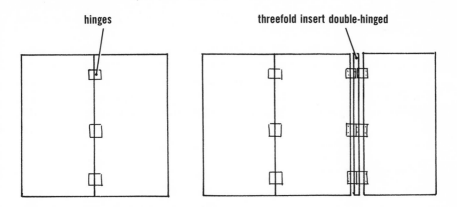

hinges                                        threefold insert double-hinged

### The hardwall frame

The frame for the hardwall flat is made of 1 × 3 stiles and rails that are glued and screwed together on edge. Corner braces and keystones are not necessary, since the hardwall covering supplies the necessary bracing.

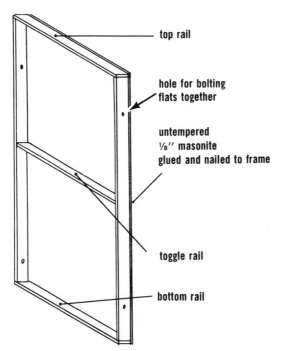

top rail

hole for bolting
flats together

untempered
⅛″ masonite
glued and nailed to frame

toggle rail

bottom rail

Hardwall flat: rails and stiles all 1 x 3 pine on edge

### Covering hardwall flats

The covering material for the hardwall flat can be any of the many varieties of fiberboard available. Usually, ⅛-inch untempered masonite is used. You can put the untempered masonite (which is more flexible and does not shatter as easily as tempered masonite) on the frame with a power stapler, or you can glue it and tack it on with small nails. Molded plastic or any one of the available plywood cutouts can also be fastened to the hardwall frame.

### Bracing and joining flats

Bracing television scenery is somewhat different from bracing theatre scenery. Theatre flats are usually supported by stage braces screwed into the wooden floor. In the television studio, scenery must be braced by jacks or braces, which are held to the hard studio floor by the weight of sandbags or metal counterweights. You can attach the jack to the toggle rail of the flat by either a pin hinge or a short piece of lashline looped through the toggle rail. You can also attach a regular stage brace to the flat and fasten it to a special floorplate, which you then weigh down with metal weights or sandbags.

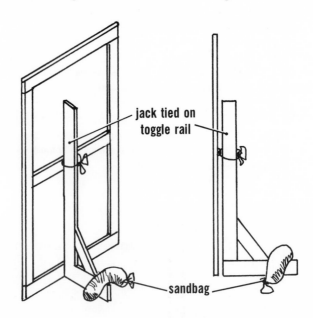

jack tied on
toggle rail

sandbag

Aluminum- or iron-pipe "pole cats" are sometimes used for bracing softwall scenery. A pole cat is a device similar to modern lamps that are held between ceiling and floor by spring tension. In low-ceiling or low-grid studios, you can brace the pole cat between the studio floor and the ceiling or lighting grid and tie the flat to the pole cat.

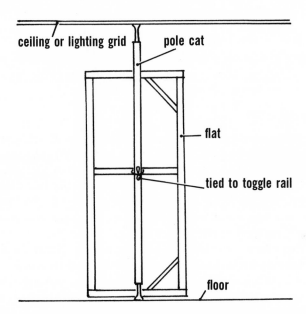

Don't overbrace the scenery. In a well-designed set you may need very few or no jacks at all. Slightly booked twofolds (a) or threefolds (b) are completely self-supporting.

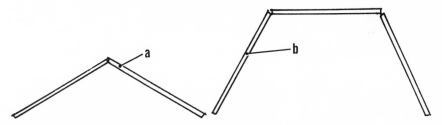

Softwall flats are tied to each other by the traditional lashline method. When lashing a flat, snap the lashline of one flat into the upper lashcleat of the second flat. Then pull the lashline through the lashcleat of the first flat, bring it over to the second flat, and tie it off with a slipknot around both tie-off cleats.

You can find the correct length of the lashline by tying the line to the lashline eye, letting it drop to the studio floor, and cutting the line just where it touches the floor.

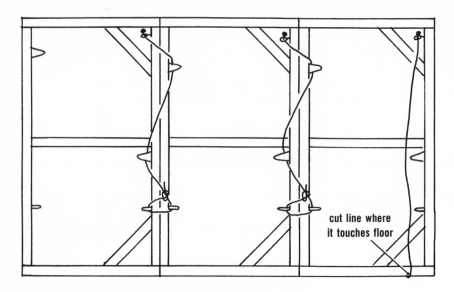

cut line where
it touches floor

One of the major problems in joining old or slightly warped flats is a crack between two lashed flats, which becomes quite apparent when viewed with a close-up camera. Very tight lashing will usually eliminate the crack or reduce it so that it becomes unnoticeable. The tightest lash can be achieved by booking the flats slightly toward you when you lash them together. Then push the flats out in a reverse angle. Be careful, however, not to push too hard or you may snap the lashline or rip out one or both tie-off cleats.

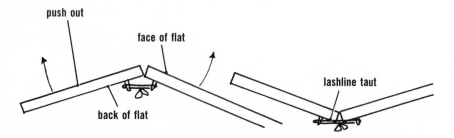

push out

face of flat

lashline taut

back of flat

If tight lashing does not help to eliminate an obvious crack, you can always cover the crack with strips of masking tape painted the color of the flat. You may do well, however, to put up the complete basic set before you pay attention to these relatively minor details.

If you join flats at a 90-degree angle, the blocks or stop-cleats, which have been indicated as part of the flat hardware, become important bracing agents. The blocks on flat "a" prevent flat "b" (called a "return") from being pulled in by the tension of the lashline.

When lashing "returns" (usually a narrow flat), always watch that the returns are lashed *behind* the main flat. This method will give the setup additional support. Also, the main flat will cover the returns and thus eliminate unnecessary cracks. The more angles (returns, booked twofolds and threefolds) you put into your setup of flats, the sturdier your set structure becomes. The returns and angles act as solid braces.

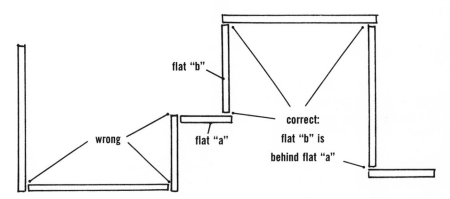

Hardwall flats are often bolted together or held together with clamps at the top and bottom parts of the stiles. When the flats join at an angle, you can nail a small piece of 1 × 3 across the top where the two flats join.

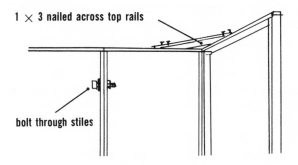

Strong rubber bands, called "shock cords," have also been used successfully in joining hardwall scenery, since they stretch around any angle of the joint.

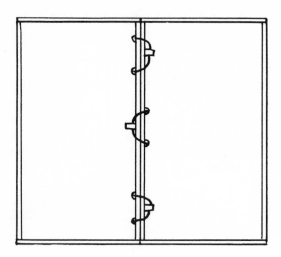

Sometimes single pieces of scenery are held up by "sailboats." A sailboat is a metal gallow fastened to a box with casters; it contains enough metal weights to balance the weight of the flat. Two "sailboats" can hold an amazing array of scenery.

In general, hardwall scenery is considered to be superior to softwall scenery and is therefore used extensively in television operations.

Hardwall scenery has several advantages. (1) It is good for permanent or semipermanent sets. (2) It is sturdy and needs little or no maintenance. (3) Small objects, such as pictures or small commercial props, can be fastened anywhere on the solid flat surface. (4) If, as in a dramatic production, a door is slammed, the hardwall scenery will not flutter and shake.

However, for small station operation, hardwall scenery is not without serious disadvantages. (1) The construction is fairly expensive. (2) The scenery is heavy, if properly constructed; it cannot be moved by one man; if it falls, it gets badly damaged; there is always the potential danger of someone being hurt by the heavy scenery. (3) It is hard to store and to move about. (4) It is difficult to brace and join. (5) It may cause audio problems; if the microphone is too close to a hardwall flat, sound is greatly reflected, creating unpleasant echo and noise effects.

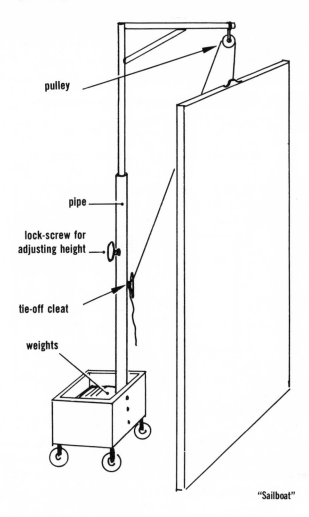

pulley

pipe

lock-screw for
adjusting height

tie-off cleat

weights

"Sailboat"

## Special Set Units and Scenery Devices

Special set units include special flats that are interchangeable with the stock unit scenery, door flats with door plugs (a door plug is the actual door, which is "plugged" into the door frame), window flats with window plugs, special frame doors (like French patio doors), library flats, fireplace flats with holes for fireplace plugs, and similar units. All special set units are compatible with standard set units in basic size and hardware. The method of construction and the construction material, however, may differ widely from that of standard units.

### Windows and doors

You will find detailed information on how to build window and door flats and their corresponding plugs in theatre handbooks. You may also find it convenient to construct both left-wing and right-wing door and window flats.

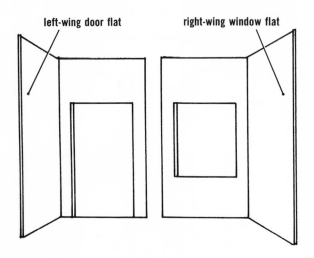

left-wing door flat        right-wing window flat

### Bookcase flats

You can make a simple but extremely realistic-looking bookcase flat by gluing the backs of old books directly on the flat. Small strips of molding indicate the bookshelves (see page 183).

### Sliding scenery

In cramped quarters you may find it very convenient to provide for an area in which backgrounds can be changed quickly and easily. In this case, an effective scenic device is to hang four or five different softwall flats on parallel tracks like closet doors. To change the background, you simply slide one flat over the other (see page 183).

### Special scenery devices

Frequent repainting of stock scenery is not possible in small station operation. Special, inexpensive scenery devices have to be found that can quickly transform stock scenery into specific settings. The most important of these special scenery devices are (1) seamless paper, (2) corrugated cardboard, and (3) masking tape.

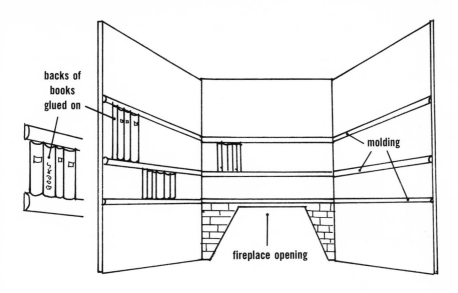

backs of
books
glued on

molding

fireplace opening

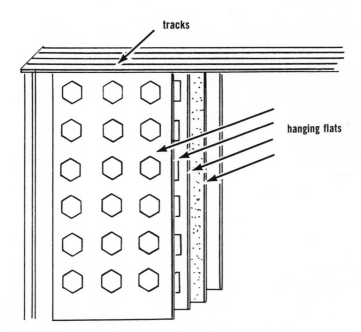

tracks

hanging flats

*Seamless paper.* Every display house carries rolls of paper 9 feet high and 36 feet wide, and these rolls come in a great variety of colors. You can simply staple this paper drop on the flats of stock scenery and use it in two ways: (1) plain, as a substitute for a cyclorama, if

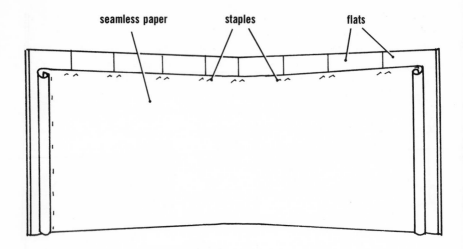

a continuous background is needed; or (2) painted, as a scenic back-drop, similar to a photomural or a canvas drop.

To attach seamless paper to flats, first lash stock scenery to a slightly arched, continuous wall. Start to staple the beginning of the roll on the camera-left side of your flats. Roll the paper out to your right, tacking it lightly to every stile of the flats. Tacking the seam-less only at the top of the paper and letting it hang will make it look smoother. With someone to help you, the whole operation is easy and quick. Have your helper stand on a rolling table. While you unwind the paper and pull the table, he will staple the paper to the flats. Be sure to put the staples in at an angle. This speeds up the striking of the paper roll considerably, since you can roll up the paper with-out having to remove the staples.

Seamless paper comes in many subtle and intense colors that will assure good compatibility.

Orange and light blue seamless papers photograph as excellent light grays; brown and olive green give medium grays; and dark blue and purple give good blacks.

Regular showcard colors can be used to paint your seamless drop. Very effective results have been achieved by painting dark seamless with different shades of gray and white. The use of a wet sponge instead of a brush will give you interesting special effects similar to a watercolor painting.

You can achieve quick and effective scene changes simply by roll-ing up one drop and exposing another beneath it.

Seamless paper drops can be re-used a number of times until the tears and wrinkles caused by frequent handling begin to show on-camera. Always label the seamless rolls according to subject matter and style, such as: Paris rooftops, realistic; or: Carnival scene, stylized.

*Corrugated cardboard.* Corrugated cardboard is a good medium for cutout profile pieces and special scenic details. The big (4 × 8 feet) sheets can be cut with a razor blade or an Exacto knife to any desired shape and stapled to standard scenery. Corrugated cardboard is especially suitable for constructing stylized scenery, such as fairy-tale trees, arches, or rockets.

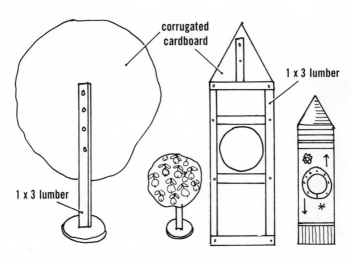

*Masking tape.* Masking tape (½ or 1 inch wide, black or beige) can be used to create many interesting designs. Just put strips of masking tape directly on flats, on the studio floor, or even on the cyclorama. If you tear the 1-inch-wide masking tape lengthwise and use the irregularly torn pieces for specific designs, you will achieve the effect of a sensitively drawn line. The great advantage of masking tape is that it is extremely quick and easy to apply and remove. And it can be put on most scenic surfaces without special preparations. If you make a mistake, or if you don't like your creation, you can quickly pull the tape off and start all over again.

### The studio floor

One of the great headaches of the scenic designer is the proper treatment of the studio floor. In long shots, the floor usually looks unattractive. Properly treated, however, it can become an important part of the set. In general, the scope of small station operation does not warrant an extensive treatment of the studio floor for each show. But there are a few special occasions that call for additional scenic efforts. Four easy methods of floor decoration should be mentioned: (1) masking tape, (2) paint, (3) masonite boards or rubber tile, and (4) glue-on sheets.

*Masking tape.* Black masking tape will lend itself to many interesting patterns on the studio floor. It is easy to apply and to take off. Perspective lines and suggestions of floor tiles are the most effective and most common taped floor decorations.

*Paint.* If you need a more elaborate floor treatment, you can paint a simple pattern directly on the studio floor. Use only fast-drying poster paint, which can be easily mopped off after the show. A few light gray painted outlines will give a nice flagstone effect for a patio set. The most effective patterns are simple geometric figures, such as stars, triangles, circles, and squares.

*Masonite or rubber tile.* You can achieve an excellent tile effect by laying dark and light masonite or rubber squares (3 × 3 feet) in any desired order. You don't have to tape the individual pieces on the floor; if the squares are tightly laid, natural adhesion will prevent the tiles from slipping. The minor cracks between tiles will not hinder cameras and booms from dollying smoothly.

*Glue-on sheets.* Some stations use large plastic sheets with an adhesive backing for specific floor decorations, such as rugs, hallway runners, or ornamental tile. The sheets are quite expensive and not always readily available. For special projects, however, they are an excellent means to decorate floors. The camera can travel freely over the thin plastic sheet, which can be ripped off after the show without any damage to the floor.

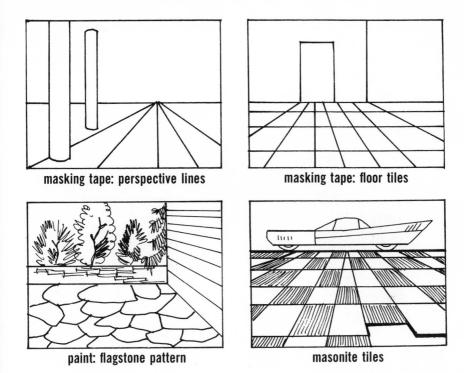

masking tape: perspective lines          masking tape: floor tiles

paint: flagstone pattern                 masonite tiles

## Hanging Scenery

Hanging scenery includes everything that is suspended from the lighting grid or from standing scenery. The most important units of hanging scenery are (1) the cyclorama, (2) the canvas drop, (3) the traveler, (4) draperies, and (5) the photomural.

### The cyclorama

The most versatile backdrop is the cyclorama or "cyc," as it is called. The cyc consists of a continuous piece of heavy canvas stretched along two or all studio walls. It serves as a continuous multipurpose backing for scenery or live action. The cyc usually hangs from a U-shaped pipe or track which, in small stations, might be tied to the lighting grid. A second pipe or drain is pushed through the floor sleeve of the cyc, keeping the cyc stretched taut. Large U-shaped cycs are usually not permanently stretched but are pulled to one side of the studio, where they are gathered like draperies, leaving important wall space free for general use.

The common light blue color of cycloramas is actually not a good television color; it does not photograph too well on monochrome television, and in color it is not the best background for light reflection. Off-white and pale green have proved to be more workable cyc colors.

The ideal cyclorama consists of a sharks-tooth scrim hung approximately 10 inches in front of the regular canvas cyc. This scrim breaks

Cyclorama (Studio 1, San Francisco State College)

the light before it hits the cloth cyc and produces an effective "infinity" feeling.

Slightly curved cyc ground rows help to blend the floor with the cyclorama, thus enhancing the infinity illusion.

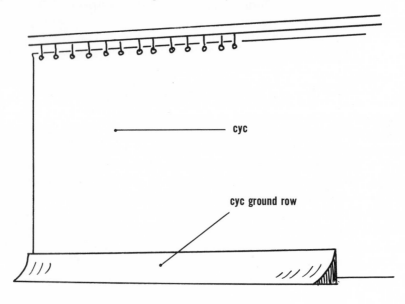

### The canvas drop

The canvas drop used in small television studios is similar to the theatre background drop, only considerably smaller. The canvas drop serves as a specific backing integrated into a particular set. Regular cloth dyes are generally used for paint. The most versatile canvas drop is a cloud drop—a large piece of canvas with realistic clouds painted on it. The cloud drop can be used as backing for a great variety of settings.

The canvas drop is usually hung from the lighting grids. Since most small studios have no provision for flying (that is, hanging) scenery, special flying arrangements will have to be made. You can attach simple pulleys to the lighting grid, which serve as loft and head blocks for the flying rig. Good quality clothesline (No. 8 sash cord) can be used for flying ropes. Make sure that you have adequate tie-off facilities on the studio wall. A 2 × 8 board with four or five large tie-off cleats is, in general, sufficient to hold medium-sized drops. Heavy and particularly wide drops will require four fly lines. In most cases, three lines will be sufficient for the safe handling of this type of hanging scenery.

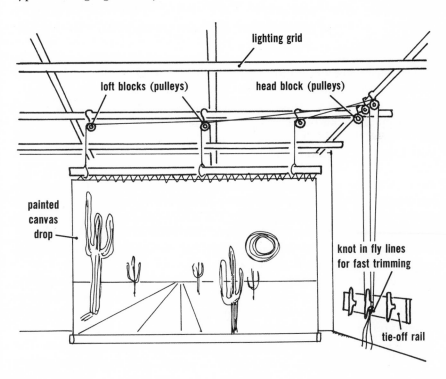

To fly the drop, lower the whole drop to the studio floor and roll it around the floor batten. Tie the rolled drop together with a few short pieces of lashline and fly it back up to the lighting grid.

There are many other methods of flying drops, such as the wind-unwind method with a permanently tied grid batten. This type of flying is successful only with very light and comparatively narrow drops. For heavy scenery you should have a regular counterweight fly system installed.

### The traveler

The traveler is a curtain, similar to the traditional theatre curtain. The traveler usually parts in the middle and opens to each side of the stage. There are many types of light travelers available, which can be easily hung from the lighting grid. When selecting a traveler, watch for good curtain material and a pleasing color.

The traveler should be made of heavy, slightly textured material. A small chain or individual lead weights sewn into the bottom seam will give the traveler added weight, which is needed for the smooth opening and closing of the curtain.

Any color that reproduces well on the television monitor is acceptable. Light green and orange have proved to be most satisfactory for both color and monochrome television operation.

### Draperies

Draperies are an important item of hanging scenery. One good way of using draperies in a television studio is to run them along a curtain rod parallel to and in front of the cyc in place of the scrim. If a draped background is needed, certain legs of drapery are pulled in front of the cyc at any place along the curtain rod. This parallel rod, however, requires a fairly expensive installation. A much simpler but very effective use of draperies is to hang individual drapery legs on flats of the stock units. You can staple drapery legs in neat folds on a short (2- or 3-foot-long) batten. Simple U-hooks attached to the batten make it possible to hang the draperies from the top of the unit flats. Several drapery legs give the impression of a solid width of drapery. Two of them can be used on each side of a window flat, acting as regular window draperies.

When you select drapery material, look for good color and gray-scale response and an interesting but not too busy texture. Some metal-threaded materials look quite festive on camera, especially when you are working in color.

Black velour draperies are sometimes used for special effects. The more light-absorbing the velour, the better it is for special effects

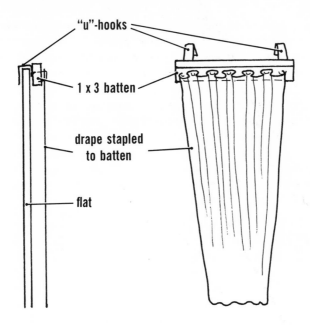

lighting. For instance, black velour draperies are ideal for the rather popular cameo settings that emphasize performers or actors against a completely black background.

### The photomural

Photomurals are either mounted on an inflexible cardboard or plywood backing or attached to a flexible canvas backing.

Of these two types, the flexible photomural is definitely more useful. It can be rolled up, used exactly like a canvas drop, and easily stored anywhere in the studio or prop room.

Photomurals make ideal backings for windows, doors, or gates, wherever realistic backgrounds are desirable. One or two photomurals should be sufficient for small station productions. A prominent landmark, such as the City Hall or any other well-known structure of your city, will always lend itself to a great variety of applications. Photomurals of a particular store interior provide excellent backgrounds for commercials.

If you are in or near a metropolitan area, you can rent many different murals from any theatre supply house.

If you have a counterweight system for the light battens and enough ceiling height, you can "fly" your scenery—raise the flats out of the picture with the help of the counterweight system. In small station operations, this technique is generally used only to lift individual pieces of lightweight scenery, such as single softwall flats or cardboard cutouts. Flying heavier pieces is often quite risky and not recommended if special flying arrangements are not available.

## Set Pieces

Set pieces are another important element of television scenery. You can create excellent sets simply by placing properly selected set pieces in front of the cyclorama. They can act as dividers of studio space, designating foreground, middleground, and background without interfering with camera view and movement.

The following paragraphs describe some of the more useful set pieces:

*Pillars.* Pillars are made out of simple cardboard carpet tubes, either painted or wall-papered. A number of different diameters is desirable. Small pillars can be put over microphone stands for support.

*Pylon.* A pylon is a three-sided structural piece, similar to a pillar, constructed of a 1 × 3 wooden frame and hardwall cover. The bottom of the pylon is usually weighted to make it stand up.

*Periaktos.* A periaktos is a set piece similar to a pylon but much larger. It is constructed of a 1 × 3 frame and covered with muslin or hardwall material. Three free-wheeling casters are attached for maximum mobility. Each side of the periaktos is usually painted differently, permitting quick and efficient set changes.

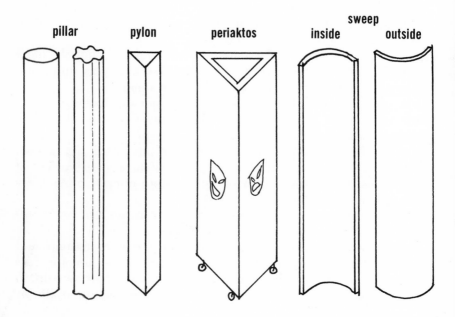

pillar        pylon        periaktos        inside        outside

sweep

*Sweep.* A sweep is a curved piece of scenery, similar to a cutout section of a huge pillar. There are inside sweeps and outside sweeps, depending on the set requirements. A sweep should fit standard unit flats.

*Step unit.* The step unit consists of a series of steps leading up to a height of no more than 5 feet. The unit may be slightly curved for maximum effect. Collapsible step units can be stored more easily and are, therefore, preferred.

**¾″ plywood boxes for step unit**          **pie-shaped unit for curve effect**

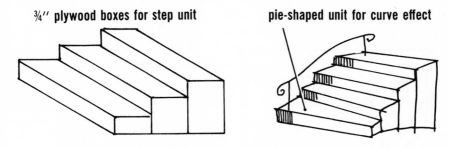

*Blocks and pedestals.* Different-sized plywood blocks and pedestals are quite useful for display purposes. One long stretched block (2 × 2 × 8 feet) with a brick pattern lends itself to a variety of out-door settings.

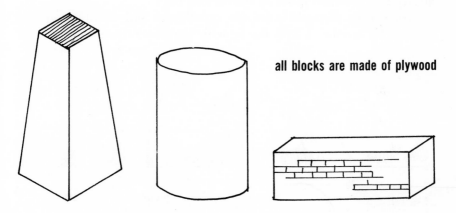

**all blocks are made of plywood**

*Platforms and wagons.* These set pieces are important for every television production. The most useful dimensions for platforms are 3 × 6 feet and 4 × 8 feet, with a height of from 1 foot to a maximum of 3 feet. All platforms are usually constructed of collapsible parallels and heavy ¾-inch plywood tops. The most useful wagons are 3 × 6 feet, with a height of 6 inches. They should be constructed

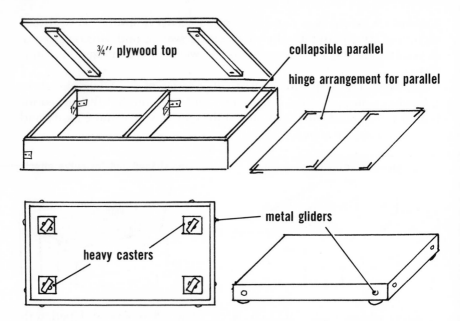

¾'' plywood top

collapsible parallel

hinge arrangement for parallel

metal gliders

heavy casters

of solid ¾-inch plywood. The heavy casters are free-wheeling and sometimes have provisions for locking in at least two directions. Both riser tops and wagons should have metal gliders for easy maneuverability from storage room to studio and back.

*Ground rows.* Ground rows are usually cut out of plywood and backed by a solid 1 × 3 frame with permanently attached jacks.

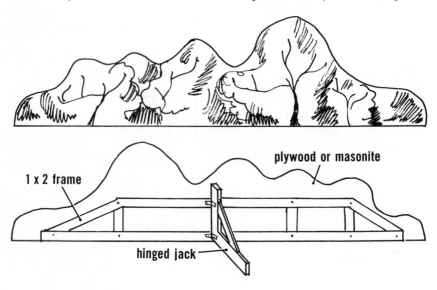

plywood or masonite

1 x 2 frame

hinged jack

The most useful subjects for ground rows are bushes, city skylines, or rolling hills. Ground rows are put in front of cycloramas and serve as background set pieces.

*Screens.* Double-hinged screens serve as excellent background for simple displays or for additional cover of interior settings. You can set a screen anywhere in the studio without bothering to brace it or lash it to other pieces of scenery. The most useful screens have four or five panels, each panel 2 feet wide and 8 or 10 feet high. Factory-made louvered screens or wallpapered hardwall screens are equally versatile.

### multipanel screen double-hinged            hardwall screen double-hinged

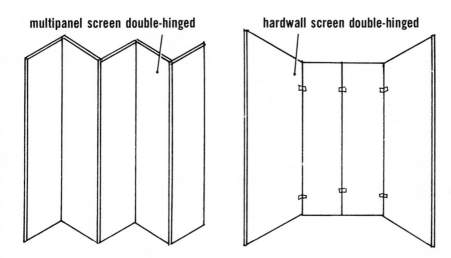

### Special Effects Scenery

Special effects scenery like the gobo, the cucalorus, and the rear screen are discussed in Chapter 7 as special effects. Sometimes, however, you may need to adapt the stock unit scenery for some special effects. The possibilities are virtually unlimited. You can mount stock unit flats on wagons and thus create one of the most simple special effects scenery: a parting wall. At a preplanned moment you can pull the set apart just enough to let a camera take a shot from behind the wall. After the shot, you can close the gap again and restore the shooting field for the other camera.

You can also put a periaktos or a large hexagonal column behind a window flat. By turning the periaktos, you can change the window scene. The window flat also provides a good frame for maps and charts, and the periaktos is especially effective when you are working with a variety of maps.

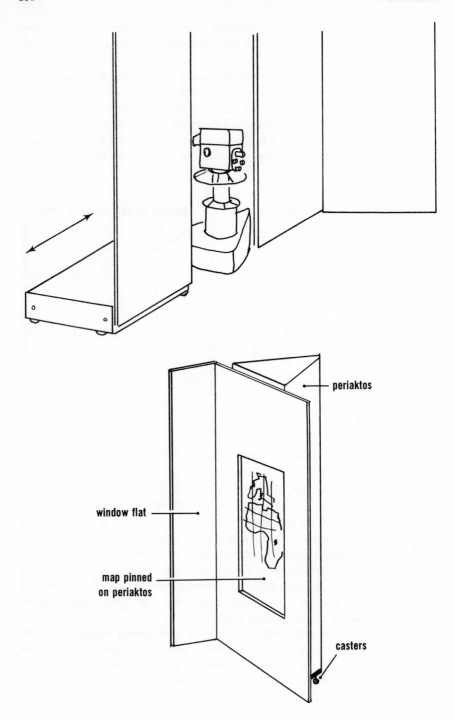

periaktos

window flat

map pinned
on periaktos

casters

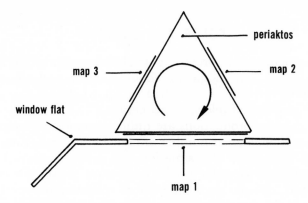

Simple automobile inner tubes can also help to convert your standard set units into special effects scenery. The rocking effect of a boat, for instance, can be easily achieved by putting a small boat on two half-inflated inner tubes. Inner tubes are capable of holding a great amount of weight. You can build a whole set section on inner tubes for an earthquake effect. But remember that in most cases the rocking of the television camera can create the same or similar effects much more easily. The rocking of parts of the set is important only if other parts must remain stationary.

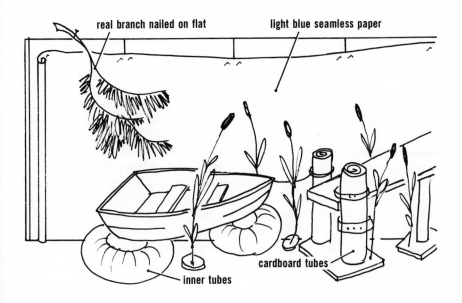

## COLOR AND SCENERY

In constructing and preparing television scenery, you need not only good taste and judgment about pleasing and effective color combinations but also a considerable knowledge of the color and gray-scale response of television cameras.

Although color productions are quite common now even in small station operation, a great number of monochrome television receivers are still in operation. This situation will probably prevail for some time to come. Since color productions must satisfy not only color receivers but also the great number of monochrome receivers, you should acquaint yourself with some basic color fundamentals and their relationship to both color and monochrome television.

Let us, therefore, look briefly at (1) some fundamentals of color, (2) the gray scale, and (3) color combatibility.

### Color Fundamentals

Color is determined by three factors: (1) hue, (2) saturation, and (3) brightness. *Hue* refers to the color itself—that is, whether it is blue, green, red, or yellow. *Saturation* (sometimes called *chroma*) indicates the color strength—a strong red or a pale blue, a washed-out green or a rich purple. *Brightness* (sometimes called *value*) indicates whether the color is dark or light.

If we had color production and color reception exclusively, hue and saturation would be our primary concern. In other words, you would be concerned primarily with the aesthetics of color—whether, for example, subtle greens and subtle reds would harmonize (concern with hue), or whether you would like to have a stronger, more intense color instead of a pastel tone (concern with saturation). The lightness or darkness of the color (brightness) would, in this case, be strictly incidental. Since, however, the monochrome camera and receiver are insensitive to hue and largely to saturation (unless a very light saturation happens to make a color brighter), you must also, if not primarily, be concerned with the brightness factor. In fact, the monochrome camera and receiver are colorblind; they respond only to shades of gray. Hence your color combination must satisfy not only the aesthetics of the color picture but also the brightness variations—that is, the variations of gray of the monochrome picture. These variations are ordered into clearly discernible steps called the *gray scale.*

## The Gray Scale

The brightness of a color is basically determined by how much light it reflects. We have already talked about reflectance percentages in our discussion of lighting (Chapter 4). You will remember that the television system is not capable of reproducing pure white (100 per cent reflectance) or pure black (zero per cent reflectance); it can at best reproduce an off-white (of about 70 per cent reflectance) and an off-black (of about 3 per cent reflectance). We call these extremes "TV white" and "TV black." If we now divide the brightness range between TV white and TV black into ten steps, we will have the television gray scale. This gray scale has been closely modeled after the brightness scale by Munsell, a well-known color theorist. Only under the most ideal conditions is the television system capable of differentiating among ten gray-scale steps. A gray scale of seven steps from television white to television black is more realistic. Some production people work with only five gray-scale steps to make sure of reproducing the desired contrast.

the seven-step gray scale

tv white                          medium gray                          tv black

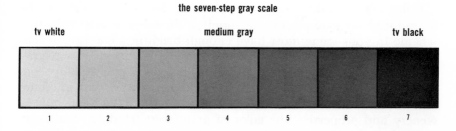

1          2          3          4          5          6          7

Since it takes relatively little reflected light to produce a dark gray or even a medium gray on the television monitor, approximate the middle of the gray scale (step five on a ten-step gray scale, or step four on a seven-step gray scale) does not coincide with the middle of the light reflectance range (50 per cent). In fact, a color with a reflectance of 50 per cent is in the upper ranges of the gray scale, and actually registers as a step two on the ten-step gray scale. A color that reproduces under normal circumstances in the middle ranges of a gray scale usually measures only about 18 per cent reflectance.

In practice, the gray-scale steps are more common as a unit of measurement than are reflectance percentages. If two very different hues, such as red and green, have the same brightness value, they are clearly discernible on the color monitor; on the monochrome

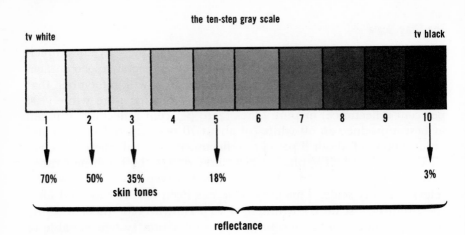

the ten-step gray scale

reflectance

monitor, however, they will show up as the same gray. We are now faced with the problem of color compatibility.

## Color Compatibility

Color compatibility means simply that the color signal can be reproduced on a monochrome monitor. In other words, the color scheme in your scene must have enough brightness contrast so that the colors will reproduce as distinctive steps of the television gray scale (see the color illustrations on the following pages). This contrast is often very difficult to achieve. Even if you work only in monochrome, you will find that it is not easy to combine the colors of your scenery and properties, the color of performers' clothing, and especially the lighting to obtain a picture that extends over the full range of the gray scale, with distinct separations of grays wherever necessary.

In the early days of monochrome television, several stations painted their scenery in several distinct tones of gray in order to assure good contrast and a crisp picture. Surprisingly enough, this technique was not too successful in most instances. There are several reasons for not painting scenery gray: (1) Gray paint does not necessarily reproduce the best grays on the television screen. Different shades of green have been found to produce a better gray scale than grays. You may sometimes run across the term "green scale" instead of gray scale. (2) Performers and production crews quickly grow weary of the uninteresting gray color. (3) In case of color shows, gray flats would have to be repainted.

Even if you are working only in monochrome television, your scenery and properties should be painted in colors that have sufficient variations in brightness. What constitutes a "sufficient variation in

*Plate III*

## COLOR COMPATIBILITY: Gray-Scale Response of Color Pictures on Monochrome Television

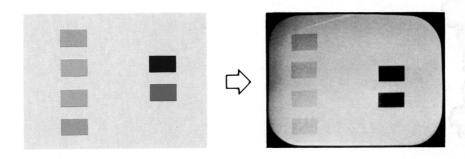

The colors on the left appear on the monochrome monitor as shown at right. The monochrome camera responds to the brightness of a color, not to its hue. The orange, green, purple, and pink all have approximately the same degree of brightness and thus appear as virtually the same gray. The magenta and the blue register as TV black. (Camera: TK-15 vidicon.)

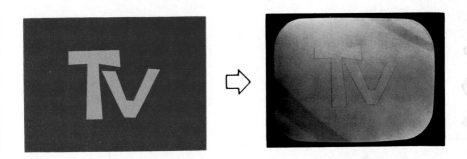

The studio card on the left appears on the monochrome monitor as shown at right. Although the card itself shows a sharp contrast of hues, the monitor shows that the card has virtually no brightness variation. Only their shadows enable us to distinguish the letters. Obviously, this combination is not practical for monochrome reception. (Camera: TK-15 vidicon.)

*Plate IV*

## COLOR COMPATIBILITY (Continued)

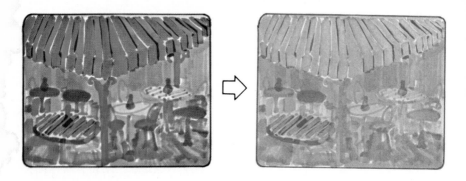

This painting of a French café will reproduce well on color television, because the hues are sufficiently different to emphasize the various objects and areas. However, since the brightness of the colors is quite similar, we would see little more than undifferentiated grays on the monochrome receiver.

In this cityscape backdrop (which could be used for a dance number), the distinct brightness contrast among the colors ensures good reproduction on monochrome television. Notice the colors that produce similar grays and those that produce contrasting grays.

brightness" is not always easy to determine. You rarely have time to measure the exact amount of reflected light under uniform laboratory conditions, thereby determining the brightness value of the color. The few serious attempts to label a specific type of scenic paint with the corresponding gray-scale numbers, such as the Chromachron system developed by Bill Wagner of KRON Television in San Francisco, have not worked out too satisfactorily. Even if you use the same color, it may reflect quite differently, depending on whether you paint a hard surface or a soft surface with it. Also, lighting influences color reflectance to a great extent, as we have already discussed. If you increase the light level drastically on a dark color, it may look lighter than a fairly light color that is darkly lit.

The surest way to determine whether you have enough brightness contrast in your color scene—that is, whether your color scheme is compatible—is to watch the scene on your monochrome monitor. If the picture looks sharp, if it has "snap," your colors are compatible. If it looks washed out, lacking proper contrasts, your colors are not compatible. Often it is enough just to put a few color swatches in front of the camera under normal lighting conditions to see just how they register on the gray scale. In fact, with a little experience you will find that just by squinting your eyes you can determine fairly well whether two colors have enough brightness contrast in order to be compatible.

Experienced scenic and graphic artists often devise highly compatible color schemes without ever consciously checking relative brightness. A good painter usually juxtaposes colors that differ not only in hue but in brightness. You might want to look up some good monochrome reproductions of famous paintings to see just how "compatible" the color schemes are (see the color and monochrome illustrations on the preceding pages).

## Scene Painting and Texture

Stock units are usually painted a neutral color, such as tan, green, light blue, or beige. The convenient rubber-base latex or polyvinyl paints have replaced the cheaper but more cumbersome dry-powder scenic paints. Latex paint is easy to apply, dries quickly and smoothly, and will not rub off.

Unit flats should be textured. Texture will give the broad, plain surface of the flat more body and dimension; it will also hide inevitable fingerprints and smudges on the flat surface.

The texture must be neat and accurate. The usual theatre techniques of chicken-feathering, stippling, and puddling often look like sloppy smudges when viewed on the television monitor. The easiest and most effective texture for television scenery is a clean spatter or a simple rolled-on pattern.

The texture is usually the same color as the flats, but is one or two gray-scale steps darker. A lighter-than-base color texture will appear brilliant and sparkling. A darker-than-base color texture will be less obtrusive.

If you like variety, you can paint some pieces of your stock scenery with a simple pattern, such as a diamond or curved-line pattern. For outdoor scene units, a brick pattern is most useful.

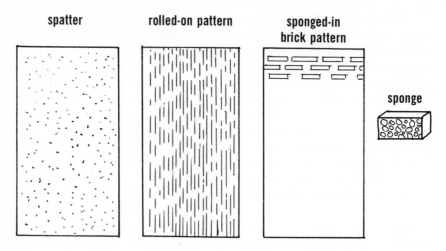

Special scenery can be painted according to standard theatre practice. If you want to achieve an especially realistic effect, you can wallpaper the flat or cover it with the more expensive vinyl plastic "wallpaper" or molded plastic bricks, rocks, or decorative wall patterns. If you use the commercially available plastic patterns, be sure to back them with foam rubber or some other pliable material before you staple them on the hardwall flat. If not backed properly, the large plastic sheets will ripple under stress, as the softwall scenery does.

## SCENERY STORAGE

Proper scenery storage is one of the biggest problems in small station operation. You will find that often there is no other room to store scenery than inside the studio.

The great advantage of scenery storage within the studio is that the scenery is readily available. You will save energy and time if you don't have to carry bulky scenery through small cluttered hallways, elevators, and doors. The great disadvantage, on the other hand, is that the scenery stored inside the studio takes up valuable studio space.

Scenery storage outside the studio is usually preferred, if the storage area is fairly close to the studio and if large hallways and doors allow you to move flats and other pieces of scenery quickly and easily into the studio.

Scenery is usually stored in (1) scene docks and (2) scene areas.

### The Scene Dock

The scene dock is an excellent storage place for television scenery. A good scene dock has predesignated slots for each type of scenery. It protects the scenery from damage and makes it easy to pull out and return quickly. The parallel-slot scene dock is a rather expensive but most effective installation.

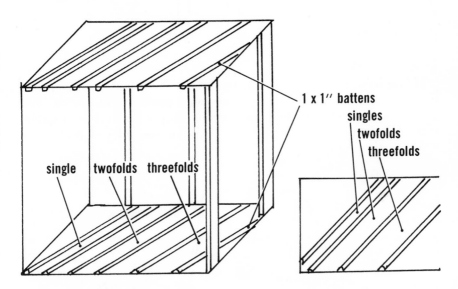

The individual flats fit into the scene dock like books in a bookcase. Maximum protection is provided for the scenery, since no flats are stored on top of each other.

You can build a less elaborate scene dock of several large $2 \times 4$ frames. The individual frames provide special stalls for larger groups of scenery; one stall holds singles, one holds twofolds, and one holds threefolds. The disadvantage of this attractively inexpensive arrangement is that the flats lean against each other, thus making it difficult to locate and pull a specific flat quickly. The flats also become damaged more easily.

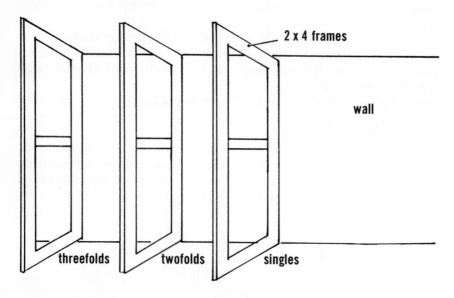

If you have to move the scenery through long hallways, you may find it convenient to load the scenery on a special scene wagon. You can adapt any of your existing wagons simply by adding a gable-type ½-inch pipe structure. Tie-off cleats on the sides of the wagon hold the tie ropes.

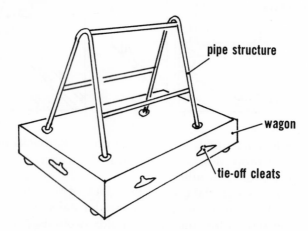

If the hallways and studio doors are large enough, you can put whole sections of your scenery on wagons and move them quickly into the studio. Scenery is sometimes moved on "tip-jacks"—metal frames with casters on which the individual flats rest.

## The Scene Area

Not all stations have room for even the most simple scene dock. In this case, the scenery must be stored alongside the studio walls, in hallways, or against any other available wall space. Usually, flats are piled on top of each other, and it is hard to free a specific flat buried under five or six heavy twofolds. The flats may also cover important wall outlets, which will force you to move half of your scenery just to plug in an extension cord.

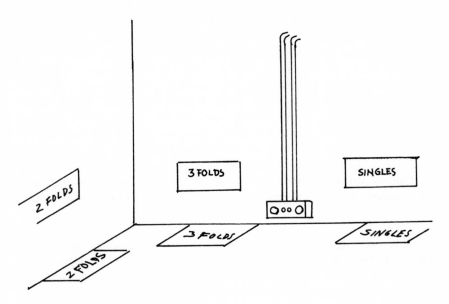

The only way out of this dilemma is to assign specific floor and wall space to specific scenery units. For instance, one area can be reserved for singles, one for twofolds, and one for threefolds. This arrangement makes it easier to find a particular flat. To avoid excessive damage to the flats, be sure to store them back-to-back and face-to-face.

## ELEMENTS OF SCENE DESIGN

Quite frequently you can clarify your thinking about a show considerably if you think of the scenery it will require. This will force you to think in pictures rather than in abstract ideas. Thinking in pictures is vitally important for anyone concerned with the visual art of television.

A strong asset of the good set designer is a flair for style. As a set designer, you should be familiar with basic stylistic principles of art and architecture. There are many good histories readily available to give you relevant information.

Before you begin to design scenery, you must also be thoroughly familiar with (1) the content of the show, its literary and artistic concepts; (2) the style of the show—contemporary or period, Victorian, Baroque, etc.; and (3) the locale of the show—indoors or outdoors, park, office, etc.

Then you must examine the script within the framework of your production facilities. You must answer a number of questions: (1) How many cameras are to be used for the production? (2) What audio facilities are to be used? (Big boom, hanging mikes, etc.?) (3) How many sets are required? (4) What is the sequence of scenes? How are the sets related? Where, therefore, must they be placed? (5) Can the sets be put into easily lighted set areas? If not, what additional lighting facilities are needed? (6) What is the general blocking of action? What are the performers doing? (7) Are fast set changes required? (8) Does the planned set allow for optimum camera angles? (9) Can the set be easily set up and struck?

The set must be functional—it must function properly for cameras, microphones, lighting, performers, and general studio traffic.

### The Open Set

Only one suggestion concerning a specific type of set design will be made here. We will call this the "open set" method. "Open set" means that the set is not closed or boxed in by walls, as it often is in a livingroom design. The open set consists only of the most important parts of the room, such as a door, active furniture, and a few characteristic set props. The walls may only be suggested by putting some 3-foot singles into space. A continuous cyc backing is almost essential for all open set designs. You can achieve the most desirable depth staging simply by placing particular set pieces into the foreground, middleground, and background.

There are several advantages to the open set method: (1) It gives the director many opportunities to shoot through the set from a great variety of angles that would otherwise be blocked by background scenery. (2) It is easy to set up and to strike. (3) It is easy to light. (4) It is easy for performers to work in. (5) It enables the microphone boom to move quickly and freely. (6) Since the camera generally looks at details rather than at the entire set, the open set technique

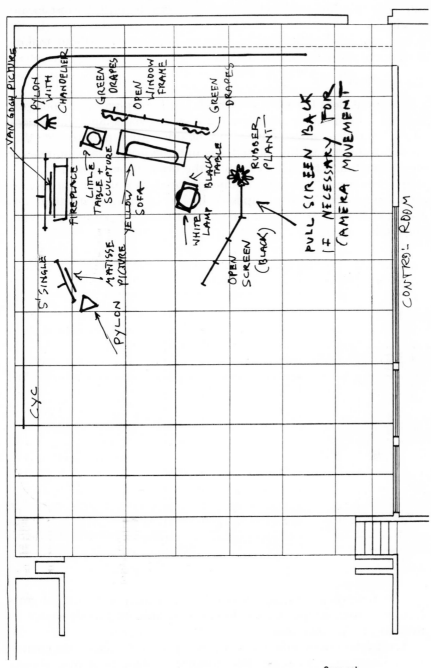

Open set

does not rule out extremely realistic set treatment. (7) Most locally produced shows lend themselves very well to stylization. (8) Set pieces and stock units can be used in many ways without making the repetition of usage too obvious.

### The Floor Plan

The final detailed set is drawn on the floor plan. The floor plan shows the studio floor area, the main studio doors, and the location of the control room. To have a specific orientation pattern according to which the sets will be placed, the lighting grid usually appears on the floor plan. The plan resembles the orientation squares of a city map. Sometimes, linoleum seams are used as guiding lines, or an artificial pattern is superimposed. In the latter case, numbers and letters that correspond to the floor plan lines are painted alongside the studio walls.

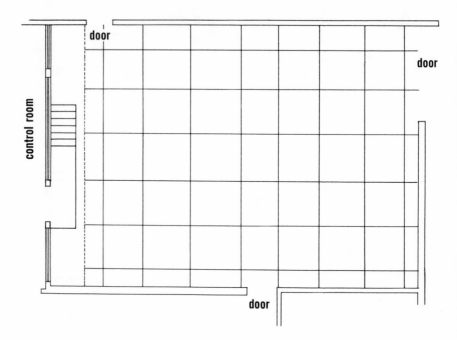

The scale of the average floor plan is ¼ inch = 1 foot. All flats, hanging units, set pieces, set decorations, and set properties are indicated on the floor plan.

A mistake commonly made by inexperienced scene designers is the inconsistency in scale. For instance, a floor plan may show a threefold as backing for a whole set of livingroom furniture. The tendency is to draw furniture and other set pieces too small in proportion to the covering flats. It may help to have small cardboard cutouts or plastic templets of the most frequently used furniture; you can easily and accurately trace these templets on the floor plan.

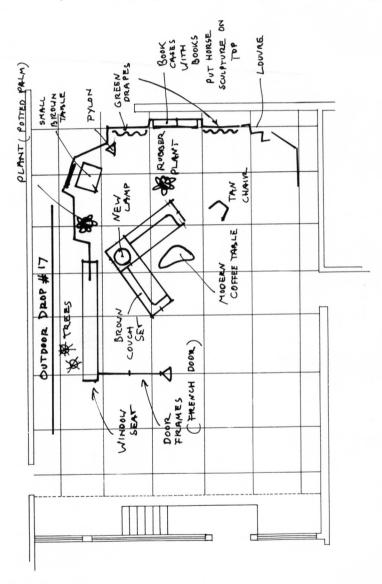

During your setup you will notice that the available studio floor is always more limited than your floor plan indicates. Make sure, there-

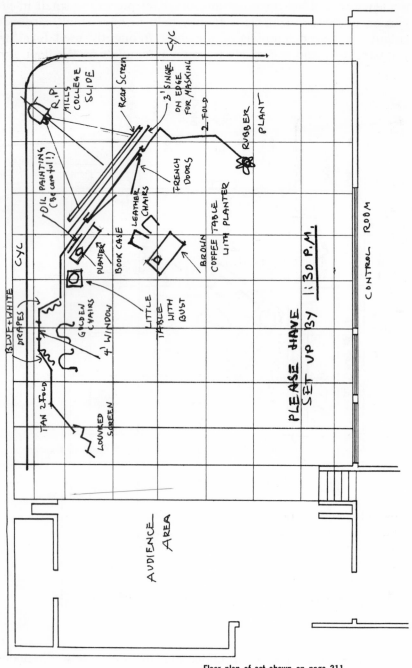

Floor plan of set shown on page 211

fore, to limit your set design to the actual *available* studio floor space. Don't forget that the jacks for bracing the flats take up space, too.

Always place your active furniture (furniture used by the performers) at least six feet from the set wall, so that proper backlighting effects can be achieved. The director can also use the space to move his cameras behind the furniture for unusual or reverse-angle shots.

If certain set or prop changes occur during the show, indicate these changes on a tracing paper overlay.

The floor plan is an important production aid for all production and engineering personnel. It is essential to the floor crew, who will set up the scenery according to floor plan instructions. The lighting man will be able to plot the general lighting layout. The director will be able to visualize the show and block the movement of performers, camera, and boom. The audio engineer can familiarize himself with specific microphone placements and other possible audio problems. The performers will see the relationship of the different sets and can acquaint themselves at least superficially with the basic blocking problems.

## PROPERTIES AND SET DRESSINGS

Properties and set dressings are essential set items. Although flats and other pieces of stock scenery supply most of the neutral backgrounds and other necessary structural units, properties and set decorations give the set character and style.

There are three types of properties: (1) stage properties, (2) set dressings, and (3) hand properties. Properties are usually called "props" for short.

### Stage Props

Stage props include (1) indoor furniture, (2) outdoor furniture, (3) special furniture units, and (4) landscape props.

#### Indoor furniture

Ideally, every television station should have enough indoor furniture to create at least partially the following settings: a modern livingroom, including couch, table, chairs, lamp tables, and bookcase; a Victorian livingroom, including couch, table, chairs, and buffet; a general study, including desk, bookcase, end table, and reading chair; and an office, including desk, file cabinet, bookcase, coatrack, and chairs.

The couch and chairs should all be comfortable but not overstuffed. The furniture, and especially the chairs, should not be too low, or else sitting and rising will become a major problem, especially for women. Look for a sturdy, nicely textured material that does not show smudges too easily. Stay away from light colors.

#### Outdoor furniture

For outdoor furniture, choose only a few but characteristic pieces. White wrought-iron chairs with matching tables (ice cream parlor furniture) are sturdy and attractive on camera. A sun umbrella that fits through one of the tables is also useful. Be sure, however, that you can angle the umbrella back far enough so that it will not block important lighting.

A decorative park bench is also an important outdoor prop.

#### Special furniture units

Special furniture units include (1) desks, (2) special tables, and (3) counters.

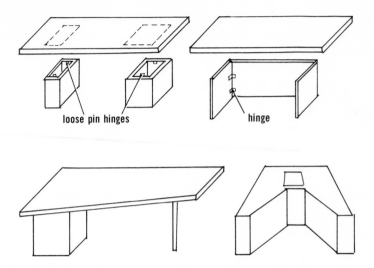

loose pin hinges                                    hinge

*Desks.* You will need a large modern desk and at least one smaller, more conventional desk. Special desks are usually built for newscasters. Some newscasters' desks come equipped with a built-in monitor. But this is not always successful, since the light falling on the newscaster's desk may wash out the monitor picture.

*Special tables.* You will need at least two or three work and display tables. The most useful table dimensions are 3 × 5 feet and 2 × 3 feet. A small 2 × 2 table makes an excellent display table for simple commercial setups. You should skirt all display tables with either plywood or heavy draperies. Special discussion tables are essential for small station operation. The designs vary from semicircular to

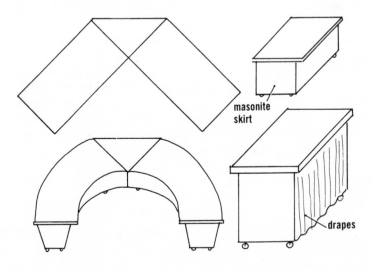

masonite
skirt

drapes

triangular shapes. Usually they are constructed to allow the most advantageous camera angles during the discussion program.

*Counters.* You will need a set of at least two different counters. They can be used for classroom demonstrations and other display purposes, and for bookcases, bar counters, etc. They can also be built as collapsible units.

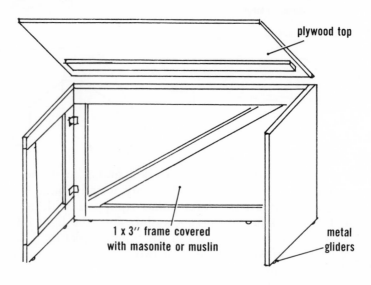

plywood top

1 x 3″ frame covered with masonite or muslin

metal gliders

### Landscape props

Landscape props include standard landscaping items, such as trees, fences, rocks, grass mats, potted palms, artificial flowers, bird baths, tree branches, and the like. Most of these items can be purchased ready-made from any one of the larger display houses. However, you can make some of the simpler landscape props yourself.

Old different-sized cardboard carpet tubes, for instance, make excellent tree trunks. Just paint or wallpaper the tube to give it the necessary bark-like texture. You can put the tube over an extended microphone stand to give it some support, attach some tree branches to the top of the tube, and your tree is ready to be planted. Remember that background trees must always be a little higher than foreground trees. If you need a large, detailed tree, you can find full construction information in any of the many theatre construction handbooks.

Flowerbed borders for patios or other outdoor sets can be easily laid with real bricks, or any assortment of decorative concrete blocks.

You can make simple rocks of crumpled seamless paper (use a wornout paper drop) stapled to some wooden blocks.

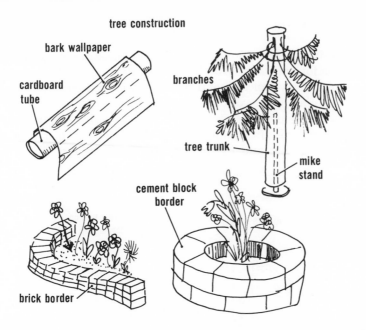

tree construction

bark wallpaper

cardboard tube

branches

tree trunk

mike stand

cement block border

brick border

If you use grass mats, you can blend them into the background (ground rows) by spreading some tanbark on the studio floor. Tanbark pieces around tree trunks also help to create a realistic landscape effect.

The extent of your outdoor set depends entirely on the particular need and on studio facilities. A few characteristic landscape props placed in front of a neutral cyc or a painted sky drop will usually give you the desired effect. Try to accomplish as much depth staging as possible. A few branches in the foreground (which might consist of a twig held by one of the floormen) will contribute greatly to a realistic outdoor effect and will give your setting realistic dimensions.

## Set Dressings

Set dressings help to determine the style and character of your set. The set dressings most frequently used in television production include: (1) draperies, (2) pictures, (3) lamps and chandeliers, (4) fireplace plugs, and (5) miscellaneous decorative pieces, such as flower vases, candles, tablecloths, and other small decorative items.

### Draperies

Draperies have already been discussed in the section on hanging scenery. You should acquire a certain amount of different drapery material so that you can dress a large variety of settings, such as modern living rooms, Victorian drawing rooms, and offices.

### Pictures

Inexpensive reproductions of well-known paintings make good wall decorations for your sets. Watch that the style and period of the picture match the style of the total set. To avoid undesirable reflections, remove the glass from your pictures.

You can hang pictures on softwall flats by using regular hanging wire or special picture hangers. You can also attach a thin string to the hanging wire and fly the pictures from the top of the flat.

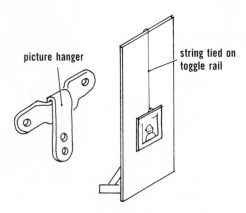

picture hanger

string tied on toggle rail

On hardwall scenery, a small tack will be enough to hold an average-sized picture.

Pictures should be hung rather low so that they show in a majority of shots. Also, in a television setting, pictures can be hung close together without giving the appearance of being crowded.

### Lamps and chandeliers

In purchasing lamps, look for the possibility of using the lamp for different set styles. One neutral lamp with interchangeable lamp shades can often fulfill several different style requirements. Lamps should be functional; you should be able to turn them on and off. A 15- or 25-watt bulb is usually enough to show that the lamp is turned on. Use either opaque or very dense translucent lamp shades.

Chandeliers are usually available in secondhand stores. You can easily renovate an old chandelier by adding a generous amount of plastic crystal pieces. A modern candelabrum with matching candles is also useful.

### Fireplaces

If your storage space is limited, you may prefer to construct only one fireplace that can be easily adapted to different stylistic requirements.

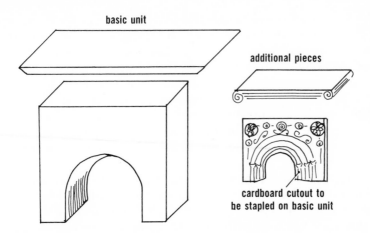

Only the mantelpiece and the fireplace opening must be interchangeable. The fireplace openings can be made out of cardboard and stapled against the basic fireplace unit. The mantelpiece, however, must be strong enough to hold standard decorative items, such as plates, plaster busts, and figurines.

### Decorative pieces

You will undoubtedly collect a great number of miscellaneous set dressings within a short time. The most important pieces, those that you should acquire first, are flower vases, a variety of tablecloths and drapery material for commercial displays, an assortment of candles, decorative plates, figurines and a plaster bust, fireplace screens and andirons, old books, and a variety of ashtrays.

## Hand Properties

Hand properties consist of all the objects with which the television performer works during a show. They include such items as cigarettes, dishes, silverware, and food; and, depending on the type of show, they may be extremely varied. A few of the more frequently used hand props should be mentioned here.

*Dishes.* A set of dishes is frequently used in commercial displays. Dishes are also important properties in dramatic shows. A plain-designed, off-white set of dishes with great durability (plastic preferred) is generally sufficient for small station operation.

*Silverware.* Stainless steel silverware of neutral design is most practical.

*Glasses.* A variety of inexpensive water, wine, and beer glasses will be adequate for standard productions. In glasses, look for durability rather than quality trademark.

*Bottles.* An assortment of old wine bottles is needed for many setups. You should alter the bottle labels, however, so that a close-up will not show specific brand names.

*Food.* Although complex food commercials are rarely produced by local stations, you should nevertheless know how to display food on camera as attractively and as appetizingly as possible.

Meat, vegetables, and fruit look better on camera if you sprinkle them with water just before the show. If the food will not be eaten, you can tint the sprinkling water with ink, which makes the water-drops more visible.

If coffee or tea must look steaming hot, heat it on a small hotplate right in the studio. Or, if the steam has to be sustained for a greater length of time, drop a small piece of dry ice into the pot.

If you have to work with ice cream displays, be sure to take the ice cream out of the freezer some time before the show. Ice cream that is too hard is as difficult to work with as ice cream that is too soft. If it is too hard, put it under a hot lighting scoop for a few moments. It should be mentioned here that you will need a good refrigerator with a large-size freezer compartment somewhere in the prop room.

All carbonated drinks, such as cola beverages and beer, should be well chilled before being shown on camera. If possible, the glasses should also be refrigerated. A foam head of about 1½ inches seems to please most beer manufacturers. Carbonated drinks look most re-freshing if they are specially lighted from the bottom of the glass, since bottom lighting greatly enhances the effect of carbonation. You will have to build a simple display lightbox. The size of the box may vary with the size of the display (see page 219).

If real products are used during rehearsals, make sure that enough of each product is left over for the on-the-air performance.

There are many tricks that will make a product look better than it really is. Be aware, however, that even a "little helping along" can be a severe misrepresentation of the product. You should be very careful to present the product as truthfully as you can. This does not mean, of course, that you cannot fill an actor's glass with tea instead of 90 proof whiskey, even though, in the script, he is having highballs before dinner. But you *are* deceiving the audience if you put dry ice into soap suds to make them appear twice as effective as they really are. Good judgment should always be your principal guide in these matters.

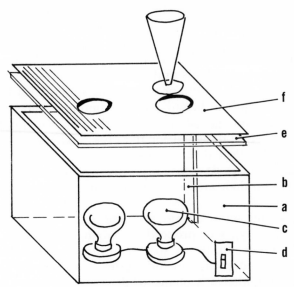

a) sides of box, ½-inch plywood, b) 1 × 2 structural members, c) one or two internal-reflector bulbs, d) light switch, e) glass cover, f) black cardboard with circular cutouts for beer glasses and bottles.

## SUMMARY

Television scenery must be designed for the camera. It must allow for (1) optimum camera angles, (2) good, functional lighting, and (3) maximum action of the performers.

All scenery for small stations should be designed so that it can be easily set up and struck. There are four types of television scenery: (1) standard set units, which consist of interchangeable unit flats; (2) special set units and scenery devices, which include window and door flats, bookcase flats, sliding scenery, seamless paper, corrugated cardboard, masking tape, and special floor-decorating devices; (3) hanging units, consisting of the cyclorama, the canvas drop, the traveler, draperies, and the photomural; and (4) set pieces, of which the more important ones are the pillar, the periaktos, the sweep, the step unit, blocks and pedestals, platforms and wagons, ground rows, and screens.

The construction of all scenic material should be done so that the different pieces of scenery are readily interchangeable. This requires uniformity in size (8 feet or 10 feet high) and in ways of joining flats.

In painting the scenery, a compatible color scale must be used so that the color will photograph adequately on monochrome television.

To prolong the usefulness and protect the appearance of scenery, good storage facilities within or outside the studio must be provided.

Any scene design is begun with a thorough knowledge of the show's content and format. Again, it should be pointed out that the scenery must be designed for the *camera*. The style of the entire show should be reflected in the scenery.

The final detailed set is usually drawn on the floor plan, which shows the studio floor area in juxtaposition to the studio doors and control room.

Properties and set dressings are also important scenic devices. There are three types of properties: (1) stage properties, including indoor and outdoor furniture, special furniture units, and landscape properties; (2) set dressings, including draperies, pictures, lamps, fireplace units, and other miscellaneous decorative pieces; and (3) hand properties, including dishes, silverware, glasses, bottles, and food.

### EXERCISES

1. The choreographer of a modern jazz ballet asks you to design an effective set. He wants a good background (abstract or stylized, such as a city skyline) and also some "objects" in the middle of the studio, which his dancers can use "to dance around." What would you suggest? What types of scenery do you need for such a set?

2. You are asked to design a news set for one male newscaster. What would you suggest?

3. The format for a new mid-day news show calls for three areas: a news area, an interview area, and a weather area. The newscast will be handled by two newscasters, a man and a woman. You have a very small studio with limited lighting facilities. What type of set would you design?

4. Your director asks you to come up with an exciting set for his less-exciting interview show. The format calls for one interviewer and one or two interviewees. What would you suggest?

5. The advertising agency representative tells you that he will bring in his own scenery for the proposed fashion show. He tells you that the brightly colored set has been used successfully in many department store shows. What is your reaction? Why?

6. The script calls for four important set changes. How can you indicate these changes on the floor plan?

7. The producer of the new educational show asks you to create the illusion of a livingroom window with an extremely realistic-looking exterior. The acute space limitations do not allow you to use your rear screen. What can you do?

8. You are asked by the head of the radio and television department of a college to suggest some basic scenery that will be needed in the department's new medium-sized studios. They intend to produce all kinds of shows, from simple two-man interviews to rather complex dramatic performances. What would you suggest?

9. The director asks you what type of scenery you need for a cameo setting. What would you tell him?

10. How can you create the illusion of a dense forest with as little material and expense as possible?

# 6

# Graphics

Television graphics include a multitude of material. All two-dimensional visuals that are especially prepared for the television camera, such as title cards, special illustrations, maps, and charts, can be called graphics.

## PREPARATION FACTORS

The television camera again dictates certain rules that must be observed in the preparation of graphic material. The major factors

to be considered are (1) style of art work, (2) size and clarity of layout, (3) color and gray-scale response, and (4) ease of operation.

## Style

The style of the art work must match the style of the entire show.
Even the opening titles should give some indication of the type and
character of the show. In a comedy show, for instance, cartoon lettering or an amusingly animated film opening helps to get the viewers' attention and prepare them for the show content. A dramatic
show, on the other hand, may be identified by supering simple and
unobtrusive titles over live action. But don't go overboard on style
and identify your guest performer from China with Chinese lettering,
or your newsreel of the downtown fire with flame letters. Don't aban-
don good taste for effect.

The art work for the opening of a show must be as exciting and
attention-getting as possible. This is the moment when you want to
catch the audience and get them interested enough in your show to
watch it. For the same reason, intensely dramatic preliminary scenes,
called "hookers" or "teasers," are standard practice in dramas and
mystery shows, in which excitement is generated even before the
identifying titles appear.

Art work for the closing of a show, on the other hand, should not
be so final that the viewer feels inclined to turn off the set for the
rest of the evening. It should indicate the close of a certain period,
but not the close of the day's telecasting. There is no ready-made
formula on just how to achieve the right close. Artistic sensitivity
and a good knowledge of the television medium and its audience
will again be your best guide.

## Size and Clarity

The relatively small, proportionally fixed screen size of the television set, as well as the quality of the picture reproduction, demand
maximum clarity for all television graphics.

### Aspect ratio

The proportions of the television screen are three to four—that is,
the picture is always three units high and four units wide. All picture
information must be contained within this three-to-four aspect ratio.

### Scanning and essential area

Within the aspect ratio, there is a peripheral loss of picture area
caused by transmission and reception. The picture seen in the control
room monitor generally includes more area than the picture on a

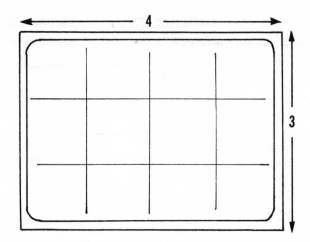

home receiver. The amount of area loss depends on transmission factors and, to a greater extent, on the degree of misalignment of the home receiver. The picture height as well as the picture width may be simultaneously misadjusted on the receiver. Although this misadjustment may not change the general proportions of the image, it crops the top, bottom, and sides of the picture.

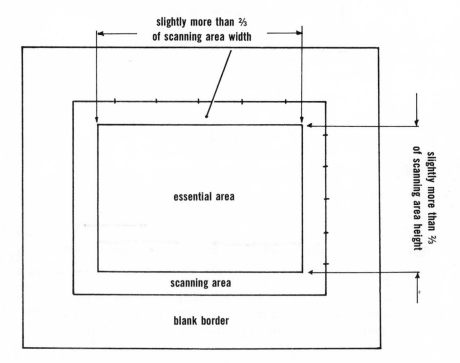

The area framed by the camera and transmitted by the station (and, under ideal conditions, received on the home set) is called the *scanning area*. Centered within the scanning area is the most important part of the picture area, the *essential area*. All pertinent copy and picture information must be contained within the boundaries of the essential area, if the information is to be seen on a majority of television receivers. In general, the essential area is slightly more than ⅔ of the height and width of the scanning area.

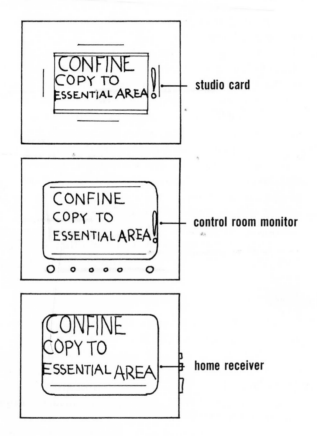

studio card

control room monitor

home receiver

### Layout

The amount of information that can be simultaneously projected on the television screen is limited. You should confine your copy to no more than ten words. By limiting the number of words, you can use a letter size that is easily legible even to people sitting at a considerable distance from the screen. Large letters are especially important for color television. The limited resolution power of the television system will not reproduce detailed art work or small print satisfactorily. Screen size and resolution, therefore, demand great simplicity in the general layout of television graphics. Your main purpose in using television graphics is to communicate; the simpler your presentation is, the better your communication will be.

### Color and Gray-Scale Response

In preparing television graphics, you must, of course, work within the limitations of the gray scale. In graphic arts for monochrome television, different shades of grays are used instead of colors. Some artists find it convenient to purchase ready-made grays that are numbered according to the gray scale.

As with the painting of scenery, the preparation of graphics requires attention to color aesthetics and to some technical aspects of the color camera. First, your color combination should be appropriate to the intended communication. If the title is humorous, the colors should reflect the same feeling; if the title is somber, the colors should communicate somberness in their own way. Second, the combination of hues (often called palette) must be compatible. Proper brightness contrast is essential in graphics, since some sort of written information is almost always used. Letters that fall within the same gray-scale step as the surrounding colors are of no value at all: they will not show up on the monochrome screen. Make sure, therefore, to use colors with a good strong brightness contrast whenever written information is to be communicated. On the other hand, remember that you must stay within the contrast range (20:1) appropriate for color television.

### Ease of Operation

Ease of operation is as important a factor in graphic arts as it is in any other phase of production. The studio card, for instance, must be large enough so that the cameraman can quickly frame up and focus on it; yet it must be small enough so that the floor manager can handle and store it easily. The cost of illustration board will usually limit studio cards to a specific size. A large card with large lettering does not necessarily look bigger on the screen than a small card with small lettering. The size of the lettering as it appears on the screen depends entirely on the position of the camera in relation to the card. A standardization of card size will greatly simplify both art work and studio operation.

## STANDARD GRAPHICS

The graphic material most frequently used in small station operation falls into two big groups: (1) standard graphics, including studio cards, slides, telops, and crawls; and (2) special graphics, including product labels, maps, charts, and simple animations.

## The Studio Title Card

All studio title cards, or easel cards, are designed for the camera. There are three types of title cards: (1) the plain title; (2) the illustrated title, and (3) the super card.

### The plain title card

The over-all dimensions of the plain title card are 14 × 17 inches. (You should not go below 11 × 14 or above 15 × 20.) The *scanning* area is 9 × 12 inches centered within the 14 × 17 studio card. There is thus a 2½-inch border from each edge of the card to the respective edges of the scanning area. You should define the boundaries of the scanning area by placing an inch-long blue pencil line midway along each side of the scanning area borders. The *essential* area is a 6¾ × 9¾-inch rectangle centered within the scanning area. There is a 1⅛-inch border between the scanning area and the essential area.

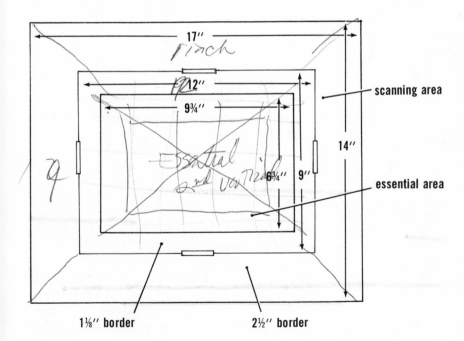

17"

12"

9¾"

scanning area

14"

6¾"  9"

essential area

1⅛" border

2½" border

Large (30 × 40 inches) sheets of illustration board are cut into individual studio cards. Illustration board is available in white, several shades of gray, and black. For color work, you can purchase it in a variety of colors. All illustration board should have a mat surface (with a light reflectance not to exceed 40 per cent) to prevent glares. A medium-dark gray works best for monochrome titles.

*Preparation technique.* Before you start to letter the title card, mark the scanning and essential areas. A simply made framing guide will speed up this task considerably. Take a standard studio card and cut out four small slots to indicate the scanning area; then cut the essential area from the center of the card. By placing the guide on top of the studio card, you can accurately mark scanning and essential areas.

**cut out 1″-long slots (⅛″ wide)**

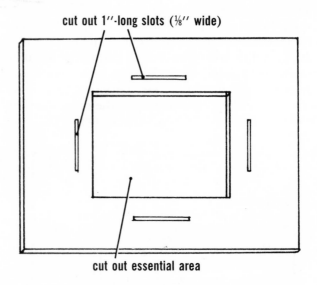

**cut out essential area**

*Lettering.* When lettering a studio card, remember the following points: (1) The letters must be simple and bold. Extremely fine stems and serifs may look attractive in a woman's fashion magazine, but they are difficult to read on a television screen. (2) Don't crowd your letters. Since the resolution power (which affects clarity) of the television picture is rather limited, narrow spaces and fine lines will get lost on the screen. (3) Unless you intend to create a special effect, make sure that your letters are parallel with the bottom edge of the studio card. (4) Make the letters as sharp as possible; in other words, draw well-defined lines. Fuzzy letters look even fuzzier on camera.

The most commonly used lettering methods in television graphics are (1) handlettering, (2) handlettering with lettering guides, (3) Artype, Fototype and rub-on letters, (4) printing, and (5) feltboard letters.

1. *Handlettering.* Good handlettering is not easy to do. If you are not an expert in this art, you will probably spend entirely too much time preparing studio cards and end up with a neat but uninspired-looking job. Amateur handlettering lacks style. You may do well to have your cards done by a handlettering expert.

Materials for television handlettering are the usual graphic arts tools: different-sized lettering brushes, lettering pens, India ink, and showcard colors. As mentioned before, different shades of ready-made television gray are available.

2. *Lettering guides.* As an amateur letterer, you may want to use one of the many handlettering guides. They come in a great variety of sizes and types, from a simple cutout ruler, which gives you the basic shape of letters, to a fairly complicated machine like the Varigraph, which works on the pantograph copying principle. It is usually cheaper in the long run to buy a simple printing machine than to struggle with complex lettering guides.

-ΔPᏰCDE-ⅡJKᐱ⟋OPꞁST

3. *Artype, Fototype, and rub-on letters.* Ready-made letters that can be either photostated or pasted directly onto your art work produce good lettering results.

Artype comes in strips of acetate paper upon which the individual letters are printed. You can tear off the letters and paste them directly on the illustration board.

Fototype is very similar to Artype. The more popular Fototype is printed on opaque paper. You tear the letters off small letterbooks (similar to a miniature calendar) and put them face down into a Fototype guide. This guide consists of a small metal ruler that keeps the individual letters in proper alignment. When you have finished the line of copy, you put a strip of transparent tape along the backs of the letters and lift the whole strip out of the lettering guide. This strip is then pasted onto the particular studio card. Fototype lettering is intended for photostating. It should not be used directly for on-the-air reproduction. Before the copy of Fototype letters is photostated, you must touch up the cracks between letters with white showcard color.

Rub-on letters are even simpler to use than Artype or Fototype. The rub-on letters are printed on a thin plastic sheet (usually 8½ × 11 inches). You simply put the plastic sheet over your art work and rub over the letter with a hard object, such as the reverse tip of a ball-point pen. Through the pressure, the letter is immediately and permanently transferred onto the card.

4. *Printing.* Printing will always be the quickest and neatest method of lettering. There are two types of printing machines that have proved valuable in the preparation of television graphics. One is the simple Linoscribe machine; the other is the more complex Kensol hotpress.

The *Linoscribe* is well suited to small station operation. It is comparatively inexpensive and does an adequate job of printing. This machine uses standard lead type, which you can later use for the Kensol hotpress, if you like. To operate the Linoscribe, you set the type face up in reverse and lock it in place by two small metal wedges. You then ink the type with a roller, lock your studio card face down on the type, and move the pressure roller attached to the machine quickly over the card. Finally, you unlock the card and carefully lift it off the type. The card should be allowed to dry for a few minutes, or the type may smear (see page 231).

It is a good practice to check the layout of your type quickly by placing your framing guide over the set type. You will see immediately whether the copy lies within the boundaries of the essential area.

The disadvantage of the Linoscribe is that the thin printing inks may cause undesirable contrast variations in the lettering, and may also cause fuzziness around the edges of the letters.

The *Kensol hotpress* is the ideal printing method for television and motion picture graphics. Unfortunately, the hotpress is a fairly expensive machine. However, if you have a great amount of printing to do (including special art work for promotional advertisements) you can hardly afford not to purchase this type of printing machine. Its use is comparatively simple (see page 232). First, you lock the reversed standard type (the same as used in the Linoscribe machine) into a special chase. Then preheat the type on a small hotplate (which comes with the press) to a temperature of approximately 250 degrees. As soon as the type is sufficiently preheated, put the chase face down into the heated (250 degrees or slightly higher) head of the hotpress. When you have lined up your studio card with the type, put a plastic film (shiny side up) over the cardboard and pull the pressure lever. Don't hold the type too long on the art work or the heated plastic may seep into the fabric of the card.

pressure roller

type being inked

finished card

Linoscribe ink rollers and ink

pressure roller is pushed over card

The great advantage of the Kensol hotpress is that the edges of the letters are sharp and clear, making it possible to use very small type successfully. Also, the hotpressing method allows you to print on cellulose acetate, the so-called "cells," which is an important advantage in the preparation of art work for television slides.

5. *Feltboard lettering.* On remote location you may need a lettering device that permits a variety of rapid title changes. An assortment of plastic letters that can be pushed into a slotted feltboard seems to fulfill this requirement most adequately.

chase being inserted into hotpress

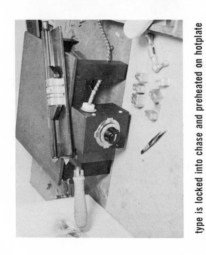

type is locked into chase and preheated on hotplate

card is printed

film is removed

hotpress lever is brought down

plastic film is put on card

232

### The illustrated title card

The illustrated title card has the same dimensions (size, scanning and essential areas) as the plain studio card. There are three types of illustrated title cards: (1) the illustrated title for show identification, (2) the "shared I.D.," and (3) the commercial product illustration.

All illustration material should touch the borders of the scanning area. The important parts of the art work, however, must be confined to the essential area. The lettering within the illustrated title must also be kept within the essential area.

The illustrated title communicates through pictures and the printed word. The illustrated title for show identification, therefore, should convey a show's content and mood. Also, it should make the show's title interesting and attractive to the audience.

There are no set rules on how to illustrate a title card effectively. Anything is acceptable as long as illustrations and lettering are consistent with the mood and the style of the show. Again, observe proper gray-scale and color-response relationships. Keep your design as simple and clear as possible. Complex and cluttered illustrations, as meaningful as they may be, do not communicate on the television screen.

Photography plays an important role in the preparation of graphic art work. In fact, you can use straight 8 × 10 prints as illustrated title cards. Often it is much simpler to take a good photo of a complicated display than it is to take the display directly into the studio —as with complicated automobile displays in elaborate showrooms, for example. Of course, photos are possible only when the announcer is not required to demonstrate the product.

There are several ways of combining illustration with lettering. (1) You can either handletter or print directly over the art work on the title card. (2) You can letter the card first and then illustrate around the lettering. (3) You can letter on a cell and overlay the lettering on the illustrated card. The cell overlay card, however, will have to be photographed again before it can be used as a studio card. The advantage of the cell overlay is that you can place the lettering wherever you want without affecting the original art work whatsoever.

The *shared I.D.* is a title that shows, in addition to a commercial message, the station logo. The station identification is shared with a commercial or a public service announcement. In general, the essential area is divided into four equal parts. The upper right-hand area of the card is reserved for the station logo. The other parts of the

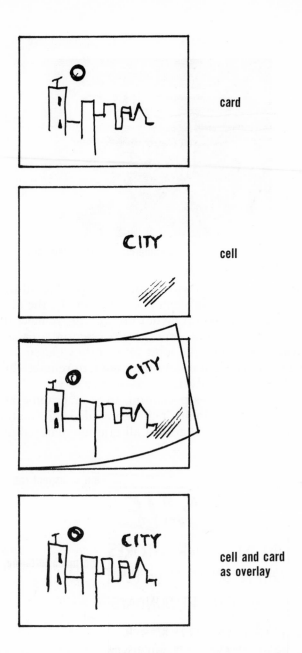

card

cell

cell and card
as overlay

essential area are used for the commercial message, which may include copy and illustrations. Shared I.D.'s are rarely used as live
studio cards; they are usually photographed and made into a 2 × 2
slide (see page 243).

station logo

commercial or promotion copy

Quite often, studio cards with commercial product illustrations are supplied by the advertising agency. Unfortunately, the dimensions of these cards and their general layout do not always meet the requirements of television graphics. Aspect ratio, essential area, and amount of information are among the most frequently violated factors. If the account is important to you, you may have to remake the entire art work. It will be to your advantage as well as to your client's to issue a few mimeographed rules pertaining to your graphic arts requirements. This pamphlet should include detailed information on size, scanning area, and essential area of all graphic material used at your station.

out of aspect ratio

too much lettering

If you prepare title cards with commercial illustrations, you can sometimes speed up your art work by photographing the sponsor's products and pasting the photographic cutout on the card. This cut-out will always look more realistic than a hurriedly drawn sketch. New ideas in layout and execution of graphic art work are always encouraged. If you watch today's commercials from a technical point of view, you will be pleasantly surprised to find a great many elements of modern painting realized in television graphics.

### The super card

A super card is used when the lettering or art work is shown super-imposed over, or keyed into, an object or live action. The general dimensions of the super card are identical to the standard studio card. Scanning and essential areas have to be taken into consideration.

Standard super cards are cut from black illustration board. The less light reflectance the super card has, the better the superimposure will be. The lettering and the art work of the super card are white.

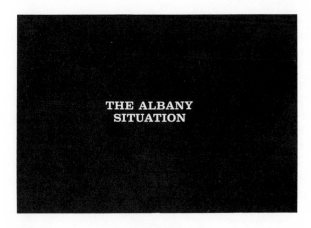

Since the black on the card reflects no light, only the white lettering will be transmitted by the studio camera. The white lettering can then be electronically superimposed over, or keyed into, another camera's picture.

In preparing super cards, make sure that your art work and letter-ing will produce a good, clear image. Since the information contained on a supercard is always superimposed over a more or less busy back-ground, your lettering must be extremely simple and clear. Also, the amount of information given on a super card is limited. Five to seven words are usually all that a single super card should contain.

If you must include art work other than plain lettering, reduce it to a simple white line drawing. Large white areas do not super well and should be avoided.

If you have to make a super card showing the name of a guest performer, put the lettering as close as possible to the lower border of
the essential area. This positioning will enable the cameraman to
frame the super in the lower part of his viewfinder screen, thus preventing the lettering from cutting across the guest's face.

Sometimes you may be asked to super a title over a very light background. In this case, the standard white on black super does not work;
the white lettering will blend in with the light background. To avoid
the problem, you can eliminate the super entirely and print a straight
title card, or you can prepare a black super. A black super consists
of black lettering on a white card. This method is not recommended,
however, because the high light reflectance of the white card clouds
the picture and makes the black lettering appear slightly washed out.

### Operation Techniques for Studio Title Cards

Studio title cards are usually put on studio easels for easy camera
pickup. Many different kinds of easels are in use. A simple, mobile,
and practical studio easel can be built with little effort and few
materials.

A more elaborate type of easel allows you to drop your cards onto
a wide lip and store them in a built-in container. You can also use
this easel for simple displays.

At least two easels are needed in each studio. There may be times
when you want to use an easel on-camera, and the style of the show
may require a more decorative easel than the functional type used
regularly.

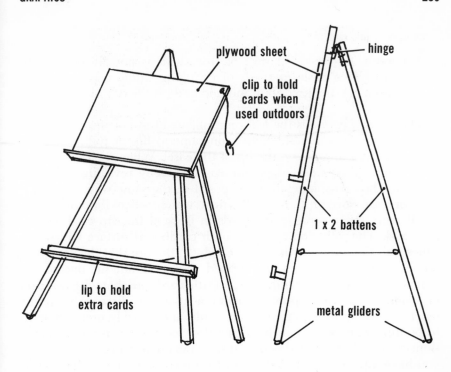

plywood sheet

clip to hold
cards when
used outdoors

hinge

1 x 2 battens

lip to hold
extra cards

metal gliders

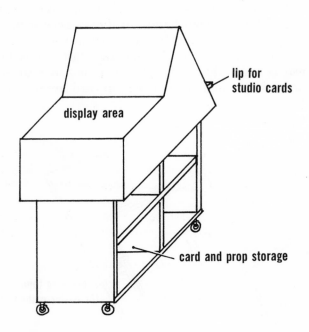

lip for
studio cards

display area

card and prop storage

### Changing of title cards

A smooth, on-the-air change of title cards is not always easy to accomplish. Two basic methods of changing studio cards are most widely used: (1) the flip or pull method and (2) the drop-in and drop-out method.

The *flip card method* is the least complicated but not the easiest way of changing cards. For the "hot" (on-camera) flip or pull, place the cards perfectly aligned on the lip of the easel. When the director signals, simply flip one card off the easel, thereby revealing the card behind. The cards beneath are exposed in the same way.

There are several things you must watch when flipping cards: (1) Be sure that you hold the cards in back of the flip card against the easel. The adhesion of the smooth cardboard surface will sometimes pull the under-cards off the easel. (2) Be sure that the camera is far enough away so that the flipped card will not hit one of the longer lenses. In general, however, all title cards are shot with a 75mm or 90mm lens, which puts the camera at a safe distance from the easel. (3) Make sure that you can easily and quickly grab the card to be flipped, especially if the flips follow each other in rapid succession. (4) Watch that you do not cast shadows on the flip card. (5) When you have flipped a card, don't throw it on the studio floor, but put it gently on the lower ledge of the easel. If the flips are fast, get someone to take the cards off your hands, or use an easel with a long lip. (6) Try to flip the cards as quickly and neatly as you can. A neat slow flip, however, will always look better than a fast sloppy flip.

A *card pull* is easier than a flip, but it is not as neat-looking. To pull the cards, simply take hold of the top card in the middle of the

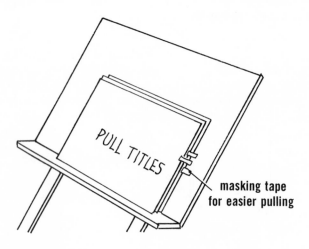

masking tape
for easier pulling

side edge and pull it smoothly toward you. Make sure that you keep the card horizontal with the easel during the entire pull. A piece of masking tape on the edge of the card helps to get a better grip.

Even if your pulls and flips occur while the camera is not on the air, you should take the utmost care with them. They will not only give you good practice, but will guarantee you clean, professional-looking card changes in case the camera is left on the air unintentionally.

The *drop-in and drop-out method* requires the cards to be specially rigged. Drop cards work like pages in a ring binder. They are threaded through three large-sized rings. Drop-in cards have the rings threaded through the top edge; drop-out titles have the rings threaded through the bottom edge. When you change a drop-in title, the card falls *into* camera range; that is, it *appears* on the screen; a drop-out title drops *out* of camera range or *disappears* from the screen.

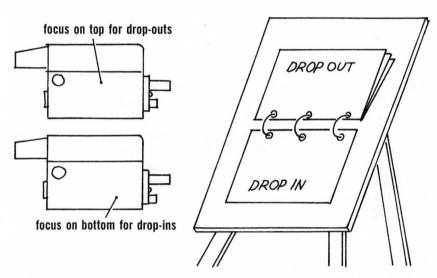

focus on top for drop-outs

DROP OUT

DROP IN

focus on bottom for drop-ins

Always make sure that the holes in the cards are big enough so that they will not bind. If the title cards are frequently used, you should install metal grommets to protect the holes from getting torn.

If you undertake many remote telecasts, you may want to build a title card drop box. This box has seven to ten slots in which masonite leaves can freely move up and down. The cards work on a drop-out principle. The masonite leaves with the title cards attached to them are pulled up and held in place by metal pins. In order to change cards you simply pull one pin after the other, causing the cards to drop back into the box.

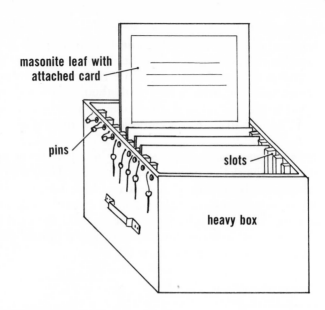

masonite leaf with
attached card

pins

slots

heavy box

The advantage of this box is that the title cards are solidly attached to the leaves, a factor you learn to appreciate when you have to handle several loose studio cards in a windy football stadium. The box can be put anywhere—on steps, old boxes, bleachers—wherever the camera can most easily reach. Another advantage of the box is that the studio cards are protected from scratches and tearing.

The disadvantages of the drop box are that it is fairly heavy and that the leaves may get stuck in the slots from time to time, especially if the masonite leaves are allowed to warp in damp weather.

### Special title card problems

Sometimes you will have to work with light-reflecting cards or glossy photographs mounted on studio cards. Spraying with Krylon dulling spray helps in most cases. If you don't like the light fog a dulling spray puts over card surfaces, or if you don't have time to spray the cards, you can simply tilt the card toward the camera. Tilting takes the glare off the card and renders the reflection harmless.

Another problem to be met in using studio cards is the proper alignment of camera with easel. A good floor manager usually places the easel so that the cameraman has little or no framing adjustment to do. But if the easel is not square with the camera, the card will look "keystoned" on the monitor screen—that is, one corner of the card will appear higher than the other, compared with the lower edge of the monitor screen. If the card looks "high on the right," turn the

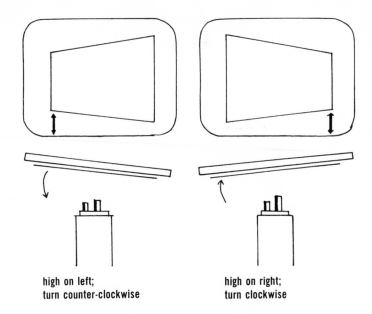

high on left;
turn counter-clockwise

high on right;
turn clockwise

easel clockwise to correct the keystone effect. If the card looks "high on the left," rotate the easel counter-clockwise.

## Slides

Television slides are used in a special projector and picked up by a stationary television film camera. (Slide and film chain operation will be discussed in more detail in Chapter 8.)

In this discussion on preparing television slides, we will be concerned mostly with the preparation of art work for the slides. Information on how to make slides is available from many training films (the audio-visual department of every college has a film of this nature on file) or from special literature by the Eastman Kodak Company or other major photographic companies. In general, a slide is made by photographing the original graphic presentation on 35mm film and mounting the film between two glassplated or other available ready-mounts.

The easiest way to prepare art work for 2 × 2 slides is to proceed as though you were making a studio card. In fact, it is best to do all the necessary art work directly on a 14 × 17 studio card. If you have a hotpress you can print the lettering on acetate cells and photograph the cell overlay with the art work. The cell overlay method is especially advantageous if used over photographs that cannot be marked up with lettering. If you don't have a hotpress, you can use a special crawl-free lettering ink for writing on acetate cells.

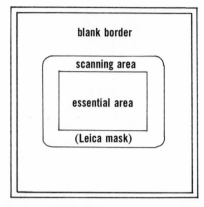

Dimensions:

Over-all size: 2 × 2 inches.

Scanning area: $2\frac{7}{32}$ × $1\frac{1}{8}$ inches. The scanning area is the area outlined by the standard Leica mask.

Essential area: $\frac{5}{8}$ × $2\frac{9}{32}$ inch centered within the scanning area.

Instead of using plain backgrounds for lettering, you can back your lettering with any number of materials, such as roughly textured monkscloth, woodgrain wallpaper, old boards, sand, rugs, and other texturally interesting objects. These backgrounds are either photographed and then rephotographed with your cell overlay lettering or photographed with three-dimensional plaster letters placed directly on the background material. Some graphic artists even build huge structures to get some genuine three-dimensional effects into their title slides. A quick and simple way to produce slides is to photograph the art work with a Polaroid camera equipped with special 2 × 2 slide accessories.

Although the vidicon television camera is capable of handling slightly more contrasting pictures than the I-O studio camera, you should try to stay within the gray-scale range. Simplicity in layout and lettering is also essential in the preparation of television slides.

In making standard white-on-black super slides, you must prepare your art work in reverse—black lettering on white cardboard. Because the photographic process reverses the polarity of your art work— whites become black and blacks become white—you can use the film negative directly as a super. In preparing color slides, you should avoid pure black and white lettering on a multicolored background.

There are several advantages in using a slide instead of a studio card. (1) All studio cameras will be free to pick up live action, since the slide is televised by a special camera. (2) Slides are always lighted evenly and brilliantly, thus producing a better, livelier picture. (3) The slides can be automatically changed, permitting a smooth transition.

There are two disadvantages in using slides, however. (1) The slide is in a fixed position—the camera can neither pan nor dolly on a slide—whereas the studio card permits the camera to move and pick out certain details. (2) If the slide is not properly mounted or is inserted incorrectly into the projector, the televised image will appear slanted or slightly out of focus and cannot be immediately adjusted.

## Telops and Balops

In some stations you may still find telop (television optical projector) or balop (Balopticon) machines in use. These machines project photos and other opaque art work, as well as three-dimensional objects, into the television film camera. A telop, for example, can be a 4 × 5 photo, or a 4 × 5 piece of thin cardboard with a title hot-pressed on it. Balopticon uses 11 x 14 materials.

The only real advantage the telop machine has over the 2 × 2 slide machine is that the titles do not have to be photographed and

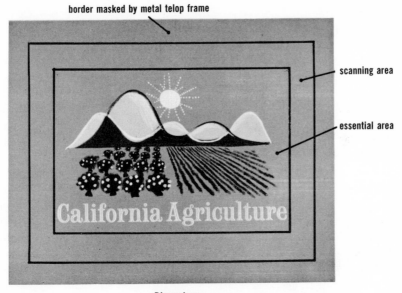

border masked by metal telop frame

scanning area

essential area

Dimensions:
Over-all size: 4 × 5 inches.
Scanning area: 3 × 4 inches. The scanning area is masked off by the metal strip holding the telop cards.
Essential area: 2¼ × 3¼ inches.

mounted before being projected. The fast production methods of television slides (with Polaroid cameras, for example) and the sophisticated slide projection equipment now available have made the rather
bulky and unwieldy telop and balop machines obsolete.

## The Crawl

To show a great amount of copy successively, as in closing credits,
you should prepare a television crawl. There are two basic types of
crawls: (1) the studio crawl and (2) the telop crawl. Both work on
the same principle. The lettering is put on a long, narrow strip of
heavy paper that is moved mechanically in front of the camera.

### The studio crawl

The studio crawl consists of a large drum rotated by hand or by an
electric motor. The whole unit is mounted on a free-wheeling caster
base for easy maneuverability. The drum can be used either open or
masked. The masked drum makes framing easier for the cameraman,
although the construction of a masked drum is somewhat more involved than that of an open drum.

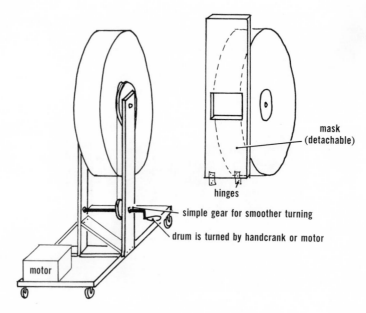

mask
(detachable)

hinges

simple gear for smoother turning

drum is turned by handcrank or motor

motor

The size of the crawl drum may vary considerably. A 12-inch-wide
drum with a 30-inch diameter will hold a crawl strip long enough for
extensive credit copy.

The crawl is generally used for supering a long list of credits at the
end of a show. You will sometimes have to speed up the crawl con-

siderably to get all the credits on the air before going to black. At other times you will have to slow down the credit roll to fill time. A variable speed control for the crawl drum is, therefore, almost essential. A manually operated crawl is sometimes preferred because of the required flexibility in speed. But a motor-driven crawl is much smoother. You can install a simple rheostat that will give you a great variety of speeds when coupled with the crawl motor.

The preparation of a crawl strip is fairly simple. For a super crawl, prepare a strip of heavy-weight black paper, its width equal to the width of the crawl drum, its length equal to the circumference of the drum. The white lettering will run from the top of the strip to the bottom. Be sure to space the individual lines fairly widely so that they will not blend into each other on the television screen. Leave room at the top and bottom of the strip to allow time to stop the crawl before the top credit line appears again. The crawl strip can be either stapled or taped to the drum.

A plain (non-super) crawl is prepared exactly the same way as the super crawl. Instead of white lettering on black paper, black lettering on medium gray paper is used.

Make sure that you roll the crawl in the right direction. The crawl should always roll from the bottom of the screen to the top. Therefore, the drum should roll away from the camera, not toward it.

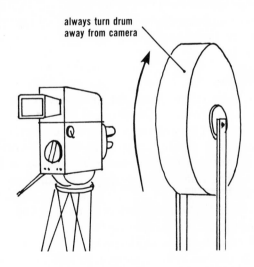

always turn drum
away from camera

### The telop crawl

If you have a telop machine available, you can get a mechanical attachment for a telop crawl. The telop crawl attachment usually takes a 3⅞-inch-wide photostated crawl strip.

The best way to prepare a super telop strip is to paste black photo-type letters on a strip of white illustration board. Again, the cracks between the individual letters must be touched up with white show-card color. After photostating, the strip can be used directly as a telop crawl.

## SPECIAL GRAPHICS

The more frequently used special graphics are: (1) product labels; (2) maps; (3) charts; and (4) simple animated titles. With the exception of film animation, all discussed graphics are processed for the studio camera.

### Product Labels

Some production people still insist on photostating every product label that is put before a monochrome studio camera. This procedure is unnecessary. Most labels on food cans, boxes, and bottles televise quite clearly. Some light red or orange lettering, however, has a tendency to wash out on the television monitor, and may require retouching. To retouch the label, carefully loosen it from the can or package, lighten or darken either lettering or background, and photostat the retouched label. The photostated label is then glued back on the can or box. If the letters and other important details blend into each other when you look at the label with your eyes squinted, put it in front of a camera and watch the result on the monochrome monitor. If the label reads properly, leave it alone. If it does not reproduce clearly, retouch it.

### Maps and Charts

Maps are an important visual aid for many television programs. Commercial maps are usually too detailed for good television pickup. You must, therefore, prepare the map for the television camera by either re-emphasizing certain map areas or by redrawing the map entirely. If you want to emphasize a certain border or highway, simply trace the existing lines with a heavy India ink line. To emphasize a whole area, such as the state of Nebraska on a map of the United States, first retrace the borders and then darken the state area with a green- or blue-tinted watercolor wash.

If your news commentator works in front of a large map, you can usually pick up certain details simply by taking a close-up of the area he is pointing out. However, if the indicated area must include more clearly defined detail, you can redraw this particular map section on a special easel card. Redrawing allows you to include all the necessary detail in a controlled way. As soon as the news commentator indicates the area on the large map, another camera can take a close-up of the specially prepared easel card. Some production people call this technique the magniscale method.

Sometimes it is quicker to redraw the whole map than to do extensive touchup work. When you draw a map for television, include only the most necessary details. Dark art work on light gray cardboard photographs best. For a color rendering, be sure to give the individual colors enough brightness contrast for good black and white reception.

If large water areas are to be set off against land, as in a map of the San Francisco Bay area, you will have to decide whether to make the water areas darker or lighter than the land areas. Your mind may play a trick on you and make the map appear to be in reversed polarity, which will make water areas look like land and land areas look like water. In general, lighter land areas help to overcome the reversed polarity problem in special graphics.

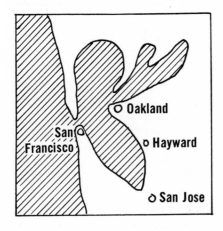 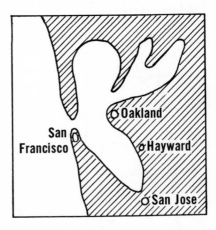

Charts, showing comparisons of percentages and other statistical data, are always specially prepared for on-the-air use. Charts are usually drawn on oversized illustration board so that the performer can stand next to it and point to certain pertinent data. You should, however, keep the special chart in aspect ratio. And if you use different colors to indicate the curves of a frequency polygon, make sure that the colors have sufficient gray-scale contrast to distinguish properly the different curves. A chart should have as little written copy as possible. If many figure groups are necessary to explain the significance of a chart, draw large figures and space them properly. You may be able to put all the figures on a second, separate chart. Maximum clarity must be your chief objective in drawing charts for television.

Sometimes you may want to dramatize the steep, successful rise of a curve by putting it on a long strip of illustration board out of aspect ratio. If you have art work out of aspect ratio, you should always find out how it is going to be used. Sometimes a card must be shown in its entirety, in which case it must have a backing that is in aspect ratio. But if the chart is going to be panned on a close-up, no special backing is necessary. A slow, tight tilt frequently reveals information more clearly and dramatically than a long shot of the whole chart.

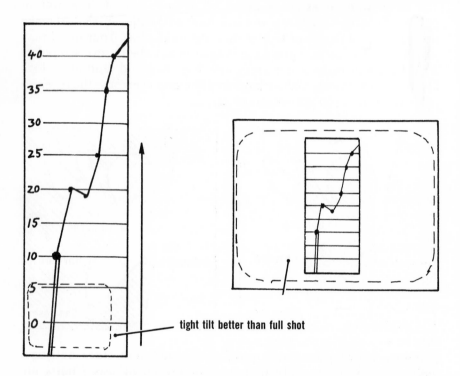

tight tilt better than full shot

All charts, maps, and other title material should be mounted on a stiff cardboard backing so that you can put them on studio easels. Large maps and charts can be stapled or taped to the cardboard backing or directly to the flat. Tape, however, frequently tears the paper of the graphic material when removed. Staples, carefully put through the tips of the four corners, cause less damage. Large charts can also be attached to one or two "pole cats."

Small items should be glued on studio cards with rubber cement. This will give a neat appearance even if the camera overshoots the visual on a tight close-up. If you "wet mount" your visuals, you will be able to separate the mounted material from the studio card with-

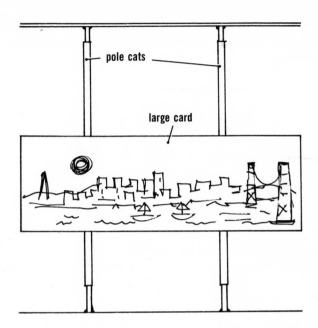

out doing too much damage to either item. Rubber cement wet mounting means that you apply the cement to one side only and that you press the picture on the backing while the cement is still wet. In rubber cement dry mounting, you place the cement on both the picture and the backing and let the cement dry thoroughly before placing the visual on the backing.

## Simple Animations

If you can, try to avoid live animation with graphics. They are not only time-consuming to prepare but also especially difficult to handle in the studio. They are never quite as satisfactory as you would like them to be. There are a few simple animations, however, that work fairly well—at least most of the time.

### The pull-off card or strip

To show lettering or graphs appearing gradually, you can use a pull-off strip or card. Assume that you would like to have the program title "Read Along With Me" appear as a super, letter by letter. The animation process is simple. First, prepare a super card with the title printed on it. Then take a plain black studio card and darken the left-hand edge so that the white of the edge will not bleed through during a super. This card will cover the supercard. By pulling this cover card from camera left to camera right, you will gradually reveal the letters of the title. The faster you pull, the faster the letters will appear. By gradually pushing the card over the letters, you can make the title disappear.

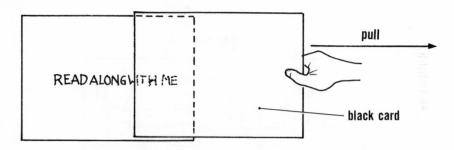

You can animate graphs by gradually revealing rear-lighted cut-outs. To demonstrate the flight path of a satellite, for example, cut a small slot in the studio card indicating the flight path. Then place opaque masking tape over the slot to prevent the backlight from shining through. When you pull off the strip, the rear-lighted slot becomes visible. You will need a special frame to hold the studio card securely without blocking off the special back light.

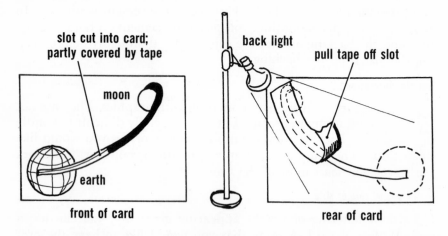

Other animations can be achieved by pulling a cardboard strip behind a large cutout slot. A rise or drop in temperature, for instance, can be shown by this simple pull-strip arrangement.

There are many possibilities for creative title animations. You can show a hand drawing titles on a piece of glass right on camera. Or a credit crawl may be lettered right onto the roll of an old player piano;

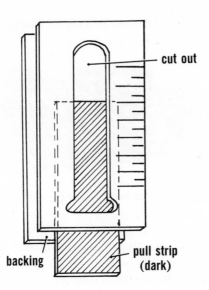

while the performer is pumping the piano, the camera dollies in for a close-up of the moving roll on which the credits appear. Title cards are often arranged as the pages of a large book, which are turned on camera by the performer.

### The ferrotype plate

Interesting title effects can also be achieved with a ferrotype plate, which you can purchase in any photo-supply shop. The ferrotype plate is a highly polished, thin metal plate that is flexible enough to be bent and twisted to a certain degree. When used for animation, unwanted areas of the ferrotype plate are covered and the exposed areas reflected onto a rear screen or a simple white cardboard. Compared with other animation techniques, ferrotype animation is relatively simple.

In order to animate the title *The Moving Image,* for example, this is what you do:

1. Cut black construction paper to the size of the ferrotype plate (11 × 14 inches is a workable size).

2. With a sharp pen knife, cut the title out of the construction paper. Don't worry about the center of the "o" falling out. You can glue the center pieces back on the ferrotype plate.

3. Turn the paper around so that the letters appear as a mirror image, and glue the paper with rubber cement firmly on the plate. Make sure that all edges are clean and glued on tightly; otherwise you will project fuzzy letters.

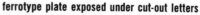

ferrotype plate exposed under cut-out letters

black construction paper glued on ferrotype plate

4. Take the ferrotype plate, which is now exposed only through the cut-out letters, and shine a strong, directional light (such as a projection bulb or a small spotlight) onto the plate. Direct the reflections of the exposed ferrotype letters toward the rear screen or the white card. You should now see *The Moving Image* clearly projected on the screen. (If you work from the back of the rear screen, with the camera on the other side, you do not have to reverse the lettering before gluing the paper on the plate.)

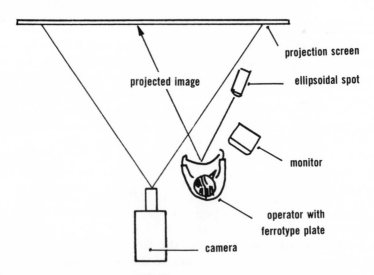

5. Now twist the plate. The more you twist it and bend it, the more distorted the projected letters become. Continuous bending and twisting of the plate results in "dancing" letters.

6. The television camera treats the projection like any other title; the animation can now be superimposed on, or keyed over, any other video source.

## Video Tape and Film Animation

If your video tape recorder is equipped with an automatic editing system (such as Editec) you can do complicated animation directly on video tape. The animation techniques for video tape vary from moving cut-out cardboard figures over various backgrounds to the more sophisticated film-animation techniques. Nevertheless, the more complex animation projects are almost always done on film, mainly because film animation is such a well-established and efficient industry. Also, film-animation equipment is more versatile and more accurate than the television system. The advantage of video tape animation, of course, is that it permits you to play back the animation immediately and correct possible errors.

### The storyboard

Even if you don't intend to do the animation yourself, you should present your idea for an animation sequence in the form of a storyboard. A storyboard is a sequence of small sketches with accompanying text depicting the most important points of your story. Storyboards are often prepared to clarify important scenes in all types of television shows (see page 256).

### Film openings

Special animated openings for a show series should always be put on film. The use of film will free your studio cameras from complicated opening maneuvers and will give you a chance to concentrate on the show itself. For more information on animated film techniques, you can find reference material in your library. Eastman Kodak Company has special film bibliographies available.

## OPERATIONAL REQUIREMENTS

### Storage

You need good storage facilities for your many title cards and other graphic materials. A large rack with individual boxes for title cards will greatly ease the problem of putting the cards away and finding them quickly when needed. Oversized material can be stored in larger slots adjacent to the standard card boxes. Interchangeable paper labels in a metal holder will simplify the relabeling of slots.

**Storyboard**

studio cards in slot        metal strips with labels                    oversized material

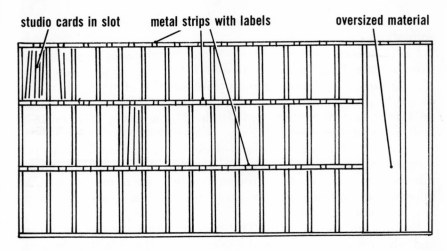

## Copyright

Whenever you present printed material, such as reproductions of famous paintings, professional photographs, illustrated books, and similar material, you must obtain proper permission from the copyright holders of the item. Television is considered a means of mechanical reproduction and demands copyright clearances.

## Reference Material

You will find it helpful to have some graphic arts reference material handy. Illustrated encyclopedias and dictionaries are almost essential tools for the graphic artist. Two or three standard works on calligraphy and printing should also be on your desk. A pocket edition of art history may prove very useful. Most art directors collect their own reference material. Out of old magazines and books, you can cut pictures that look as though they might sometime be useful. Either mount the cutouts on the leaves of ring binders or file them in large envelopes. A picture file of that sort is generally referred to as a picture morgue, an expression that television has taken over from the newspaper business.

## SUMMARY

Television graphics include all two-dimensional visuals that are especially prepared for the television camera.

Standard graphics include (1) the title or easel card, (2) the 2 × 2 slide and the rear screen projector slide, (3) telops or balops, and (4) the crawl.

Special graphics include product labels, maps, charts, and simple animations.

*Size of standard television graphics.* Since the television screen is comparatively small and the resolution of the picture reproduction somewhat limited, only a small amount of information of maximum clarity should be shown on the screen. The amount of copy on a studio card or slide should not exceed ten words. The lettering itself must be bold and easily legible.

*Aspect ratio.* The aspect ratio of television is three to four. All picture information must be contained within this aspect ratio. Since transmission and reception processes cause a loss of picture area, all information must be confined within an area that is sure to arrive at any television receiver.

*Scanning and essential areas.* The area on which the camera frames and which is transmitted by the television station is called the scanning area. Centered within this scanning area is the most important part of the picture area, the essential area. All information (copy or pictures) must be kept within the essential area.

The relationships of over-all size to scanning and essential areas of most standard television graphics are as follows:

| Type | Over-all Size | Scanning Area | Essential Area |
|---|---|---|---|
| Studio card | 14 × 17 inches | 9 × 12 inches | 6¾ × 9¾ inches |
| 2 × 2 slides | 2 × 2 inches | $^{27}/_{32}$ × 1⅛ inches | ⅝ × $^{29}/_{32}$ inches |
| Telops | 4 × 5 inches | 3 × 4 inches | 2¼ × 3¼ inches |
| Telop crawl | 3⅞ inches wide and as long as needed | | |

Special graphics may be any size, depending on their use. If possible, all graphic material should be designed with the 3 × 4 aspect ratio in mind.

Lettering is an important aspect of television graphics. There are five lettering methods most commonly employed by the graphic artist: (1) handlettering, (2) handlettering with a lettering guide, (3) Artype, Fototype and rub-on letters, (4) printing, and (5) felt-board letters. The most useful printing machines are the Linoscribe and the Kensol hotpress.

There are three types of studio title cards: (1) the plain title (usually black or white lettering on gray cardboard), (2) the illustrated title card (the same as the plain title card, but with illustrations), and (3) the super card, a black (or dark gray) card with white (or light blue) lettering.

A 2 × 2 slide is prepared the same way as a title card. The slide is made through a photographic process. Sometimes cell overlays are used for the preparation of illustrated slides. The art work for a super slide is black lettering on white, which is then reversed by photography.

A telop can be made simply by printing on a 4 × 5 cardboard, or by making a mat print from a 35mm negative.

A crawl can be prepared for a crawl drum or for the telop machine.

In the preparation of special graphic material, attention must be paid to the simplicity and clarity of all information to be televised.

## EXERCISES

1. What is aspect ratio?
2. Define scanning and essential areas.
3. How can you make sure that your lettering does not expand over the essential area?
4. You are asked to prepare a super card showing the ten locations of your sponsor's stores. What would you suggest? Why?
5. The agency representative asks you to make the drawing of their dog food can on your studio card as realistic as possible. What preparation techniques would you suggest?
6. Your guest performer brings a studio super card with him with extremely big lettering on it. The reason for having the letters that big, he tells you, is so that they will look very large on the screen. Do you agree with him? If so, why? If not, why not?
7. You are preparing art work for a super slide. What color lettering will you use on what color illustration board? Why?
8. The sponsor would like to show his three new automobiles simultaneously to compare size. He prefers to have the copy read off-camera. He would also like to have the camera remain in one position so that the viewers would not be distracted by possible distortions. In addition to all that, he would like the set to resemble his showroom. What procedures would you suggest? Why?
9. At the end of his last television lecture, Professor Dart would like to give name credit to all twenty students who have helped him with the preparation of his television shows. What graphic method would you suggest?
10. Your director insists on supering five different titles over the opening of your half-hour drama. All available studio cameras are used for the live action. Can you fulfill the director's wish? How? If not, why not?

# 7

# Special Effects

Special effects should be employed sparingly. If they are overused, the "special" will soon lose its uniqueness and effectiveness. Some special effects are so readily available that they present a great temptation to the inexperienced television director, especially the one who thinks that the degree of creativity is proportional with the number of special effects he can use. Other effects are so difficult to achieve that most small stations are not capable of handling them properly. Whenever you intend to use a special effect, you should ask yourself the following questions: (1) Is the effect really necessary? (2) Does the effect contribute positively to my visual presentation? (3) Can the effect be easily produced? (4) Is the effect reliable?

We can divide special effects for television into the following three large groups: (1) electronic effects, (2) optical effects, and (3) mechanical effects.

## ELECTRONIC EFFECTS

There are nine types of major electronic effects: (1) superimpositions, (2) sweep reversals, (3) polarity reversals, (4) beam control effects, (5) electronic stretching and compressing, (6) the wipe, (7) the split screen, (8) electronic matting, and (9) flexitron effects.

### Superimpositions

A superimposition is a form of double exposure. The picture from one camera is electronically superimposed over the picture from another. In effect, both pictures are simultaneously projected on the monitor screen.

Since a "super" shows two pictures at once, you must be careful in choosing the right background and position for the supered objects. If you superimpose two "busy" (very detailed) pictures, you will notice that both pictures (and with them the superimposition) will become unidentifiable and meaningless. Detailed objects should always be supered over plain areas. If you cannot avoid the superimposition of two detailed pictures, you must quickly decide which one of the pictures is more important to the viewer. Your technical director will then electronically favor the more important picture; that is, he will make it more visible than the other. Like the white letters on a black super card, the objects to be supered should be put in front of a dead black background. The background will eliminate unnecessary detail and prevent distracting light reflections.

You can use a super for the purpose of identification or information, decoration, and unusual effects.

The most common identification or information super is the supering of titles over live action. Another example of an identification super is a shot of the inside of a machine supered over the machine's housing, such as the picture of a clock mechanism supered over the clock housing, or the picture of a high powered engine supered over the hood of a racing car. You can use photographs and illustrations instead of three-dimensional objects for most of your identification supers.

A variation of the informative super is used when the hands of a pianist are supered over a full shot of the piano. Informative supers of this sort, however, are usually more distracting than informing. Superimpositions of piano keys in all possible variations and directions reveal more often the director's bad taste than the musician's brilliance.

Decorative supers should not be used as a substitute for good composition and interesting visual material. The superimposition of candles and twinkling stars, for example, rarely helps to disguise the mediocre performance of a singer. If the performers on your show are good and your studio properly set up and lighted, you will find little need for decorative supers.

However, if you want to express the complexity of an event or a person's thoughts and emotions, superimpositions are quite appropriate. For example, you may want to express visually the complex structure of a particular jazz sequence by supering the various instruments involved. Or, to show a high state of emotional excitement, you may show a close-up of a performer with various images superimposed over the face. You are probably familiar with the portrayal of dream sequences, whereby objects and happenings are superimposed over the sleeping face. The same rule applies for superimpositions as for all other special effects: if the effect is meaningful, its utilization is justified.

A few of the more frequently used super techniques shall be mentioned briefly.

For a ghost effect, have your performer dress in the traditional white bedsheet and move slowly in front of a black threefold. Make sure that he remains in one spot so that the camera does not overshoot the black backing. The ghost image is then superimposed over the picture from another camera, which may be slowly panning through the set of the haunted house. Although the ghost actually remains in one spot, the panning of the second camera will create the illusion of the ghost floating weightlessly through the room. If you cannot find anyone with the strong desire to play a ghost, you can make one out of a handkerchief. Tie the handkerchief ghost to a string and move it violently in front of a black easel card.

Mystical writing that suddenly appears on a blackboard while the surprised professor looks on is no problem in television production. One camera frames up on the blackboard and the professor. Another camera is focused on a black easel card on which you can write (with white chalk) the mystical letters. You must wear a long black glove so that your hand and arm become completely invisible when supered over the blackboard. If you want the lettering to appear on the camera-left side of the blackboard, the easel card writing must be framed on the left side of the viewfinder. If your writing is to appear on the right blackboard area, the card must be framed on the right half of the camera viewfinder.

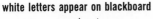

white letters appear on blackboard

white chalk on black illustration board

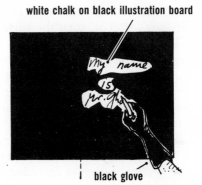

black glove

To show a variety of dream pictures, use $8 \times 10$ photos mounted on studio cards for the dream sequence. One camera takes an extreme close-up of the actor, while the other takes the studio cards to be supered. The cards can be used as hot (on-camera) flips while the superimposition is still in effect, or they can be changed with the super temporarily taken out.

Sometimes you must quickly set up for an unexpected superimposition. There may be no time to place a special black background be-

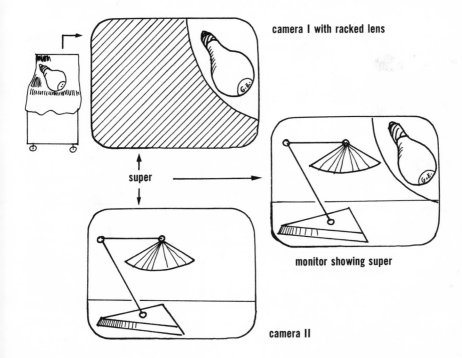

camera I with racked lens

super

monitor showing super

camera II

hind the objects to be supered. In this case, you can rack the on-the-air lens—that is, turn the turret as though you would change lenses—so that most of the picture is blocked out (which leaves a black area) except for the image of the object, which has been moved by the racking into the corner of the viewfinder. You can now super-impose this image over the picture from the other camera. This effect is called "lens-rack super" or an "offset-turret" effect.

## Sweep Reversals

Most monochrome television cameras are equipped for horizontal and vertical sweep or scanning reversals. If you change the horizontal sweep you will get the effect of a mirror image; right and left will be reversed. You can use the horizontal sweep reversal to correct an image taken off a mirror, for instance.

The vertical sweep reversal projects a picture upside down. It is frequently used for comedy effects. You can make a performer stand on his head or show a whole set upside down merely by flicking the

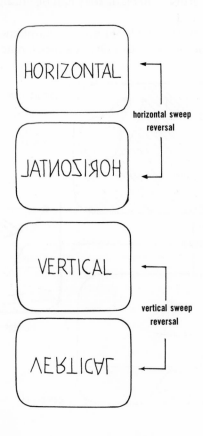

horizontal sweep
reversal

vertical sweep
reversal

**SPECIAL EFFECTS** *special effect generator*
*wipe-machine*
*special effects amplifier*
265

reversal switch inside the camera. You can reverse horizontal and vertical sweeps simultaneously, if you like.

## Polarity Reversals

Reversed polarity means that the gray scale is reversed. The white becomes black and the black turns white. A polarity reversal switch in the film chain camera, for instance, permits the projection of negative newsfilm. Be sure to alert your engineers if you plan to project a negative newsfilm so that they can reverse the polarity. You will have little use for this special effect in studio productions. In case you need it, a polarity reversal switch can be easily installed in the camera.

## Beam Control Effects

You can make a picture gradually turn negative by having the engineer turn up the beam control. This gives the effect of extreme brightness, which you can use to simulate chemical and electrical fires, lightning, and explosions. If properly handled, this special effect can look extremely convincing.

## Electronic Stretching and Compressing

The width and height of the television picture can be electronically stretched and compressed. You can make a person appear long and thin or short and fat, according to the desired effect. The image, however, will appear distorted, similar to the images in a distortion mirror. Engineers are generally not too fond of this special effect. First, stretching and compressing is hard on the camera tube. Second, once a picture is pushed that far out of alignment, it is hard to return it quickly to normal without using a test chart.

All the above-mentioned electronic effects can be produced with standard electronic television equipment. More complicated electronic effects, such as wipes and electronic matting, need an expensive and rather complicated special effects generator and amplifier. Unfortunately, many small stations do not have such equipment. Colleges and universities, however, may feel it necessary to purchase a special effects amplifier not only to give their students proper professional training but also to conduct thorough research in the field of television production techniques.

## The Wipe

The two simplest wipes are the vertical wipe and the horizontal wipe. A vertical wipe gives the same effect as pulling a window shade down. Just as the window shade "wipes out" the picture you see through the window, the image from one camera gradually pushes the picture from the other camera off the screen, or "wipes it out." The horizontal wipe works the same way, except that it is pushed out to the side of the screen by the other picture.

vertical wipe                    horizontal wipe

The more complicated wipes can take on many shapes. One picture can start in the middle of the other picture and wipe it off the screen in the shape of a diamond. Or the wipe can start from the edges of one picture and shrink the other picture off the screen. Wedge wipes and rectangular wipes are also frequently used. The illustration on page 267 shows some of the more common types of wipes.

Operationally, you can select the appropriate wipe configuration either by pressing a wipe button or by turning a rotor selector to the proper wipe position. The speed of the wipe is determined by how fast you move the special effects levers, which look exactly like the fader levers on your switcher (see Chaper 11 for more detail). If your switcher is equipped with a "joy stick," a small lever that can be moved in all directions, you can move certain wipes anywhere on your screen. For example, if you have activated your circle wipe and would now like to move the circle to the upper left-hand corner of your screen, simply move the joy stick to your upper left until the circle is in the appropriate position. Of course, these effects can be achieved only with rather complex video switchers.

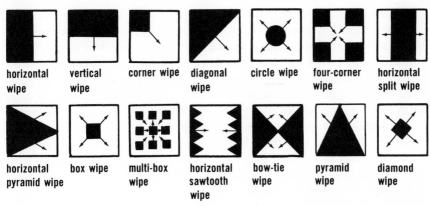

| horizontal wipe | vertical wipe | corner wipe | diagonal wipe | circle wipe | four-corner wipe | horizontal split wipe |

| horizontal pyramid wipe | box wipe | multi-box wipe | horizontal sawtooth wipe | bow-tie wipe | pyramid wipe | diamond wipe |

Basic wipes

## The Split Screen

You can get a split screen effect by stopping a wipe in the center of the screen. Each half of the screen will show a different picture. To set up for a split screen, one camera must put the object in the left half of the viewfinder, the other in the right half. The unnecessary part of each picture is then wiped out.

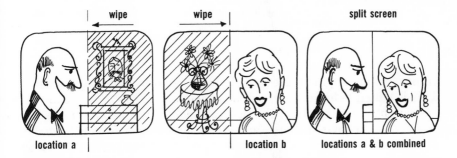

location a | location b | locations a & b combined

A split screen effect is especially useful if the different pictures originate from different locations. The man in the left half of the picture may be located in Los Angeles, the woman on the right in New York. This, in effect, suggests that they are talking to each other face-to-face.

## Electronic Matting, or "Keying"

In electronic matting, one picture is electronically cut into the other. One of the most common matting effects is the "keying in" of program titles over a background scene. The effect looks very similar to a supered title, except that the matted title looks somewhat cleaner and sharper. The titles are prepared exactly as they would be for a super. The only difference is that the title is not put over the background picture, it is cut into the picture. With electronic matting, you can combine any two images without having one show through the other as in a super. For example, you can use the picture supplied by one camera as background for the live action picked up by the other camera.

Let us assume that you would like to show a ballet dancer perform on the steps of an old Victorian house. One camera can focus on a photograph of the house, the other on the dancer performing in front of a black or very dark background. The matting amplifier will then continually cut the dancer's shape out of the photograph and put her image into the blanked-out spots. As a result, the dancer appears to be dancing on the steps.

camera 1 on card
showing photo of buildings

camera 2 on dancer
in front of black
(or nonlighted) cyc,
standing on black cloth

camera 2
keyed over camera 1:
dancer on steps of building

An improved matting process has been developed for color television, which uses the more flexible blue signal for matting purposes. This is called "chroma key matting."

In chroma key matting, the neutral background is blue instead of black, as in regular matting, and everything that is blue will let the picture of the second camera show through. If the performer wears a blue shirt, the other picture will show through the shirt area. Blue eyes can become a problem on a close-up, turning into transparent holes when keyed into a background scene. Fortunately, most blue eyes contain or reflect enough other colors to render the few transparent spots harmless.

If the video switcher is equipped for "double re-entry"—which means roughly that the matting effect is piped through the switcher again so that another effect can be keyed in—and if a third camera is used (which may be the television film camera), further matting effects can be achieved. One camera takes the background, another camera provides the signal that cuts the moving shapes out of the background picture, and the third camera supplies the material to fill the cutout holes, which may be anything that has textural interest, such as rough cloth, an old brick wall, or water. With this technique you can create any number of surrealistic effects, as, for example, a number of heavy concrete blocks in the shape of a man swimming along a busy downtown street.

Such visual adventures, however, are strictly experimental and can rarely, if ever, be justifiably integrated into standard show formats.

### Flexitron Effects

The flexitron can electronically dissolve an image into wavelike motion. You have probably seen the effect when sound is made visible on an oscilloscope (an electronic testing scope, which shows images of green lines). The flexitron works in a similar way, except that the sound is fed into the television camera and coupled with the picture scanning. Depending on the volume and frequency (pitch) of the sound, the wavelike motion becomes more or less violent. Since the flexitron effect needs highly specialized equipment, it is rarely used in small station operation. Other transitional devices are usually easier to obtain and often equally effective.

## OPTICAL EFFECTS

The category of major optical effects includes: (1) rear projection, (2) front projection, (3) mirrors, (4) gobos, (5) special lens prisms, (6) mat boxes, (7) effects wheels, and (8) defocus effects.

### Rear Projection

Rear projection is a widely used and very important special effect. With the aid of rear projection you can quickly and easily create a variety of realistic indoor and outdoor backgrounds for a limited performing area.

The rear screen is a large (the most common size is 10 feet high and 12 feet wide) sheet of translucent frosted plastic stretched with rubber bands into a sturdy wood or metal frame. The frame should ride on four free-wheeling casters for quick repositioning.

Contrary to a regular slide projector, which projects a slide on the front side of the screen, the rear screen projector throws the slide image on the back of the screen. The translucent screen, however, allows the camera to pick up the projected image from the front.

There are three basic disadvantages of using a rear screen in small station operation: (1) the purchase or rental of a complete rear projection unit, including a screen and projector, involves considerable expense; (2) the rear projection takes up valuable studio space and complicates lighting procedures; and (3) the performing area becomes quite limited.

The advantages of rear projection, however, substantially outweigh the disadvantages, especially if you do not have a matting amplifier with which to produce many of the R.P. (rear projection) effects more easily.

Even without the projector, a rear screen lends itself to several interesting studio effects. If you place a particular object between the screen and a small but strong light source (usually a simply mounted projection bulb), you can project a great variety of shadow patterns on the screen. This projection technique is especially effective when integrated with a stylized set.

You can make simple cardboard cutouts of skylines, houses, trees, mountains, and ships, and project these on the rear screen; or you can use three-dimensional objects for projection, such as ladders, bird cages, fireplace units, or candle holders. You can also put your performers behind the rear screen for simple silhouette effects. A modern dance number, for instance, looks quite effective when at least partially performed in silhouette behind the rear screen.

rear screen                                      cardboard cutout clamped to microphone stands

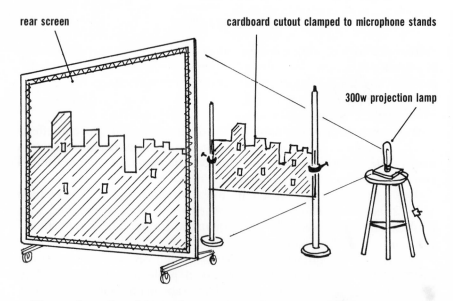

300w projection lamp

If you place the objects close to the light source and away from the rear screen, the shadow projection will be large and not clearly defined. If you place the objects close to the rear screen, away from the light source, the shadow projections will be more clearly defined and closer to the actual size of the objects. You can achieve shadow distortions by placing the light source either higher or lower than the object.

Sometimes you can create interesting R.P. effects by projecting a large sheet of plexiglass painted with showcard colors in a watercolor technique. As long as the soft plexiglass surface is not scratched during cleaning, you can use the same sheet over and over again.

### Rear screen projector

You will, of course, achieve much more realistic effects by using a specially built rear screen projector. A good rear screen projector must have a short, undistorted wide-angle throw and must be capable of projecting an extremely brilliant and contrasting image. The short throw (which is still anywhere from 20 to 30 feet, unless you can shorten the throw by projecting the slide first into a mirror) is highly important, especially in a small studio; the high light intensity of the projector is important to combat the inevitable spill light hitting the screen. Standard rear screen projectors are usually designed for (1) 4 × 5-inch glass slides, (2) simple animation crawls, (3) special effects wheels, and (4) dissolves and supers.

### Rear projection slides

A rear projector can hold several slides that are easily (sometimes automatically) interchangeable. Rear screen manufacturers have large slide libraries containing all the important landmarks in the world as well as a great variety of other useful settings, such as snow scenes, trees, streets, and mountains. If you need an R.P. slide of a scene that you cannot obtain from the library, you can have it processed by any large photo lab.

A quick way of making R.P. slides is to paint directly on the glass plates. The extreme enlargement of the slide drawing produces interesting effects. You can also blacken the entire slide with India ink and then scratch certain designs on the black surface.

So that the projection will appear correctly on the monitor, you

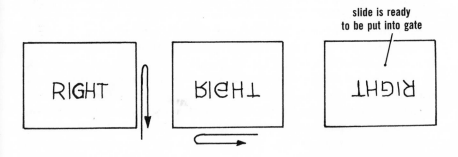

slide is ready
to be put into gate

must insert the slide in a special way. First, hold the slide right side up. Second, flip it upside down. Third, flip it sideways. The slide is now in the right position to be put into the gate.

### Animation crawls

An animation crawl is a strip of large celluloid film that moves sideways at varying speeds in front of the projector. Landscapes and street scenes are the most common subjects for the R.P. crawl. These crawls are used in connection with specific foreground pieces, such as a train or wagon window. The moving landscape behind the stationary train window will create the illusion of a moving train. If you want the performer to appear walking down a street, you can put him in front of the R.P. screen, have him face against the direction of the crawl and go through a walking motion. This, however, must be rehearsed carefully to achieve an illusion of reality.

### Special effects wheels

Special effects wheels can be attached to the standard rear projector. They are similar to theatre effects wheels, projecting certain rotating images.

### Dissolves and supers

Two matching rear projectors will enable you to dissolve or superimpose two R.P. images. To dissolve, simply turn up the rheostat control on the second projector, which will temporarily superimpose a second image on the screen. At the same time, turn down the rheostat control of the first projector and gradually take out the first image. The speed of the dissolve depends on how fast you turn the rheostats. If you stop in the middle of the dissolve, you will have a superimposition of both slides. An effective super is the projection of a cloud slide over a cloud crawl. It produces a realistic dimensional effect with the foreground clouds moving and the background clouds remaining stationary.

Many large television operations use a special rear screen film projector. Like the R.P. crawl, it creates quite realistic background motion. This technique is widely used in the film industry; a shot of the interior of a car, for example, is accompanied by a background projection showing a landscape or buildings whizzing by. Such process shots, however, are of little use in small station operation. If you must do some closed circuit experimenting with different kinds of process shots, you can use a standard 16mm film projector as your rear screen projector. To get a throw long enough to fill a major portion of the rear screen, you will probably have to project the film on a large mirror, which will reflect the projection onto the rear screen. The mirror will eliminate the necessity of electronically correcting the projected image through horizontal sweep reversal. Since the film is not synchronized with the sync pulse of the television camera, the monitor picture will flicker somewhat and black shutter bars may move up and down the screen from time to time. The image, however, is clear enough for closed circuit experiments, especially if vidicon cameras are used.

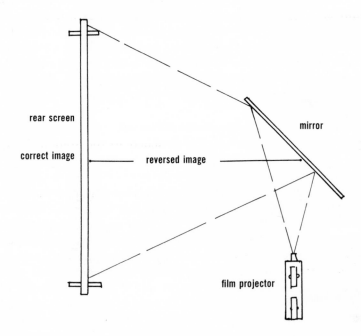

Rear screen projection is most effective when integrated with other parts of the studio set. A few simple foreground pieces that match parts of the projected scenery will produce more realistic pictures. If you have enough studio space, you can use rear projection instead of photomurals.

Whenever you use a rear screen in a small studio, you should be aware of the following problems: (1) The rear screen projector takes up considerable studio space. To achieve proper lighting, the performers must be at least six feet away from the screen, which requires even more space. (2) To preserve the illusion of reality, you cannot overshoot the rear screen. Therefore, the number of performers and their action radius must be extremely limited. A screen as large as 10 × 12 feet is usually just large enough for two performers. (3) The

rear screen with projected landscape

foreground trees

canvas or paper covered with tan bark

blower motors of the projectors are fairly noisy and are often picked up by the studio microphone. (4) A high-contrast rear screen has a narrow fall-off angle. This means that the brightness of the projected image falls off as soon as the camera moves away from its central position and shoots the screen from an angle. (5) As mentioned in Chapter 3, the lighting of the rear screen and surrounding sets involves particular and often difficult problems.

## Front Projection

Elaborate front projection, as used in the theatre, for example, is not often used in small station operation. The performer may easily get between the projection source and the background if the front projector is not properly placed. However, when the performers remain fairly stationary, front projection can be employed. For example, interesting background effects can be front-projected with two or more standard overhead projectors, which are used in nearly every school and college. Of course, any front projection demands as precise a studio lighting setup as rear screen projection. Very little if any light should spill on the projection surface, which is often the cyclorama.

The most common type of front projection is the cucalorus projection, often called "kookie." A simple cucalorus is a geometrical pattern cut out of a large sheet of illustration board or ¼-inch plywood. This pattern is hung in front of a powerful directional spotlight. The resulting shadow pattern is used to break up plain surfaces, such as large sections of the cyc or unit scenery. Cucalorus projections are sometimes used for idea-associations, such as the shadow of prison bars on the cyc to indicate a prison cell. Special ellipsoidal spotlights, which use small metal slides (kookie slides) for cucalorus projections, have been developed. These spotlights are called "pattern projectors."

## Mirrors

Mirrors are usually a hazard in studio operation. If the shots are not carefully rehearsed, the cameraman and floor manager may discover themselves looking into the lens of their own camera. In dramatic shows, however, mirrors can help you get new and unusual picture angles. The simple event of an opening door becomes significant and mysterious when seen through a mirror. And with small mirrors arranged in a specific way, you can achieve interesting decorative effects.

When you use mirrors as simple set decorations, you should spray them with dulling spray. The dulled surface will eliminate the danger of picking up unwanted reflections.

In some remote locations you may find it impossible to get certain shots because the camera cannot get into proper shooting position. A properly placed mirror may enable the cameraman to get the required shots.

Mirrors that are most frequently used are (1) the overhead mirror, (2) the periscope, and (3) the multi-image mirror.

angled mirror reflection

### Overhead mirrors

In studio operation, mirrors are generally used to get overhead shots. A mirror hung from the lighting grid over a piano will give you a good top view of the whole keyboard. Overhead shots of dancers are also very effective. If you use a mirror, make sure that the horizontal scanning has been reversed. Otherwise, your pianist will appear to be playing the bass with his right hand and the rapid treble sections with his left.

When you hang your mirror at slight angles, the reflected images will look canted. Such tilted images often help to set a mood of mystery or heightened drama.

### The periscope

The mirror periscope consists of two adjustable mirrors hung in a movable frame. The periscope permits a variety of overhead shots. When you use a periscope, you don't have to reverse the horizontal sweep in your camera, since the image will be corrected by the second mirror of the periscope.

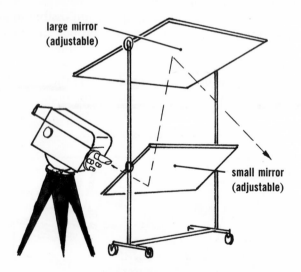

large mirror (adjustable)

small mirror (adjustable)

There are several advantages in using a periscope. (1) The mirror does not have to be hung from the lighting grid. The periscope can be moved into the desired position right on the studio floor. (2) The camera can shoot straight into the lower mirror without having to tilt up into the lights to find the overhead mirror. (3) The horizontal sweep does not have to be changed.

However, there are also disadvantages. (1) The periscope is large and bulky, and thus is difficult to move. (2) It takes up valuable studio space. (3) The mirrors get out of adjustment easily, especially when the periscope is rolled over cables that always seem to be in its path. (4) The mirror height is fixed, which limits the area that can be reflected by the mirror and, therefore, seen by the camera.

Although the use of mirrors will greatly increase possible camera angles, you should realize that mirrors require many small adjustments and time-consuming rehearsals before they give you the picture you want. In most cases, mirrors will severely restrict your action radius. When you use mirrors, make sure that the blocking has been carefully worked out and that it is slavishly followed by the performers. To assure a successful on-the-air performance, mark clearly the positions of cameras and performers during rehearsal.

### Multi-image mirrors

The multi-image effect is achieved by mirrors reflecting each other's images, like barbershop mirrors that hang on opposite walls. Toy kaleidoscopes are based on this principle. You can duplicate a kaleidoscope effect on television by taping two small mirrors or ferrotype plates together along one edge, so that the reflecting surfaces face each other. When you open the mirror plates to a particular angle and hold them to the camera lens so that the lens points

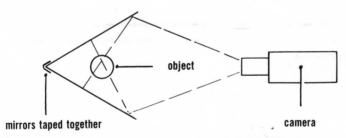

object

mirrors taped together                                        camera

Multi-image with mirror

at the "V" formed by the two mirrors, you will get a rosette-like pattern of whatever the camera is seeing. With a little experimenting you will discover that the change of the "V" angle will produce a change in the number of rosette segments.

A dynamic effect, something like a cubist painting, can be obtained by reflecting a scene off a mirror mosaic. The preparation for this effect is amazingly simple: break a thin mirror into several large pieces and glue these pieces together again on a piece of plywood or masonite. When the camera shoots into the mirror mosaic at an angle (so that the camera will not be seen in the reflection), the reflected scene takes on a highly effective mosaic effect.

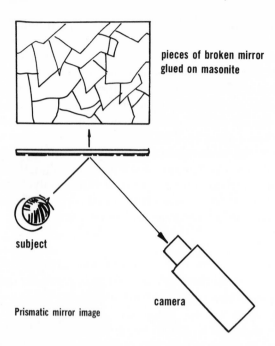

pieces of broken mirror
glued on masonite

subject

Prismatic mirror image

camera

## Television Gobos

A gobo is a special television device that helps to create an illusion of depth. A gobo acts as a foreground frame to background objects or live action. Don't confuse the television gobo with the motion picture gobo. In the motion picture industry, a gobo is an opaque shield that is put in front of the lights to keep undesirable spill light from hitting specific set areas.

There are three kinds of television gobos: (1) two-dimensional cut-out gobos, (2) translucent gobos, and (3) relief gobos and gobos with moving parts.

### Cutouts

An overused but good example of a simple cutout gobo is the picture frame gobo. This gobo gives the impression of a photograph in which the person suddenly comes to life.

The production procedure is relatively simple. First, make the gobo by cutting a medium-size rectangle out of a 30 × 40 illustration board and painting some kind of frame (usually baroque) around the opening. Then place the camera, gobo, and performer in such a way that a full shot of the gobo will show the picture frame, the opening within the frame, and the person within the opening, all in a believable perspective. When you dolly in on the gobo, the opening

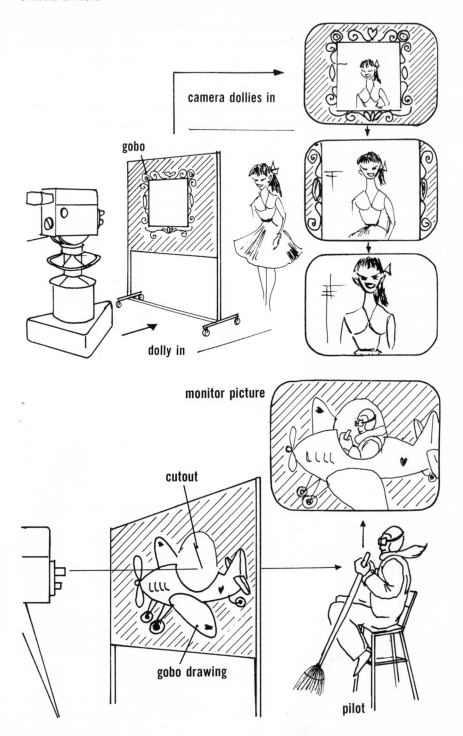

camera dollies in

gobo

dolly in

monitor picture

cutout

gobo drawing

pilot

will seem to widen out until it disappears from the screen altogether. The camera can then concentrate on the performer, who now starts his action.

Other widely used gobos are cartoon cutouts of airplanes, old automobiles, and carriages. In most cases, the performer sits on a chair behind the cutout, in front of a plain background. The camera remains stationary and shows the gobo and the performer in a correct size relationship.

### Transparent gobos

The operation technique of a transparent gobo is the same as that of a cutout gobo. The transparent gobo consists of a piece of glass or acetate cell upon which the gobo effect is drawn or printed. The camera will not be restricted to shoot only through a gobo opening, but can shoot through all the parts of the gobo that are not covered with the drawing.

Transparent gobos are excellent for identification of a set locale. A transparent gobo with the word "Sweet Shoppe" lettered on it will quickly establish the background set as a candy store. This type of set identification is especially useful in stylized settings for song and dance numbers. Little or no changes in the actual settings are neces-

cell with lettering

sary as long as the gobo titles indicate the different locales for the individual dance numbers. You can get good gobo effects by having certain designs (such as Early American lithograph vignettes) photographed directly on your cell gobo.

### Relief gobos and gobos with moving parts

Any small foreground piece that is used in correct perspective with the realistic background set can be called a gobo. Small three-dimensional arches and other models are often integrated with the set pieces in a standard set. You can also use special gobos with moving parts, which will create realistic effects. For instance, the entrance to a saloon can be made out of a gobo cutout with two small movable doors attached. The camera dollies in on the gobo with the doors closed. On cue, both doors are bent back and the background set or action is revealed.

### Gobo operation technique

Gobos are usually stapled on a gobo stand, which you can easily make out of 1 × 3 lumber. A small board attached to the lower edge of the stand frame is useful for placing three-dimensional objects. Casters or metal gliders on the gobo frame allow it to be moved quickly and silently out of the camera's way.

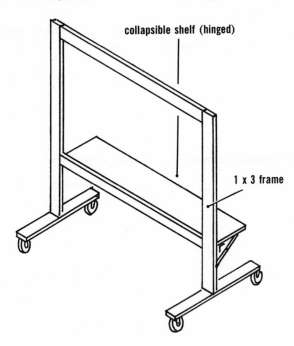

collapsible shelf (hinged)

1 x 3 frame

When using gobos you will need a fairly great depth of field in order to keep the gobo as well as the background in focus. Use a wide-angle or medium-angle lens (75mm or 90mm lens) and a high *f*-stop setting. Sometimes the cameraman will have to resort to the split focus, which means that he must compromise his focus adjustment between foreground and background.

To get the gobo away from the front of the camera, you can quickly dissolve or cut to the other camera while you have the floor stand removed. Some stations work with a split gobo frame that is pulled apart to each side of the camera. However, the construction of this frame and the making of gobos for the split gobo holder can become quite complicated; also, additional production people are required to handle the split gobo device.

## Special Lens Prisms

Special effects lens prisms are sometimes used on the television camera. The most common of these are the image inverter prism and the multiple image prism. The image inverter prism rotates an image into several positions. The studio floor can become a wall or the ceiling, depending on the rotation degree of the prism. You can make an image inverter prism rather easily by fastening a mirror to the lens at the desired angle. However, you will need a horizontal sweep reversal in order to eliminate the mirror image.

Like the multi-image mirror device, the multiple image prism literally multiplies an image several times. The objects being viewed by the camera are usually arranged in a circular fashion and are visible simultaneously on the television screen. The prism can also be turned, which causes the multiple images to rotate around the center of the screen.

## The Mat Box

A mat box is a mask that partially blocks the camera lens. It reduces the field of view without disturbing the apparent distance from camera to object. Although there is a great variety of more or less complex mat boxes on the market, you can make an inexpensive but useful mat box yourself. All you need is a small paper cup that will fit over your lens. Paint the inside of the cup black and cut a small opening (either round or rectangular) in the bottom of the cup. Then tape the finished mat box over your lens.

A mat box is employed in achieving special superimposition effects. Perhaps you want to create the effect of a tiny man trapped in a glass bottle. One camera takes a close-up of the bottle, while the other is focused on a special set. This set consists of a black background (two black threefolds or black drapes) and a blackened floor area immediately in front of the backing (a strip of black seamless paper taped on the floor is easier to put on and take off than black paint). The camera takes an extreme long shot of the performer in front of the black set, which allows the size of the performer to be reduced drastically on the screen. The mat box prevents the camera from overshooting the black set on this long shot. The image of the performer is now superimposed over the bottle to achieve the desired effect. Remember that a mat box effect cannot be done successfully without careful planning and rehearsing.

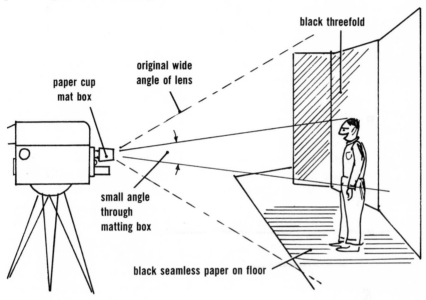

### Effect Wheels

A disc rotated in front of a camera is sometimes used as a transitional device or as a means to interpret visually certain happenings, such as a long fall, a person being hypnotized, or any number of other weird effects. The most commonly used disc design for the effects wheel is a white spiral. The effects wheel is either driven by a small electric motor or cranked by hand (see page 284).

### Defocus Effects

The defocus effect is the simplest optical effect. The cameraman turns his focusing knob and racks out of focus and then, on cue, racks back into focus. This effect is used as a transitional device, or to indicate types of psychophysical disturbances.

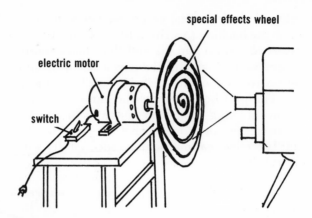

Since going out of focus will conceal the image almost as completely as going to black, it is possible to change your field of view or the objects in front of the camera during complete defocusing. For instance, you can go out of focus on a young girl seated at a table, change actors quickly, and rack back into focus on an old woman sitting in the same chair.

A slight defocusing can make the camera subjective; for instance, the camera may assume the function of the actor's eye to indicate progressively worse eyesight. Also, you can suggest psychological disturbances by going out of focus on a close-up of the actor's face.

If you want only partial defocusing, with part of the picture remaining in focus, you must use what is known in the motion picture industry as "Vaseline lens." The Vaseline lens is a regular camera lens whose edges are "fogged" with Vaseline cream. However, you should construct a device that allows for this effect without dirtying or damaging the lens itself. Simply get a cardboard tube or bottomless paper cup, tape a piece of clear glass to one end of it, and place

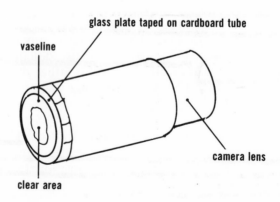

the whole assembly over the lens. You can now grease the edges of the glass, leaving a clear area in the middle. Thus, the outer edges of your picture will be out of focus (the degree of the "fogging" depending entirely on the thickness of the Vaseline grease), with the center remaining in sharp focus.

## MECHANICAL EFFECTS

Most mechanical effects are needed only in the presentation of television plays. Although small commercial stations may have little opportunity for doing television drama, colleges and universities are frequently involved in the production of plays.

The techniques for producing mechanical effects are not universally agreed upon. They offer an excellent opportunity for you to experiment and try out new ideas. Your main objectives in special effects experiments must be: (1) simplicity in construction and operation and (2) maximum reliability.

Only the most frequently used special mechanical effects will be discussed here. You can get further information on mechanical effects in advanced television publications and in theatre and film handbooks.

### Rain

Soak the actors' clothes with water. Super the rain from a rain drum (see illustration). Try to avoid real water in the studio, because even a small amount can become a hazard to performers and equipment.

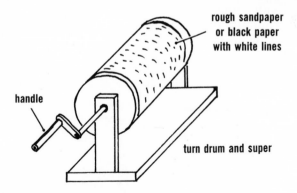

rough sandpaper
or black paper
with white lines

handle

turn drum and super

### Snow

The simplest method is to use snow out of commercial spray cans. Spray liberally over the performers and in front of the camera lens

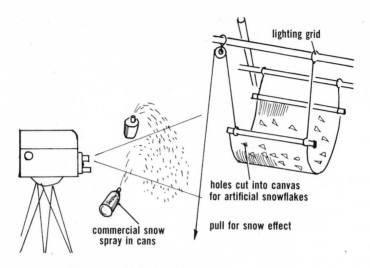

lighting grid

holes cut into canvas
for artificial snowflakes

pull for snow effect

commercial snow
spray in cans

from opposite sides. Another method is to sprinkle plastic snow (white light-weight flakes) on performers from the top of a ladder or from a snow machine rigged to the lighting grid.

### Hail

Sprinkle ice cream salt over the performers. A hail machine, similar to a small snow machine, can be used.

### Fog

Fog is always a problem. The most widely used method is hot steam blown over dry ice, or dry ice placed in hot water. However, there are disadvantages to these methods: (1) You need a great amount of steam and dry ice to produce a small amount of fog. The recommended fog machines as demonstrated in network training films rarely work properly. (2) If you throw dry ice into boiling water,

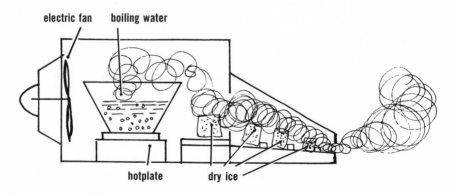

electric fan    boiling water

hotplate        dry ice

the bubbling is frequently picked up by the sensitive boom mike. (3) Dry ice fog is heavier than the warm studio air. The fog will cling stubbornly to the studio floor unless you move it around with an electric fan. Again, you will create audio problems.

Different types of fog filters, which are placed in front of a lens, are available. The fog created with a filter, however, has no movement, and looks more like a poor quality picture than fog.

### Wind

Use two large electric fans. There is rarely any audio problem, because the wind sound effects drown out the fan noise.

### Smoke

Commercial smoke powder lighted in a dish or metal pan is effective. For large smoke clouds, pour mineral oil on a hotplate. If the smoke bothers the performers too much, super a film loop of billowing smoke clouds over the scene.

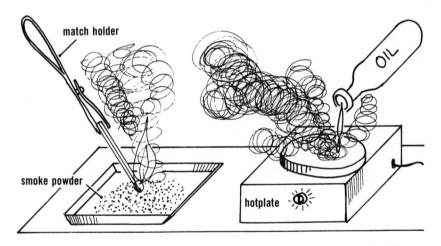

### Fire

Be careful with real fire inside the studio. Sometimes a flickering light is all that is necessary to produce a fire effect. For real flames, light a few blocks of solid fuel in a metal pan and place it directly in front of the camera lens. Have flickering light effects in the background. A film loop with flames supered over a shot of the set is also effective.

For a fireplace fire, buy one of the commercially available artificial fire units for fireplaces. The units work on a light-reflecting principle.

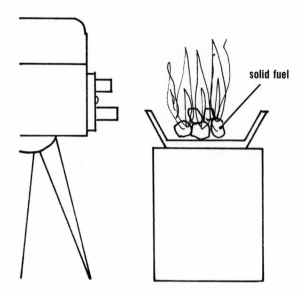

solid fuel

Always have a fire extinguisher handy when you work with real fire in the studio. And watch local fire laws.

For fire reflection, you can staple silk strips onto a batten and project the shadows onto the set.

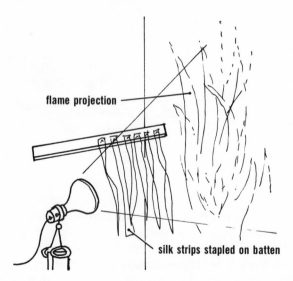

flame projection

silk strips stapled on batten

If you do not have to get too close to the fire effect, you can also glue red, blue, and yellow silk strips around the periphery of a drum and activate the silk strips with a fan inside the drum.

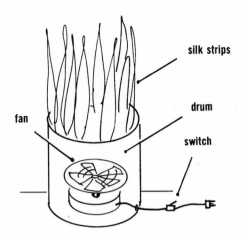

## Lightning

Combine four or six photofloods or two photo flashes and wire the units to a single switch. Lightning should always come from behind the set. Do not forget the audio effect of thunder, if the lightning is supposed to be near.

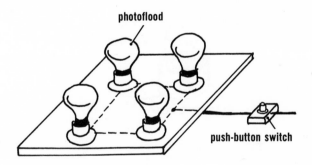

## Gunshots

Live shots have already been discussed in Chapter 3. It is best to use a small-caliber pistol with blanks. Don't shoot too close to a performer; a blank at close range is almost as dangerous as a bullet. When shooting, hold your gun away from the microphone.

### Water reflections of sea and lake

Put strips of twisted transparent tape on the cyclorama. Light it with directional spots.

You can also hide a trough full of water behind the cyclorama and ground row and light it in such a way that the actual water reflections appear on the cyc.

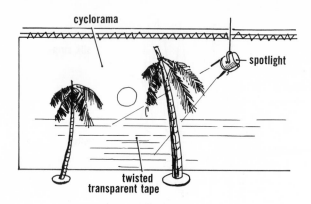

cyclorama
spotlight
twisted
transparent tape

### Explosions

Ignite flashpowder in a metal box with a protection screen over the opening. There are two reliable methods for igniting powder in a flash box. (1) For a small amount of flashpowder, remove the glass from a 3-amp household fuse. Screw into a socket. Pour flashpowder into the fuse and turn on the switch. (2) For a large amount of powder in a flashbox, carefully break a lightbulb so that the fila-

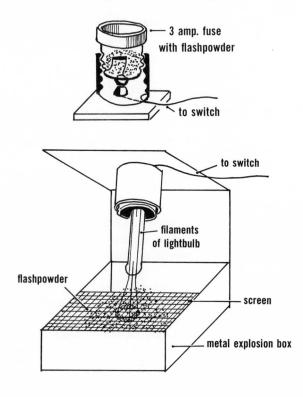

3 amp. fuse
with flashpowder

to switch

to switch

filaments
of lightbulb

flashpowder

screen

metal explosion box

ment wires are not disturbed. Screw the bulb base into a light socket and stick the filaments into flashpowder. Turn on the switch for the explosion. For maximum effect, throw flour into the set to simulate explosion dust.

Remember that extreme caution should be exercised when explosions are necessary.

### Telephone rings

Although telephone rings are usually handled in the audio booth, a mechanical ring machine should be kept handy. With the machine, the rings can be timed more accurately on the studio floor. Also, a

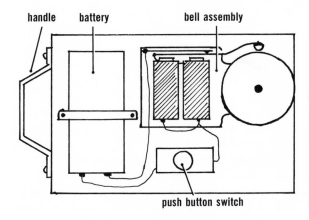

push button switch

mechanical ring keeps the turntables free for other sound effects. A buzzer can be mounted on the same box.

### Breakaway furniture and props

Breakaway furniture is rarely used in small station production. If you need this effect, however, take old prop furniture, cut certain parts diagonally, and hold them together with thin wood pegs. If

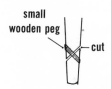

you break this type of furniture on a performer's body, do it with a short quick stroke. Don't try to do it gently; you may break the performer's arm before you break your breakaway props.

Small breakaway props, such as bottles, are manufactured in special effects departments. Thin, brittle plastics are generally used. In case of emergency, use pottery that has not been fired. Paint it for a realistic appearance.

### Black background effects (half image effects)

You need a completely light-absorbing black background (black velour). The performers must be covered with black cloth except for the parts that will appear on the screen. If only the legs of the ballet dancers are to be seen, for example, the dancers must wear black hoods that cover everything but the legs. Careful lighting is essential.

### Substitute effects

When you use special video effects, don't overlook the possibility of substitute effects. In many instances, you can curtail or eliminate complicated video effects if you combine good sound effects with your video presentation. The sound effect of pouring rain, for instance, combined with a close-up of an actor dripping wet may very well make the use of a rain machine unnecessary. To show a beach party sitting on the sand, you don't have to show a rear screen projection of an ocean to establish the proper locale; a good sound effect of ocean surf will do the same job much more easily.

On television, reaction is often more effective than action. An atomic bomb explosion can, for example, be suggested by a close-up shot of an actor's face combined with the familiar sound of that explosion. A showing of the mushroom cloud becomes superfluous. You should use special effects only when they contribute positively to your show. If a special effect is unnecessary or ill-placed, the viewer may get irritated at the presentation without even knowing why.

When you use special effects, make sure you have enough rehearsal time to try them all carefully. A special effect that misfires is worse than no special effect at all.

### SUMMARY

Special effects for television can be divided into three large groups: (1) electronic effects, (2) optical effects, and (3) mechanical effects.

There are nine types of major electronic effects: (1) the superimposition, (2) the sweep reversal, (3) the polarity reversal, (4) beam control effects, (5) electronic stretching and compressing, (6) the wipe, (7) the split screen, (8) electronic matting, and (9) the flexitron.

The category of optical effects includes: (1) rear projection, (2) front projection, (3) mirrors, (4) gobos, (5) special lens prisms, (6) the mat box, (7) effects wheels, and (8) the defocus effect.

Some of the most frequently used mechanical effects include: (1) rain, (2) snow, (3) hail, (4) fog, (5) wind, (6) smoke, (7) fire, (8) lightning, (9) water reflections, (10) explosions, (11) shots, (12) telephone rings, (13) breakaway furniture and props, and (14) black background effects.

All special effects should be sparingly used. Before employing any kind of special effect, ask the following questions: (1) Is the effect really necessary? (2) Does the effect contribute positively to the visual presentation? (3) Can the effect be easily produced? and (4) Is the effect really reliable?

## EXERCISES

1. How can you create a smoke effect in the studio?
2. What are some of the methods of showing rain on television?
3. What is reversed polarity? Why is it important in television production?
4. What is a horizontal sweep reversal? What special effects setup makes this sweep reversal necessary? Why?
5. How can you have a ghost walking around the room seemingly unhampered by the furniture and other physical objects standing in the room?
6. The talent of a weekly children's show would like to introduce an aviation film by pretending to fly in an ancient flying machine. He asks you whether it is possible for you to build such an airplane within a week. What would you suggest?
7. You have a famous pianist on your "Famous Artists" series. He asks you to get a shot from above to show the whole keyboard from time to time. You do not have a camera crane. What would you suggest?
8. You are to show a medium shot of a skier surrounded by snow-covered mountains. It is snowing. How can you accomplish the shot?
9. The choreographer of a contemporary dance group asks you to think of a method for identifying different locales, since the abstract setting cannot be changed for the different dance numbers. What methods would you suggest? Why?

# 8

# Film and Video Tape
# Recording

*academy leader*
*cue 2/3 sec.*

Film and video tape are two major program sources in television operation. A good knowledge of the basic potentials and limitations of these two sources will help you to make sensible and intelligent demands from your film technicians and video tape engineers. Also, you may sometimes be called upon to do minor film and tape editing jobs, unless union regulations stipulate specifically that these editing jobs can be handled only by union personnel. This chapter will give you basic information on (1) film and its utilization in television operation, and basic film editing and splicing techniques; (2) the film chain and its major components; and (3) video tape recording and its major application techniques in small station programming.

Whenever you plan to use film on television, you must familiarize yourself with the following three factors: (1) film subjects, (2) film specifications, and (3) preparation techniques for television transmission.

## FILM SUBJECTS

Different film subjects require slightly different preparation techniques for telecasting. We will divide the films used on television, therefore, into five major categories: (1) motion picture features, (2) television film features, (3) news films, (4) local features, and (5) kinescope recordings.

### Motion Picture Features

Motion picture features include all film originally produced for theatre presentation. All full-length feature films, the shorter travel films, educational features, and industrial features that have not been manufactured for television consumption belong in this category.

### Television Film Features

Television film features (usually syndicated films) include motion pictures specifically produced and shot for television, such as the popular westerns, situation comedies, and dramatic film series.

### Newsfilms

Newsfilms include all films produced for television by national and international news services or by local stations.

Most major news wire services also maintain an extensive film service. If you subscribe to such a service, you will receive daily the latest newsfilms and newsworthy short features.

Locally produced newsfilm is very important in small station operation. Often the newscaster himself will double as film cameraman during his "off hours" and shoot local news events. News departments of larger stations may employ several full-time cameramen and up to twenty or more part-time cameramen—so-called "stringers"—who are located at strategic spots within the coverage area of the station. The stringers shoot everything newsworthy at their location, with the hope that the television station will use the films on the air.

## Local Features

Local features include all films produced locally, such as special interviews, documentaries, and other material for editorial telecasts. Local news photographers usually take care of the local film productions. Sometimes free-lance cameramen are hired for special productions on a local level.

## Kinescope Recordings

Kinescope recordings are television recording devices. In a kinescope recording, the film camera does not shoot live indoor and outdoor scenes; it merely films images that appear on a kinescope screen. A kinescope recording can be made from a video tape recording by feeding the video signal into the tube of the kinescope recorder and then having the kinescope film camera record it as it would a live show. This process is often called "electronic film transfer." Television film programs and commercials, for example, can be video tape recorded by conventional techniques and then transferred to 16mm film for easier distribution and cheaper playback.

The finished kinescope recording (developed and printed) looks like ordinary 16mm film. Frequently, however, you will notice some loss in picture quality.

Although video tape has replaced the kinescope process to a large extent, kinescopes are still manufactured and used. If the television show is distributed to schools, for example, a kinescope is preferred, since it can be played back on any standard 16mm projector.

## FILM SPECIFICATIONS

### Dimensions

Film is labeled according to its width: 8mm, 16mm, 35mm, and the special 65mm and 70mm wide-screen film. In television operation only 16mm and 35mm film are used. Most small television stations work with 16mm film, although some stations have experimented with Super-8mm film, especially for their news shows. So far, however, its relatively poor quality has prevented 8mm film from becoming popular in television production.

Major network outlets and some "O and O" stations (Owned and Operated by one of the major networks) have 35mm film facilities. There are several reasons for using 16mm film more often than the better quality 35mm film: (1) 16mm film produces a picture that is adequate for television transmission; (2) 16mm film equipment is considerably less expensive than comparable 35mm equipment; (3)

the equipment is generally easier to handle than 35mm equipment; (4) fire hazard is reduced and storage is simpler and cheaper.

## Silent and Sound Film

Sixteen millimeter film can be silent (with no accompanying sound printed on the film), or it can be SOF (Sound On Film).

Most locally produced television films are silent films. The advantages of silent film over SOF are numerous. (1) Silent film is easier to shoot; in certain instances the cameraman may handhold his camera and his movements will not be restricted by cables, microphones, and special audio amplifiers. (2) Silent film can be shot entirely out of sequence with no consideration for a matching sound track. (3) Editing and splicing silent film is comparatively easy. (4) Negative silent film can be televised directly, eliminating the necessity of having a positive print made; the television camera can reverse the polarity of the picture portion of the film. (5) Much television film is shot on reversal film, which, when developed, comes out directly as a positive print; you can use it on the air without having to change polarity or to make a special positive print from the negative. (6) Live narration, background music, and sound effects are more flexible when used over silent film.

## SOF

There are two major types of film sound tracks: (1) optical sound and (2) magnetic sound. Many modern film projectors are equipped with optical as well as magnetic sound reproduction mechanisms. The optical sound track, however, is still common on films used in television operation.

The sound track can be put on the film in two different ways. One way is to record pictures and sound simultaneously on the same

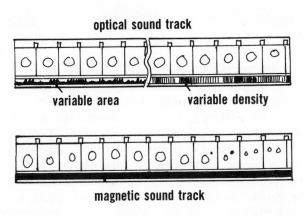

**optical sound track**

variable area                    variable density

**magnetic sound track**

SL = SLIDE

film; this method is called *single-system* sound recording. Another is to record pictures and sound separately and combine them later through printing: this method is known as *double-system* sound recording.

In double-system sound recording, the pictures are recorded on regular 16mm film and the sound on 16mm magnetic film, which is a magnetic tape that looks likes 16mm film. Quarter-inch audio tape can also be used, provided the recorder is synchronized with the film camera. The advantage of this double-system method is that the combined camera-sound unit is portable and relatively simple to operate.

Although the single system has many technical drawbacks (for instance, no high-quality prints can be struck from a single-system recording, and the sound editing is a complicated process), it is economical and faster to handle and, therefore, often preferred in local television film production.

For special interview shows, or on any other occasion where synchronized sound is essential, you must use a sound-on-film setup.

In order to make the single system more flexible, a system of "electronic A-B rolling" has been developed. "A-B" rolling is a term for film editing in which you splice the first, third, and all subsequent odd-numbered shots together for one reel, the A-roll, and all even-numbered shots for another reel, the B-roll. All shots are separated by black leader, which is spliced opposite the shots on the other reel. Both rolls are then printed together.

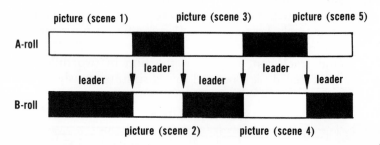

Electronic A-B rolling uses a similar principle. Let us assume that you have to cover the construction of a music center in your city. With your single-system sound camera, you cover the interview with the director of the center in one continuous take. In the interview, however, the interviewee makes many references to particular sections of the partly constructed building. After the interview, you film these sections of the building with a regular 16mm silent film camera. You then prepare a B-roll with the silent footage, making the pictures of the various building parts correspond exactly to the sound track on your SOF footage. The A-roll, containing the SOF interview, is put on one film projector; the B-roll, containing the individual construction scenes, is put on another. Both films are started at the same time. The A-roll with the interview is put on the air first. But whenever the director of the music center is referring to one of the construction sites, you simply switch over to the B-roll film projector, with the explanatory audio still coming from the A-roll. Thus, you have a running commentary from the interviewee, with the appropriate B-roll illustrations continuously paralleling the commentary. In fact, you are "editing" your film on the air, using the original sound track as your editing guide.

### Film Projector Speed

Since television film projectors (24 frames per second) are synchronized with the electronic television scanning system of 30 frames per second (60 "scannings"), most shooting of television film is geared to 24 frames per second. The sychronization is accomplished technically by the system's scanning the first film frame twice, the second three times, the third twice again, and so on. On rare occasions, especially under extremely bad lighting conditions, the cameraman may want to shoot at a slower speed. This he can do only if he is shooting silent film and if the scene he is photographing is rather static; otherwise, sound and pictures will be greatly distorted when the film is projected at the faster speed of 24 frames per second.

### Film Length

Television projectors are equipped with special film reels that can hold up to 4,000 feet of film, good for almost two hours of continuous programming. Twenty-second and one-minute commercial spot announcements are wound on 100-foot reels, the smallest reel generally used on television projectors.

## FILM PREPARATION TECHNIQUES FOR TELEVISION TRANSMISSION

In order to prepare film properly for television transmission, you must familiarize yourself with the following subjects: (1) editing, (2) script, (3) music, and (4) the television film chain.

### Editing

In this section on film editing, we will take a look at some basic problems connected with the preparation of film for television. There is no sense in duplicating specific material that is readily available in many good books on film-making. Enough detail has been included, however, to enable you to perform a simple editing job without having to search elsewhere for basic references. Major editing jobs should be left to the film specialist. An experienced, professional film editor can cut and splice a film in a fraction of the time it would take the inexperienced man.

When you edit a film, you must literally cut the film apart, pick out the sections you like, and glue them together again so that they form a continuous whole. Film editing is like editing the camera pictures during a live telecast. Your guiding principle in both endeavors is the telling of a story, as simply and effectively as possible.

In all film editing, you must first of all have the over-all story in mind. The story line is your main point of reference during all phases of editing. Second, you must cut out all superfluous shots, as visually interesting as they may look to you. Third, you must rearrange the individual shots and scenes so that they relate to and follow out of each other; the story must have a beginning, a middle, and an end.

When you are faced with editing a locally shot 16mm film intended for television use, keep in mind these specific points in the editing procedure:

1. The shorter you cut the individual strips of film (shots), the faster they will flash by on the screen. A rough yardstick measuring length of shot in relation to projection speed may be of help. Thirty-six feet of 16mm film will be projected on the screen for one minute, assuming that the film is projected at the regular speed of 24 frames per second. One foot of film, which is considered a short shot, will be projected for only $1\frac{2}{3}$ seconds. Whether a shot is "short" or "long" depends, of course, on the content of the individual scenes.

2. Make sure that the individual shots intercut. In other words, put into sequence only those shots that will maintain the direction of movement and the general film continuity. Make drastic continuity changes only if such changes are really motivated.

3. If you cannot avoid an apparent jump in continuity (simply because the cameraman did not have his camera running all the time), you can intercut certain stock shots, such as other photographers taking films, close-ups of onlookers, traffic shots, etc.

4. Whenever the cameraman stops his camera and starts it again, the first two frames of each shot will be slightly lighter than the following frames. This brightness change is greatly emphasized by the television camera and, therefore, is clearly visible on the screen. (It usually appears as a brief flash.) You should edit out these starter frames.

5. All "jump cuts" must be eliminated. A jump cut is a succession of two frames that are not perfectly matched. It occurs when the cameraman stops his camera and then continues shooting the same

scene from the same setup. In most cases, his framing will have changed slightly. This change in framing becomes a sudden jump of the picture on the screen. It can be eliminated by intercutting a different shot.

When you edit silent film, you are concerned only with the picture sequence. When you edit single-system SOF, however, you must edit the film according to the audio track rather than the visual. Since the sound precedes the accompanying picture by 26 frames (about 7.8 inches) for 16mm film and by 20 frames (15 inches) for 35mm film, you are bound to lose some picture if you are editing the sound track, or some sound if you are editing the pictures.

### Feature film editing

Television film editors who must re-edit an already beautifully edited full-length feature are faced with a real problem. Often they must shorten the feature film by at least 30 minutes to fit the film into the available time slot; and they must find good spots for inserting numerous commercials. You really should leave such a big job to the editing specialist. But if you are asked for suggestions on this undertaking, you may want to refer to some basic editing rules.

1. Always screen the film carefully. Try to understand the story line, the structure, and the mood of the film as thoroughly as possible.

2. Analyze the film and group it into organic segments, into scenes that are essential to plot and mood of the picture, and into less important, merely decorative parts.

3. Begin the cutting with the least important film segments. Be careful, however, not to cut seemingly decorative shots that are essential to the mood of the story.

4. Insert your commercial only at a logical, organic break in the story line of the film. Don't pick the place for the commercial insert merely by looking for a series of old cue marks on the film, or for a convenient fade-out, or for a place where the audio track permits easy cutting. If you splice your commercial just as the murderer lifts his knife, you run the risk not only of destroying the impact of the entire film but also of annoying your sympathetic viewer and nullifying the message of the commercial.

5. Make sure that the number of commercials spliced into a single feature complies with the programming policy of your station.

### Editing equipment

The basic equipment you will need to prepare film for telecasting consists of the following items: (1) a 16mm film projector (with optical and magnetic sound heads); (2) a pair of rewinds and different-sized reels; (3) an action viewer; (4) an optical and magnetic sound reader; (5) a film splicer; (6) splicing cement or transparent splicing tape; (7) narrow opaque cloth or masking tape for marking strips of film and hooking "out-takes" together; (8) a footage counter and/or a program timer; (9) a 2- to 4-gang synchronizer (optional—used only when double-system film editing is done); (10) opaque film leader and academy leader; and (11) a cue marker.

### Editing procedures for locally produced 16mm film

As soon as you get the processed film from the lab you must get a good description of the event. The cameraman who has shot the film will usually be on hand to tell you the story in detail, or he will· send you a note along with the film, listing the major sequences of his newsreel. When you know the story, you can start the mechanical editing procedures. The major steps are:

1. Rewind the film so that the *beginning* of the film is on the outside of the reel (heads out). Newsfilm usually comes from the lab with the *end* of the film on the outside (tails out).

2. Thread the film into a standard projector and view the whole film.

3. Make notes on the shooting sequence and on the intended editing sequence.

4. Time the film while it is running through the projector. (Because projector speeds vary somewhat, the timing can be only approximate.)

5. View the film again through the action viewer and start the cutting process. (Always cut the film with scissors; tearing may damage too many frames.)

6. When cutting single-system sound film, place the action viewer and the sound reader side by side and run the film through. When you have located the part of the audio track that you want to cut out, mark the exact spot with a soft grease pencil directly at the sound head of the sound reader.

7. After making cuts, label the individual strips of film ("clips") with white tape and hang or clamp them on the editing table. Always put the clips heads up (and with the emulsion side facing the same way) to reduce the chance of splicing the clip upside down into the reel.

8. If you have a complicated editing job to do, keep track of the order of your film clips by listing all the scenes on a paper pad and by marking the clips with corresponding numbers.

9. Link all the out-takes ("outs") together loosely with cloth tape

and wind them on a separate reel. You can then run your out-takes through the action viewer if you decide to use one of the cut-out pieces after all.

10. Put all the film clips in the order in which they are to be spliced and cut them to the desired length.

11. Splice the clips together.

12. Run the film strip through the action viewer and timer.

13. Cue-mark the individual film segments.

## Film Splicing

To learn film splicing, you must practice it. Reading about film splicing will not make you an efficient editor, although it can give you an idea of how to go about it.

Splicing means gluing two strips of film together. Every editor splices film in a slightly different way, depending largely on habit and, occasionally, on time.

There are two different types of film splices: (1) the standard cement splice and (2) the film tape splice.

### Cement splice

A cement splice literally welds two pieces of film together. Before you can make a successful cement splice, you must know the difference between film base and film emulsion. Look at a piece of film. It has a shiny side and a dull side. The shiny side of the film is the film base. The dull side is the film emulsion. The film cement will weld the film base together, but it will not stick to the film emulsion. Therefore, you must either glue both base sides together or (and this occurs much more frequently) scrape the emulsion off an end of one film and cement the base thus exposed to the shiny side of the other film. To do this properly, you must use a film splicer. A film splicer cuts the film, locks it into place for the scraping, and holds it together for the welding. In all film work for television, where the breaking of a splice may create a major programming disaster, you should use only good professional splicing equipment.

The following steps are involved in making a cement splice:

1. Lift the entire left side of your splicer. (On some models you may be able to lift only the upper half of the left side. The standard splicing procedures are the same, however.)

2. Lock one film clip into the right-hand side. The emulsion side (dull side) of the film must be up—that is, facing you.

3. Bring down the left side, thereby cutting the clip on the right.

4. Raise the entire right side.

5. Lock the other film clip into the left side. The emulsion side (dull side) must again be up. Note that in most cases both emulsion sides are up for cement splicing. However, you may sometimes have to splice together two films that have the emulsion on opposite sides. In this case, your left film is base side up (shiny side facing you), while the right film is emulsion side up (dull side facing you). No scraping is then necessary.

6. Bring down the right side, thereby cutting the left film, and raise the entire right side again.

7. Scrape the emulsion off the exposed film (width: $\frac{1}{10}$ of an inch for positive film and $\frac{1}{16}$ of an inch for negative film). If base side is up, no scraping is necessary. Some people prefer to wet the film just before scraping. A dry scrape, however, works equally well.

8. Apply film cement on the scraped side.

9. Bring down the right side and lock.

10. Wait about seven seconds for the cement to dry. A hot splicer (the plates with the sprocket teeth are electrically heated) will cut down the drying time to about three seconds.

11. Unlock and lift the upper halves of both sides. Wipe off excess cement.

12. Remove the film. Give it a short tug to make sure the splice holds.

The main advantage of a cement splice is that the splice is neat and clean, so that it cannot be noticed when the film is projected. Diagonal splices, although somewhat stronger than straight splices, are not generally used by television film editors. The splices sometimes catch in the projectors, and may even show up on the monitor screen. Another advantage of the cement splice is that it prevents you from losing too many frames during editing. And a cement-spliced film can be run through various film cleaners without affecting the splice in the least.

There are also disadvantages to cement splicing in television film operation. (1) The cement splice takes time. The time element becomes especially important when, for example, a newsfilm has to be edited 15 minutes before air time. (2) If you scrape into the film base or if you leave some emulsion on the scraped surface, the splice will be considerably weakened; it may break on the air. (3) The only sure way to tell whether a cement splice will hold is to run the film through the projector.

### Film tape splice

In a tape splice, you overlap the two pieces of film and hold them together with two pieces of translucent adhesive tape. There are two

steps 6 and 7 (scraping)

step 11

steps 3, 4, 5 (cutting)

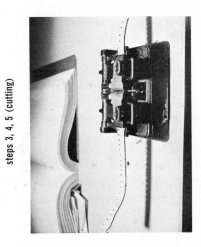

steps 9 and 10

splicing steps 1 and 2 (cutting)

step 8 (application of film cement)

different film tapes on the market: (1) a special film tape with per-forated edges that fit the sprocket holes of the film and (2) a simple straight-edged film tape (polyester transparent film tape) just wide enough to cover the film up to the sprocket holes.

The tape-splicing procedure is fairly simple:

1. Lift the entire right side of the splicer.
2. Lock the film into the left side.
3. Bring down the right side to cut the left film.
4. Lift the entire left side.
5. Lock the film into the right side.
6. Bring down the left side to cut the right film.
7. Open both upper halves of the splicer. The left film should now be lapped over the right film. This acts as an additional safety factor when the splice runs through the projector.
8. Hold both film clips with the sprocket teeth of the splicer.
9. Tear off a small piece (¾ inch maximum length) of splicing tape and press on the film overlap. Ideally, the tape should not cover more than about 1 or 1½ frames on either side of the overlap. A longer tape is hard to put on straight, and the splice is more notice-able when the film is projected.
10. Turn the spliced film over and place an additional piece of tape on the other side of the splice to give it extra strength.
11. Make sure you have placed both tapes accurately over the film. If portions of the splicing tape extend over the side of the film or partially cover a sprocket hole, the splice is bad and must be done again.

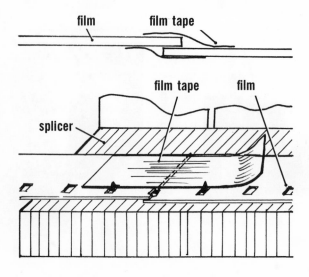

There are three main advantages to tape splicing in local television operation. (1) The splice is fast; no emulsion scraping is necessary. (2) Since you don't have to scrape the film, it does not matter whether emulsion or base sides are up. (Proper alignment of images must still be considered, however.) (3) The splice is dependable. You can see immediately whether the splice is good or bad.

There are disadvantages, too. (1) If the tape overlaps the film edge, the splice is apt to tear in the projector gate. (2) If the splice tape is too long, it may collect dust and show up on the television screen. (3) It is not a neat splice. No prints can be made from a tape-spliced negative, for instance. (4) The film cannot be run through a film cleaner. The cleaner fluid dissolves the tape adhesive and smears it over the film. As a result, the film will be dirtier than before and the splices will not hold.

These disadvantages of tape splicing seem grave enough to discourage most television film departments from using splicing tape instead of the somewhat more involved splicing cement.

### Academy leader

After you have edited all the individual newsfilms, you must put them (including the film commercials, if there are any) on one large reel. This operation is sometimes called "film make-up," a rather ambiguous term that can easily be confused with face make-up for motion pictures.

To allow for accurate cuing, a special film leader has to be spliced in front of every film. The academy leader, as it is called, consists of a strip of film showing numbers from 8 to 3 at equal one-second intervals and a dial rotating around the academy leader numbers at each second. (The old academy leader shows numbers from 11 to 3—see page 308.)

In putting your newsreel together, you must first of all splice an academy leader to the beginning of the first clip. The higher number (8) marks the beginning of the academy leader, and the lower number with an additional strip of black leader indicates the end of the cuing strip. The lower number with the black strip must always be closest to the beginning of the film to be cued.

Two films that will follow each other without interruptions can, of course, be spliced directly together. But if you plan to cut to the newscaster between films, you must place an academy leader between the preceding and following film. The leader permits the engineer to stop the projector and cue up the next film so that it can be rolled on your signal.

Always place a 3-foot opaque leader in front of the first academy

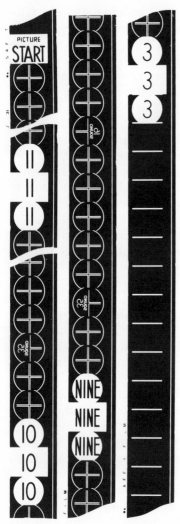

Old academy leader

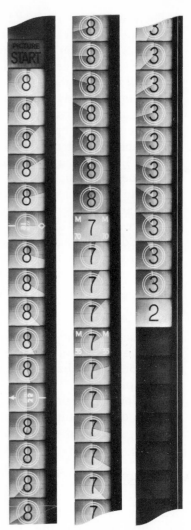

New academy leader

leader and a 2-foot opaque leader at the end of the last film on the reel. The front leader (sometimes called "head leader") will aid the engineer in threading the film into the television film projector. The end leader (sometimes called "tail leader") will keep the television picture in black for a few seconds, which will permit the engineer to stop the film and make a smooth switchover to the next program source. You should mark all head and tail leaders with a special inking pen to identify the program, the date and time of airing, and whether the leader is "heads" or "tails."

opaque leader          academy                          newsfilm

academy                     newsfilm                        academy

newsfilm                    academy                  film commercial

academy                     newsfilm                     opaque leader

*Academy leader cuing procedure.* Although most television film projectors gain full sound speed within one-third of a second, television films, especially when in color, are started at least four seconds ahead of the first frame.

When you roll the film, you will immediately see the academy leader flash by on your monitor screen at one-second intervals (for 16mm film). The older academy leader, which had numbers from 11 to 3, has intervals of slightly less than one second. As soon as the first frame of the actual film appears, the T.D. (Technical Director, who is generally doing the switching) will put the film on the air. The last two numbers (2 and 1) on the academy leader are omitted (the leader is black instead) so that you won't show the numbers on the air in case the film is punched up (put on the air) just before the film picture appears.

A 4-start (four-second start) is used in most television operations. It guarantees a stable picture when you come up on the first frame, and it also gives the performer the needed time to wind up his commentary just before the film appears on the screen. This time is especially important when he introduces a film commercial (SOF). If the performer is still laboring over the film introduction when the film appears on the preview monitor, you must switch to the film (and clip the performer's audio) if you do not want to lose part of the commercial because of "up-cutting" (switching to the commercial late). With a 4-start, the performer has more time to finish his introduction before the film comes up. An academy leader countdown makes the transition from live commentary to SOF very smooth. The academy leader countdown means that you count down the numbers of the academy leader as they flash by on the monitor. At the same time, the floor manager relays your countdown to the performer by means of finger signals (starting at number four). As soon as the performer sees the "take film" signal, he will stop talking: the film audio will take over.

The whole film integration from roll cue to the on-the-air picture generally happens in the following sequence:

1. The film engineer cues up the film on academy leader number 4.
2. The director signals to the T.D.: "Roll film."
3. The T.D. rolls the film. The floor manager gives the performer

a roll-film cue by holding his left hand in front of his face and moving his right hand in a cranking motion.

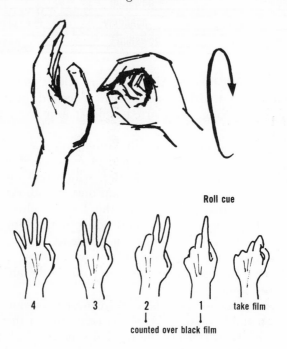

**Roll cue**

4        3        2        1        take film

counted over black film

4. The director gives the academy leader countdown aloud over the intercommunication system: "4—3—2—1—take film" (or: "dissolve to film"). If you work with more than one film island (see page 313), you must designate the number of the island, such as "Take film 2," or simply, "Take F-2."

5. At count four, the floor manager starts his finger signals.

6. The performer is winding up his film introduction.

7. The T.D. switches the film on the air.

8. The audio man brings up the audio track and kills the performer's microphone. The performer must have finished talking or he will be upcut.

Other methods of film cuing are the following:

1. The director has the roll cue pre-timed so that the film will come up precisely at the end of the performer's narration. As soon as the performer sees the red tally lights on the live camera go out, he will know that the film has been switched on the air.

2. The performer may watch a special monitor that shows the academy leader on the monitor screen.

3. Black leader is inserted instead of the academy leader and the film is rolled with a very fast start immediately after the performer's introduction. With this method, however, it is hard to avoid a slight pause between the performer's comments and the SOF.

### Timing

All film must be accurately timed to assure smooth television programming. You can run your film through either a footage counter, which gives the length of the film in feet, or a program timer, which shows a reading in minutes and seconds. The program timer is generally more convenient for your purposes, since it eliminates the use of a chart to convert feet into minutes and seconds. Make sure to time the film from the first frame to the last, but don't count the academy or opaque leaders.

### Cue marking

Although the director checks the film time with his stop-watch, he needs additional cue marks on the film to tell him when the film comes to its end. There are often two cue marks on a film. The first is meant as a warning signal that the film is running out; the second is the signal for the switchover to the next program source. The first cue mark appears as a white dot in the upper right-hand corner of the monitor screen, anywhere from four to two seconds before the end of the film. The second cue mark flashes on the screen in the same place about one to one-half second before the end of the film. (How far the cue marks are placed into the film depends entirely on station practice. The second cue mark, however, should be as close to the end of the film as possible, so that no film is lost through the changeover to another program source.)

If you run SOF silent for awhile and then want to bring up the audio track on cue, a white or black dot in the lower right-hand corner of the monitor screen will indicate the beginning of the sound.

For cue marking you must use a special cue marker. There are several types available, some of which look like a train conductor's ticket puncher. Most cue markers perforate four frames of the film with round or triangular holes. It is best to start by placing the last cue mark about four inches from the end of the film. The first cue mark is then placed ahead of the second, at a distance depending entirely on the time span desired between cues (usually four seconds).

The last thing for you to do now is to run the entire film reel through the action viewer (or, better, if time permits, through the projector) to make sure that all the films and academy leaders are right side up and that all films are properly cue-marked.

## Script

Most film scripts written for local stations have no particular format. They consist of double-spaced typewritten commentary that matches the lengths of the individual film scenes and consequently the over-all length of the film. More complicated films, however, must have an indication of each scene's action so that the performer can accurately gear his narration to the scenes as they appear on the film.

Most newsfilms from major news services come supplied with scripts of standard format, indicating the picture sequence, the running film footage, and the running film time. Even if the performer is forced to read the copy blind—that is, if he has no chance to check his narration by looking at the monitor, he can pretty well match his narration to the film simply by watching the elapsed time.

```
Traffic Safety
HX 1773 -- shot 12/30
(42 ft., 1:10)

          Running        Ft        Secs
                         (1)        (2)            (Dateline Chicago)

                 (1.       6          10        Two shots traffic, 10 secs
Traffic on the nation's streets and highways is expected to
be heavy during the coming New

                 (2.       8          13        CU shot through window, 3)
Year's holiday and the National Safety Council

                 (3.      12          20        Two shots traffic, 7)
says it fears that as many as 320 persons may die in the
seventy-eight hour weekend. Nearly five

                 (4.      20          33        Several shots Paul Jones
                                                and wrecked cars, 13)
hundred persons lost their lives in traffic mishaps during
the recent Christmas holiday. Paul Jones, spokesman for the
National Safety Council, examines wrecked cars and has these
words of caution.

                 (5.      42         1:10       SOF Jones, 37)

                 He says -- We show you this car as a reminder to you
                 to take extra care in driving during the New Year's
                 holiday. Don't drive if you drink, hold down your
                 speed. Be careful of the other driver, he may have
                 been celebrating and have (End Cue) "a happy and
                 safe New Year").

                              (END)
```

## Music

Background music and sound effects are frequently used over silent film footage. Every piece of background music you select must, of course, match the mood and action of the film story. Sound effects, if used properly, add greatly to the realism of the film. You may find it helpful to select different types of background music and keep a list of these selections so that you have them readily available when you are too pressed for time to make a careful selection. This method of selecting music, however, should not become standard practice. It is sometimes better to have no background music than ill-matching sound. Nevertheless, if the selected "standby pieces" are neutral enough to fit any number of films within one general mood, they may come in handy in an emergency. Suggested list of selections (according to music mood): (1) light and spirited (including a typical band number for sports and parades), (2) solemn and religious, (3) romantic, (4) majestic, (5) dramatic, and (6) mysterious.

## The Television Film Chain or Film Island

The basic television film chain or film island consists of at least one film projector, a slide projector, a multiplexer, and a television film camera. A second film projector may also be part of the film chain. All the components of the film chain are generally operated and serviced by the engineering staff. Production people, however, must know at least the basic operation principles of the chain if they want to use it to its full potential in television programming.

### Film projector

The television film projector is especially designed so that the film speed of 24 frames per second will correspond to the 30 frames of the television picture. If a film projector is not synchronized with the television system, you will detect a slight flutter in the television monitor and, sometimes, black shutter bars moving up and down the screen. Most film projectors can accommodate large 20-inch (4,000-foot) reels (some even 5,000-foot reels), which allow a continuous projection of almost two hours of film programs. To maintain proper tension on the film (or video tape), make sure that your take-up reel is the same size as your supply reel.

Film projectors usually have a number of devices that will prove useful to you. (1) Most projectors can show a single film frame for extended periods of time without danger of burning the film. By this means you can preview the first frame of an upcoming film or project the academy leader at full light level. (2) All television film projectors have a pickup device for optical and magnetic sound. (3) The projection lamp and the sound-exciter lamp change automatically if they happen to fail during the film projection. (4) The threading mechanism is usually kept quite simple so that, in case of emergency, the film can be threaded within seconds. (5) Projectors can bring film up to speed within one-third of a second, although longer starts are still more prevalent. (6) All film projectors have a remote starting and stopping mechanism, and some of the more complex projectors have automatic cuing systems. A film can be programmed in advance to stop and cue itself for the next segment in as many places as is desired. This system is activated by small pieces of special tape that you attach to the film at the specific cuing points.

Most film islands have two film projectors to ensure maximum continuity of programming. As soon as the film of the first projector has run out, the second projector can be started and switched on the air. Sometimes you may find it convenient to have all the programming film on one projector and all the commercial film spots on the other projector. This method enables you to eliminate certain programming film (by running it through without switching it on the air) without losing the film commercials.

RCA TP-66 film projector

### Slide projector

Transparency slide projectors have the slides arranged on either dual drums or one large carrousel drum. The more common dual drums generally have a slide capacity of 36 slides (18 each). Dual drum projectors permit reloading or changing of slides while the machine is in operation. Most new drum slide projectors are designed for forward and reverse action. Some drums are equipped with a random selection device, making it possible to have any slide punched up without waiting for the drum to rotate until the desired slide finally appears in the gate. A dual lamp slide assembly, which per-

slide holders
(36 slides)

lens

RCA TP-7A dual drum slide projector

Loading the TP-7A

mits a quick exchange of defect lamps, is also built into the slide projectors.

### Telop projector

The television optical projector (which was discussed in Chapter 5) can project opaque material into the television film camera. The telop projector usually has four projection stages or ports, at which opaque material is placed for projection. The 4 × 5 telop cards are put into long telop strips, which can hold five telops each. Telops can be lap-dissolved with each other, or even superimposed, as long as they are placed into different ports. Like any other type of opaque projector, the telop machine can project small three-dimensional objects. Vertical crawls and horizontal teletype or ticker-tape news strips can also be projected through attachments that fit one of three telop ports.

### Multiplexer

A multiplexer enables the monochrome or color television film camera to receive images from several projection sources. Through a special arrangement of half-silvered mirrors or prisms, a normal multi-

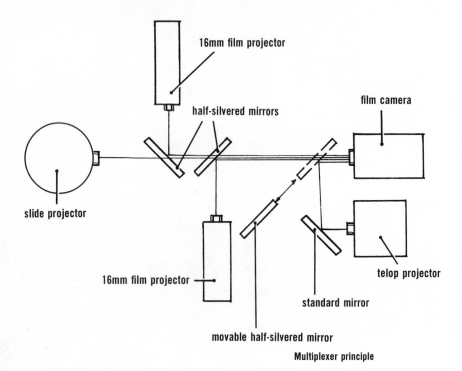

Multiplexer principle

plexer can direct signals from two 16mm film projectors, a dual drum slide projector, and a telop machine or a second slide projector into a single film camera. Since the alignment of all these video sources in relation to the television camera is rather critical, the multiplexer must be sturdy and relatively insensitive to vibrations. Some multiplexers have provisions for a second film camera so that you can preview the image from the upcoming projector while the signal from another projector is still on the air. In this two-camera system, the combination of one color and one monochrome camera is often preferred.

### The vidicon film camera

The vidicon film camera is considerably smaller than the image-orthicon or vidicon studio cameras. This stationary film camera can handle a great gray-scale contrast range without the aid of special shading controls. The vidicon film camera is also insensitive to burn-ins—an advantage that is especially important if you want to hold a super slide on the air for a period of time.

The color film camera is very similar in its design to the color

RCA TK-22 monochrome vidicon film camera

studio camera. The color film camera contains three chrominance channels (for the red, blue, and green signals) and one luminance channel. Vidicon tubes are generally used for all four channels.

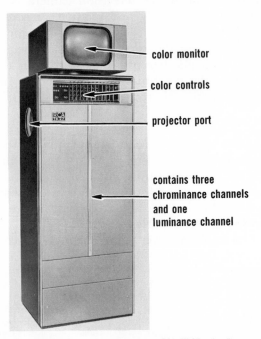

color monitor

color controls

projector port

contains three chrominance channels and one luminance channel

RCA TK-27 color film camera

Since a complete film island takes up a considerable amount of space, constant efforts are made by manufacturers to reduce the size of projection equipment and to combine the instruments in one unit. Whatever the arrangement may be, however, the basic principle of multiplexing various video sources into one or two television cameras remains the same.

You will find that there is a strong trend even in small television stations to automate the projection equipment. A computer is programmed with the necessary film, slide, and video tape start and stop cues for the various program sections, especially the station breaks. At the appropriate time, the computer activates the various video sources of the film islands and the video tape recorder. In case of emergency, the system can be quickly changed over to manual control. This initially very expensive automation equipment can reduce switching errors and save time, manpower, and ultimately money.

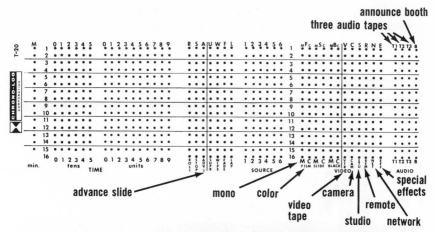

Computer card for automated station breaks.
Pegs are placed into desired dots, activating the
specific mechanisms.

## VIDEO TAPE RECORDING

Video tape recording (VTR) is quite similar to the audio tape recording process. The electronic impulses of television pictures and sound are recorded on a special magnetic video tape, which can be played back later, converting the recorded signals into picture and sound. There are two basic systems of video tape recording: (1) the transverse scanning process, and (2) the helical, or slant-track, recording process.

### Transverse Scanning Process

In the transverse scanning process, four tiny rotating (14,400 rpm) recording heads put the video signal on a two-inch-wide tape, which moves past the recording heads at speeds of either 7½ inches per second (ips) or 15 ips. In this "quad-head" (four recording heads) process, 15 ips is the speed normally used for high-quality broadcast recordings.

The "quad-head" video tape recorder puts four different tracks on the two-inch video tape: (1) the video track (the television pictures), (2) the audio track (the sound), (3) the control track, consisting of ½-inch spaced blips, called the sync pulse, and (4) the cue track, which is, in effect, a second audio track.

The control track is essential for editing and will be discussed in more detail later in this chapter. The cue track can be used for special audio information, such as the recording of a director's PL (private line) conversation to his production crew.

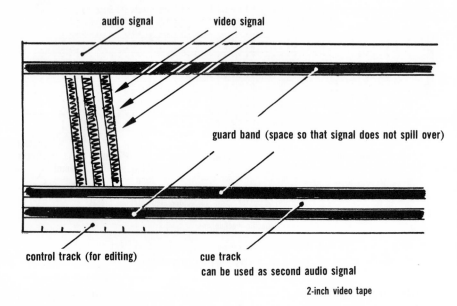

audio signal          video signal

guard band (space so that signal does not spill over)

control track (for editing)          cue track
can be used as second audio signal

2-inch video tape

You can have any part of the video or audio track erased, either separately or together. Often, the video information is recorded and edited first, with the audio track (such as a running commentary) superimposed afterward, as is done with sound dubbing in film operations.

### Helical or Slant-Track Scanning Process

In the helical or slant-track recording process, two large rotating heads put the video information on the tape in a diagonal, rather than transverse, manner. The audio track is usually at the top edge of the tape, with the control track running along the bottom edge of the tape. Some helical scanning recorders also put on a cue track. Because the diagonal arrangement of the video signal occupies a relatively large tape area, the tape speed as well as the tape width can be considerably reduced. Most helical scanning tape recorders use 1-inch tapes, but there are also models that use 2-inch, ½-inch, and even ¼-inch video tape.

Unfortunately, the helical scanning system has some serious drawbacks when compared with the transverse scanning system. (1) The pictures lack quality and electronic stability; generally, they do not fulfill broadcast quality requirements. (2) The tapes made by various

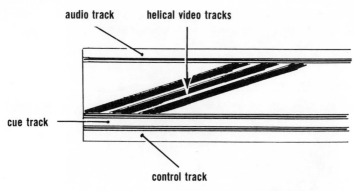

1-inch video tape for helical scanning

machines are not interchangeable and compatible. A tape that was recorded on one type of helical scanning recorder often cannot be played back on another, though similar, machine. (3) Most helical scanning models do not permit the dubbing of pictures and sound onto the larger 2-inch "quad-head" machines. (4) Mechanical editing (the physical cutting and splicing) of the helically scanned tape is, for all practical purposes, impossible. Electronic editing can be done, but it is much more time-consuming than electronic editing of tapes produced by the transverse scanning process.

## Types of Video Tape Recorders

The two distinct scanning systems provide a convenient way to group the various models of the more common video tape recorders. The recorders that use a 2-inch tape, have four recording heads, and employ the transverse scanning system can be called "broadcast video tape recorders," since these recorders are used primarily in the broadcast industry. The slant-track recorders, normally used for closed-circuit operations, can be called "closed-circuit video tape recorders."

### Broadcast video tape recorders

The two major manufacturers of broadcast video tape recorders are the Ampex Corporation and RCA. Both companies manufacture several models of "quad-head" recorders, ranging from compact, portable machines to highly complex color recorders.

The most common Ampex models are (1) the old VR-1000, which is no longer manufactured, (2) the VR-1100 and VR-1200, which are the standard monochrome recorders, (3) the suitcase-sized, battery-powered monochrome and color recorder VR-6000, and (4) the large, highly complex color recorder VR-2000-B (see pages 322–323).

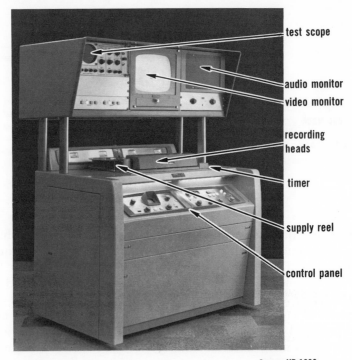

test scope

audio monitor
video monitor

recording
heads

timer

supply reel

control panel

**Ampex VR-1000**

The most common RCA models are (1) the compact TR-4, which has the tape deck arranged vertically, (2) the portable table model TR-5, (3) the larger TR-22 model, which is normally used for high-quality monochrome recordings, and (4) the large and complex TR-70 color recorder (see pages 324–325).

Both the Ampex VR-1100 and the RCA TR-22 can be converted for color recordings.

The only slant-track recorder used for broadcast purposes is the Sony PV-120 U. It uses a 2-inch tape, at a slow speed of 4½ ips, and has a variable speed control that allows slow motion and stop motion (allowing stops on individual frames for picture examination) during playback (see page 326).

### Closed-circuit video tape recorders

There is a great variety of closed-circuit video tape recorders available, ranging from high-quality 2-inch recorders to low-quality ¼-inch recorders, the latter designed primarily for home use. Among the many models, you will find these Ampex and Sony models very popu-

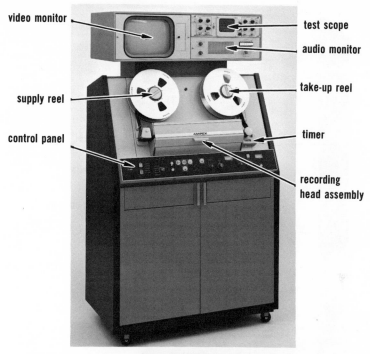

video monitor

test scope

audio monitor

supply reel

take-up reel

control panel

timer

recording
head assembly

Ampex VR-1200 (color and monochrome recorder,
similar to the 1100 model)

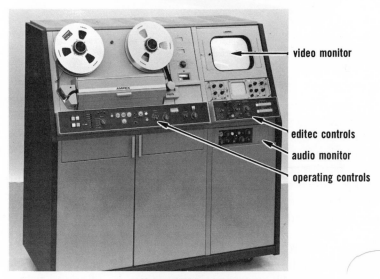

video monitor

editec controls

audio monitor

operating controls

Ampex 2000-B color video tape recorder (high-
quality recorder)

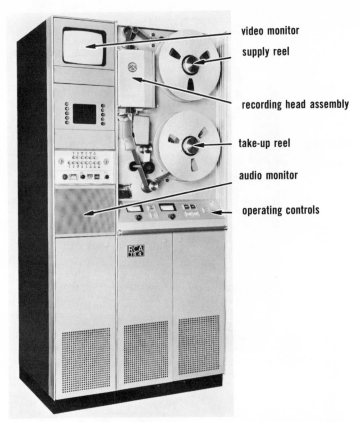

video monitor

supply reel

recording head assembly

take-up reel

audio monitor

operating controls

RCA TR-4 monochrome and color video tape recorder

lar: (1) the Ampex VR-660, (2) the Ampex 7000, and (3) the Sony EV-200 (see pages 326–327).

*The VR-660* uses a 2-inch tape, has two audio tracks, and can record and play back up to five hours of continuous program material. It is also equipped for stop-motion.

*The VR-7800* is a 1-inch tape recorder with features similar to those of the 660 but with a lower-quality picture reproduction. The 7800 is strictly a closed-circuit machine for simple observation purposes only.

The *Sony EV-200* uses 1-inch tape. This very dependable, high-quality recorder has two audio tracks and facilities for slow motion and stop motion. All important controls can be operated from a remote position.

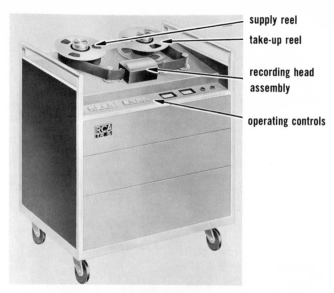

supply reel

take-up reel

recording head assembly

operating controls

RCA TR-5 mobile video tape recorder for mono-chrome and color

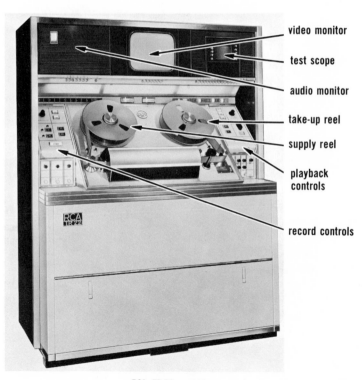

video monitor

test scope

audio monitor

take-up reel

supply reel

playback controls

record controls

RCA TR-22 monochrome and color video tape recorder (high-quality recorder)

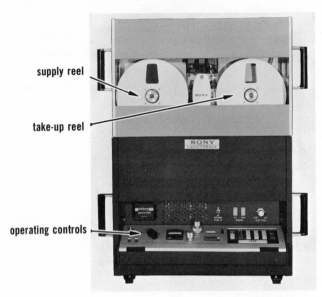

Sony PV-120U video tape recorder

Ampex VR-660 closed circuit 2-inch-tape video tape recorder

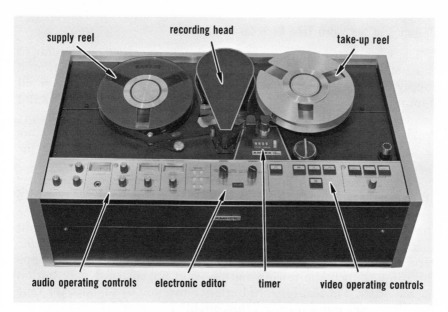

supply reel     recording head     take-up reel

audio operating controls    electronic editor    timer    video operating controls

Ampex VR-7800 monochrome and color 1-inch-
tape video tape recorder

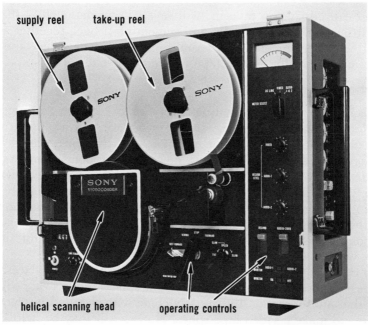

supply reel     take-up reel

helical scanning head     operating controls

Sony EV-200

## Operation of the Video Tape Recorder

The operation techniques of a video tape recorder are similar to those of a standard audio tape recorder. You thread the tape from a supply reel (which can be any size: a large 94-minute reel or a small 5-minute reel) across the erase head, the video head, the audio and cue track heads, to the take-up reel. On most recorders, the supply reel is on the left and the take-up reel on the right side of the machine; on the vertical RCA models, the supply reel is at the top and the take-up reel at the bottom of the machine.

There are five major operating buttons on the video tape recorder: (1) record, (2) stop, (3) rewind, (4) fast forward, and (5) play. To record a program, simply press the record button. This will start the machine and record at the same time (some stations prefer to split this operation into a separate start and record mechanism). When the recording is completed, press the stop button. To play back the tape recording, punch the rewind button, stop button, and play button in that order. The fast-forward button allows you to advance the tape quickly to pick out a program that might be located halfway into the reel. You can work all these buttons from remote control, if you wish.

## Video Tape Editing

You can edit video tape in two ways: (1) mechanically—that is, by cutting the tape physically and cementing it back together again —and (2) electronically—by assembling the various video tape segments electronically on one tape without ever cutting the tape.

### Mechanical editing

Mechanical video tape editing is very much like film editing. First you look at the various tape sections you want to assemble; then you cut the tape and splice the sections together again in the desired new order. Video tape splicing is, however, considerably more complicated than film splicing. You cannot see the individual frames while you are doing the cutting, and you have to be extremely precise in judging just where to cut the tape. If you don't cut the tape exactly at the marks provided by the control track, you will cause a temporary "loss of sync," causing the pictures to tear or roll at the point where they are joined.

To cut and splice the video tape at exactly the right places, you will need a special video tape splicer. The splicer models vary slightly in design and operation but usually come with detailed instructions on how to make a video tape splice. However, it may be helpful for you to be acquainted with some principal editing procedures.

1. Rough-cut the tape only with scissors or a razor blade. If you try to tear it, you will stretch the tape and ruin the recording.

2. In order to avoid loss of sync (picture roll at the splice), join the tapes only between the scanning frames. These areas are clearly marked by tiny spikes every ¼ inch along the bottom of the tape; you can make the spikes visible by applying a special iron-particle solution (sometimes called Edivue solution).

3. The video tape splicer will enable you to overlap and cut the tape ends exactly at the sync or edit marks on the control track. A splicing tape at the shiny (nonmagnetic) side of the tape holds the tape sections firmly together.

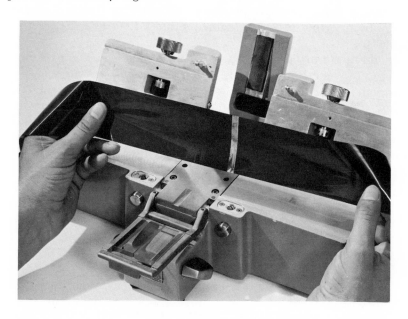

When splicing video tape, remember that the audio track leads the video track by about 9½ inches. The picture splicing, however, does not seriously interfere with the audio synchronization, since the horizontal tape speed (15 ips) cuts the time difference of sound and picture to about half a second. Even in tight dialogue, you will usually find a half-second pause that allows you to make the necessary splice.

There are three major disadvantages to mechanical splicing. (1) It is quite time consuming. (2) It requires you to cut a rather expensive tape apart; once the tape is spliced, its life and use are limited. (3) The splices may eventually loosen and possibly damage the delicate video tape heads. Electronic editing has, therefore, replaced mechanical editing to a great extent.

### Electronic editing

With electronic editing, you can insert or add video and audio information without cutting the tape. An "electronic editor" seeks out the sync pulses on the control track at the points that you have selected for editing and puts the new material on the tape exactly where you want it without the danger of picture roll due to inaccurate cutting. Since electronic editing is done on the video tape machine and not on the splicing block, you will need a second tape machine in order to combine the tape segments.

You can edit electronically in two basic ways: (1) by combining consecutive or nonconsecutive program segments (the "assemble mode") or (2) by inserting program segments into a longer tape (the "insert mode").

In the assemble mode, you can simply add scene B to scene A, scene C to scene B, and so on, or you can assemble your scenes in a "random" order; for example, you may add scene D to scene A and follow them with scenes W and B. In the insert mode, you insert short scenes in an existing tape; for example, you may want to do a short segment over again after you have already recorded the whole program.

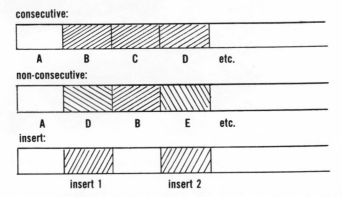

*Insert mode.* When your electronic editor is switched to the *insert* mode, you can perform both "insert" and "assemble" functions. However, to assemble while switched to the insert mode, you must first run the blank tape upon which you expect to assemble through the video tape recorder in order to prerecord the necessary sync pulses on the control track. Only then can you feed the various program segments onto the tape and add them in the desired order. The master control track, which will not be erased when the new segments are recorded, will guide the proper electronic "splicing."

*Assemble mode.* When you edit in the assemble mode, you do not have to prerecord the control track. When you record a new segment next to the old one, the tape will be totally erased and the new segment supplied with its own control track. Of course, in this assemble mode the inserting of the new material is extremely difficult. In fact, many video tape engineers find the insert mode easier to work with since it is electronically less critical and produces more stable transitions.

*Automatic editing systems.* Also available are complex automatic editing systems, such as the Ampex Editec, which work like small computers. Automatic editors will store many types of editing information, such as the exact spot of the splice and the exact length of the

Ampex electronic editing panel

Editec

segment. Such editing computers will even allow frame-by-frame edit-ing, so that you can actually do animation on video tape.

As desirable as these expensive automatic systems may be, they are not really essential in small station operations unless a great deal of complex editing must be performed. The electronic editor, however, is extremely useful, especially if you have two video tape recorders available.

### Video Tape Cuing Devices

The split-second timing that is required in all phases of television operation necessitates accurate video tape cuing facilities. There are three major types of video tape cuing devices: (1) the beeper system, (2) the video cue leader, and (3) the tape timer.

#### Beeper system

If you are set up for a video tape recording, the first thing you will record on the tape is an identification slate. The program identifica-tion slate is a small blackboard in aspect ratio, indicating the title of the show, the date of the recording, the date of the playback, the cut number, and the length of the recording.

| TITLE: | " CREATIVE MAN " |
|---|---|
| CUT: | 3 |
| RECORD: | JULY 15 |
| PLAY: | JULY 19 |
| LENGTH: | 29 : 30 |
| | DO NOT ERASE ! PLS HOLD AFTER PLAYBACK |

You must leave the slate up long enough so that it can be properly read. Some directors have the habit of briefly flashing the slate on the screen before taking the picture to black. The tape engineer, who later must identify this program by the slate as recorded on the tape, will have a hard time reading all the information given on the slate. Much confusion has been caused by not leaving the slate up long enough for proper recording. The simplest way to determine how long a slate should be kept up is to read off the monitor everything that is written on the slate. This will guarantee positive identification of the program.

As soon as you "take the slate to black," call for the beeper. The audio engineer will then throw the beeper switch, which puts a series of eight low-frequency beeps, exactly one second apart, on the audio track of the video tape. (The last two seconds before the recording remain silent; this is a safety cushion for the following program audio, similar to the black strip of film in the academy leader.)

This recorded beeper at the beginning of the taped program will now enable the tape engineer to locate the program at any point in the middle of the reel by fast-forwarding the playback. All he must do is listen to the beeps, which, because of the accelerated tape speed, will be a series of high-pitched tones. He can now cue up the tape on the first beep, which means that the picture will appear ten seconds after the start of the playback.

### The video cue leader

Since you cannot see the tape roll in your preview monitor with the beeper system, a number system was developed that is similar to the academy leader of the television film. When the tape is rolling and recording, you can put one of the studio cameras on a leader box, which projects numbers on its illuminated glass face. The numbers (similar to the dotted numbers seen on public buildings that indicate time and temperature) run from 10 to 3 in one-second intervals. The box (similar to the film leader) goes automatically to black two sec-

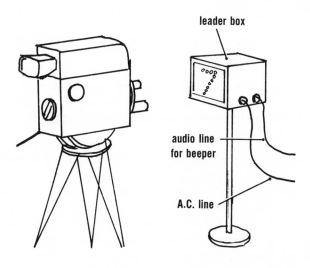

leader box

audio line
for beeper

A.C. line

onds before the beginning of the programming pictures. The numbers are all geared to the audio beeps.

When the tape is played back, you can see the numbers flash by on your preview monitor, exactly like the academy film leader. This permits you to give a tape leader countdown to the performer, who can then gear his introduction precisely to the beginning of the recorded picture portion.

Putting on this type of video leader has proved quite cumbersome, however, and the video cue leader has never gained wide acceptance in television production.

### The tape timer

The most accurate video tape cuing device, preferred by most engineers and directors, is the tape timer. This timer, which is located close to the take-up reel, indicates the elapsed time of the tape recorded program. If you prefer a ten-second cue, for example, the tape engineer will locate the first picture (frame) of the recorded program and then wind the tape back ten seconds. Seven- and six-starts for color and five- and four-starts for monochrome are generally employed, although you can bring the tape up to full speed on a two-second fast start. Quite frequently, however, a fast start does not allow the electronics to settle properly and the first picture may appear slightly out of adjustment. Usually, the video tape operator will tell you when the video tape recorder has reached the proper "speed" —that is, when the recorder is ready to accept pictures without any distortion. All three cuing devices are sometimes used together to assure accurate tape integration and, therefore, smooth program continuity.

## USE OF VIDEO TAPE RECORDING IN TELEVISION PRODUCTION

A great number of small television stations are using at least one video tape recorder, despite high purchasing cost. Most stations operate two or more recorders. A few very important technical factors make the video tape recorder one of the most valuable production devices yet developed.

1. The video tape machine can record monochrome as well as color programs.

2. The recorded programs can be played back immediately. No time-consuming developing is necessary.

3. The quality of the playback is superior to that of the best 35mm film. On a home receiver, it is practically impossible to tell whether the program originates live or as a video tape playback.

4. The tape can be partially or fully erased and used again for several more recordings (between 200 and 500 playbacks).

5. The video tape can be edited.

6. Video tapes are interchangeable. A program recorded in New York, for instance, can be played back in Los Angeles without special adjustments on any one of the existing broadcast (transverse scanning) models.

Video tape is used in three ways: (1) to record entire television shows, (2) to record show segments, and (3) to record show material at remote locations.

The advantages of video tape recording are obvious. (1) Minor or major production errors can be corrected before the telecast. (2) The recording sessions can be scheduled for the convenience of station personel and performers, regardless of actual program times. (3) Video tapes can be easily duplicated and distributed to a variety of television outlets. Many production centers have syndicated their taped shows for distribution in major and minor markets. (4) One-time-only events, such as sports, political gatherings, or difficult operations in medical schools, can be preserved for future reference and study. (5) The recording of show segments often permits a more complex and polished production than does live television, for example. And (6) video tape can be an excellent learning device. In television production, for example, the acting student can watch himself right after his performance; the student of announcing has a chance to criticize his delivery immediately after the taping. Television direction problems can be clearly shown on a video tape playback. The director is now able to see (perhaps for the first time, because now he is more relaxed and not burdened with so many different problems) his framing, video montages, camera movement, general blocking, general impact of photography, and many other aspects of his directing. Writers, producers, engineers, floor personnel—all will benefit greatly from studying the taped show segments that are most representative of their work.

However, a video tape of high technical quality and solid splices does not necessarily mean good television. In fact, indiscriminate video tape editing can often destroy television's great aesthetic potential of "aliveness," the immediate communication of the ever-changing moments of life. If the director or video tape editor does not recognize the specific requirements of the television medium—for example, editing rhythm—the various tempi of the individual segments and the over-all pacing of the show may look artificial to the sensitive viewer. In a dramatic show it is often better to record as long a segment at a time as possible than to rely on many short "takes," which must later be spliced together. The sustained action of the longer takes will often help to preserve a live, organic television quality in the performance and in the final rhythm of the play.

### Remote Video Tape Recording

There are two methods of taping shows that originate at remote locations. One method is to microwave the signal (send the signal via microwave links) to studio or transmitter, wherever the video tape machine is installed. The other way is to take the tape machine to the remote location and record the show directly on the spot.

There are two advantages to the first method. (1) The show can be simultaneously telecast while it is taped. (2) All studio production facilities, such as film chain and studio setups, can be easily integrated with the remote show segments.

However, there are disadvantages. (1) A microwave link is required, which may complicate operations considerably. Also, a complicated microwave link (usually provided by the telephone company) is quite costly. (2) The signal may be interrupted on the way from the remote location to the station's transmitter.

The second method, with completely remote tape units, is frequently used in television operations. The remote units consist of a truck or bus equipped with a large power generator, several camera chains, and one or more video tape machines. Such a remote unit is not dependent upon a working signal link with the station. You can even tape pictures while the remote truck is in motion.

The chief disadvantages of this taping method are that (1) the pictures cannot be broadcast at the same time they are taped, and (2) other program sources, such as slides and films, are generally not available.

### General Video Taping Rules

There are a few general and specific points that you may want to remember when working with video tape.

*General:*
1. Watch performances carefully. Some performers are inclined to relax too much because they know that they are not on the air and that, in case of a great mistake, retakes can be made. On the other hand, some performers may do a brilliant job just because they feel relaxed and relieved of the great and hindering "on-the-air pressure."

2. Try to record your show in one big sweep. Too many stops and retakes are not only costly but very irritating to performers and production people.

3. If you tape show segments that are to be combined with segments of a live performance, make sure that the dress, make-up, lighting, setup, and general directing procedures of the recorded segment match the preceding and following live (or recorded) segments. You will find that it is not always easy to match the television cameras for each recorded segment, especially when the recording sessions stretch over the period of several days.

4. The shooting of a show in too many segments is especially hard on the actor, who will then lack continuity as a guide for his pacing and emotional build-up. (Ill-matched performance because of segment taping is much more obvious on television than in motion pictures.)

*Specific:*

1. Make sure you have enough tape on the supply reel to last for the entire segment you plan to record.

2. Always clearly identify your tape recording with a properly labeled slate. Keep it on camera long enough so that it can be read.

3. List all your takes, including your bad takes, in the recording logbook. Label all bad cuts clearly "NO GOOD."

4. Always have your recording spot-checked immediately after the recording, before you release performers and production crews. A few playback checks of the beginning, middle, and end of the tape are usually enough.

5. Carefully label the box or can with the program title and the playback date so that the tape can be easily located for the playback. The way to start the video tape for recording purposes varies from station to station. Nevertheless, the basic procedures for starting and identifying the video tape agree at least in major points. Here is an example of a normal video-tape roll procedure:

"Ready VTR one" (if you have more than one VTR, you must call the number of the machine). "Ready slate on camera two; ready to roll VTR one, ready beeper."

"Roll VTR one." (You must now wait until the video tape machine has reached "speed"—that is, until the electronics have stabilized for proper recording. Normally, the video tape operator gives you the "speed" or "locked-in" signal, indicating that you can now proceed with the recording. This period from the start of the tape to the recording can take anywhere from four to ten seconds. If you are taping in color, the "locking-in" period will take somewhat longer than for monochrome recording.)

"Up on camera two" (assuming that the slate is on camera two). "Loose two" (or "go to black"), "and beeper!" (the beeper starts its ten-second countdown).

"Up on one" (camera one is now on the air and you have begun the video taping procedure).

Don't forget to call for the stopping of the tape at the end of the recording. Some engineers will let the tape run until the director tells them to stop it.

This discussion on the utilization of video tape is by no means meant to be exhaustive. But you may find this representative sampling valuable as an indicator of the many and extremely varied possibilities for using video tape.

## SUMMARY

Film and video tape are extensively used in all television stations. When working with film, the following three factors must be considered: (1) film subject, (2) film specifications, and (3) preparation techniques for television transmission.

*Subject:* Since different film subjects require slightly different preparation techniques, all films used on television can be divided into five major categories: (1) motion picture features, (2) television film features, (3) local features, (4) news films, and (5) kinescope recordings.

*Specifications:* In television operation, 16mm and 35mm films are used. Most small stations work with 16mm film. Both silent film and SOF (sound on film) are used.

*Preparation Techniques:* In order to prepare film for television transmission, the following subjects must be considered: (1) editing, (2) script, (3) music, and (4) the television film chain.

In film editing, the unwanted pieces of film are cut out and the desired pieces are glued together into a continuous show. There are two major methods of film splicing: the cement splicing method and the film tape splicing method. To allow for accurate film start and program insertion, academy leaders are spliced on the film heads.

Film scripts become important when there is live narration over silent film. Scripts for newsfilms, therefore, have a particular format, indicating the individual film scenes and the lengths of these scenes.

Music and sound effects may be used over silent film footage.

The television film chain or film island includes one or two film projectors, one or two slide projectors, a multiplexer, and a vidicon film camera.

In the video tape process, electronic impulses of television pictures and sound are recorded on a special magnetic video tape, which can be played back, thereby converting the recorded signals into pictures and sound. There are two basic types of video tape recorders: (1) broadcast video tape recorders, using 2-inch tape and the transverse scanning system (sometimes called "quad-head" machines), and (2) closed-circuit machines, employing the helical, or slant-track, recording system.

There are four separate tracks on the broadcast 2-inch video tape: (1) the video signal, (2) the audio signal, (3) the control track, and (4) the cue track.

Editing can be accomplished either mechanically, by cutting the tape physically and splicing it with a special video tape splicer, or electronically, using a special electronic editor.

Whenever video tape is used, special video cuing systems must be employed to allow split-second timing, necessary for all television operations. There are three major video tape cuing systems: (1) the beeper system, (2) the video cue leader, and (3) the tape timer.

Video tape can be used for both monochrome and color programs in three major ways: (1) to record entire live television presentations, (2) to record show segments, and (3) to record show material at remote locations.

## EXERCISES

1. What are the main differences between a kinescope recording and a video tape recording?
2. What are some of the problems in editing single system sound film?
3. You plan to start SOF silent and then bring up the track at a specific point. Your audio engineer is concerned about this procedure, since he cannot monitor the film audio without getting it on the air; he worries about hitting the right spot. What will you suggest?
4. The newscaster asks you to put leader between two newsfilms, because he will have to tell two long stories in this particular interval. What type of leader and how long a leader would you put between the newsfilms? Why?
5. The executive producer of your "American Cities" program would like you to begin each program with a slow pan of the city skyline. He suggests having the newsreel cameraman shoot such a sequence in "his spare time." Do you agree with this suggestion? If so, why? If not, why not?
6. The climax in your half-hour drama occurs when the antagonist falls over the sundeck railing and lands 30 feet below on the sandy beach, alive but badly shaken up. The actor suggests having this sequence prefilmed. Do you agree with him? If so, why? If not, why not?

7. You are asked to tell the cameraman to get SOF of the boat trip so that the viewers can hear the waves and the sound of the boat motor. What would you suggest? Why?

8. Your tape engineer informs you that the program timer on the tape machine has become inoperative. What other cuing devices would you suggest?

9. The guest appearance of the well-known authority on Far Eastern philosophy, Dr. Richard Marsh, would be a great asset to the opening show of your planned "Far Eastern Culture" series. Unfortunately, however, Dr. Marsh will not be able to remain in town for your opening show. What would you suggest?

# 9

## Performing and Acting

The people who appear on the television screen have varied communication objectives: some like to entertain, educate, inform; others want to persuade, convince, sell. Nevertheless, the main goal of each of these people is to communicate with the television audience as effectively as possible.

We can arbitrarily divide all television talent (which stands, not always too accurately, for all people performing in front of the television camera) into two large groups: (1) television performers and (2) television actors. The difference between the performer and actor is fairly clear-cut. The television performer is basically engaged in

nondramatic activities. He plays himself and does not assume someone else's character. The performer sells his own personality to the
audience. The television actor, on the other hand, always portrays
someone else; he projects a character's personality rather than his own.

## TELEVISION PERFORMING TECHNIQUES

The television performer speaks directly to the camera or communicates with other performers or the studio audience, fully aware of the
presence of the television audience. The television performer's audience is not a mass audience but only a small, intimate group that has
gathered in front of a television set. It may help you to imagine your
audience as being a family of three, seated in their favorite room,
about ten feet away from you.

The usual definition of the television audience, as expressed by
modern sociologists, is thus drastically changed by the television performer. The large, anonymous, and heterogeneous mass audience becomes a small group of people, a family seated in a favorite room,
watching television. With this picture in mind, there is no reason to
scream at the "millions of people out there in video land"; rather,
the more successful approach is to talk quietly and intimately to the
family who were nice enough to let you come into their home.

When you assume the role of a television performer, the camera
becomes your audience. This means that you must adapt your performance techniques to the characteristics of the camera and other
important production elements, such as lighting, audio, and timing.

### The Television Camera

#### Audience

The camera is not a dead piece of machinery; it sees everything
you do or do not do. It sees how you look, how you move, how you
sit and stand—in short, how you behave in a variety of situations. At
times it will look at you much more closely and with greater scrutiny
than a polite person would ever dare to do. It will reveal the nervous
twitch of your mouth when you are ill at ease and the expression of
mild panic when you have forgotten a line. The camera will not look
politely away because you are scratching your ear. It will faithfully
reflect your behavior in all pleasant and unpleasant details. As a television performer, therefore, you must carefully control your actions
without ever letting the audience know that you are conscious of
doing so.

### On-the-air lens

Since the camera represents your audience, you must look into the on-the-air lens, or "taking" lens, whenever you intend to establish eye contact with your viewer. Different makes of turret cameras have their on-the-air lenses in different locations. Make sure you know what lens is taking the picture. Don't hesitate to ask the floor manager or the cameraman which lens you should look at. (For a review of the lens positions, see Chapter 2.)

### Camera switching

If two or more cameras are used, you must know which camera is on the air so that you will address the right camera and thus remain in direct contact with the audience. When the director changes cameras, you must follow the floor manager's cue quickly but smoothly. Don't jerk your head from one camera to the other. If you suddenly discover that you have been talking to the wrong camera, look down as if to collect your thoughts, then casually glance into the "hot" camera and continue talking to this camera until you are again cued to the other camera. This method works especially well if you work from notes. You can always pretend to be looking at your notes, while, in reality, you change your view from the "wrong" to the "right" camera.

In general, it is best to ask your director or floor manager if there will be many camera changes during the program, and approximately when the changes are going to happen. If the show is scripted, mark all camera changes in your script.

If the director has one camera on you in a medium shot (MS) or a long shot (LS), and the other camera in a close-up (CU) of the object you are demonstrating, it is best to keep looking at the long shot camera during the whole demonstration, even if the director switches to the close-up camera from time to time. This way you will never be caught looking the wrong way, since only the long shot camera is focused on you.

### Close-up techniques

The tighter the shot, the harder it is for the camera to follow fast movement. If the camera is close to you or if it is using a long lens, you must move (if at all) with great care. When you are demonstrating small objects on a close-up, hold them steady. If the objects are arranged on a table, don't move them off the table. You can either point to the objects or tilt them up a little to give the camera a better shot of them.

There is nothing more frustrating for cameraman and director than a performer who snatches the product off the table just when the cameraman has a good close-up of it. A quick look in the monitor will usually show you how you should hold the object for the camera. If two cameras are used, orient the product somewhat toward the close-up camera. But don't turn the product so much that it looks unnaturally distorted on the wide-shot camera.

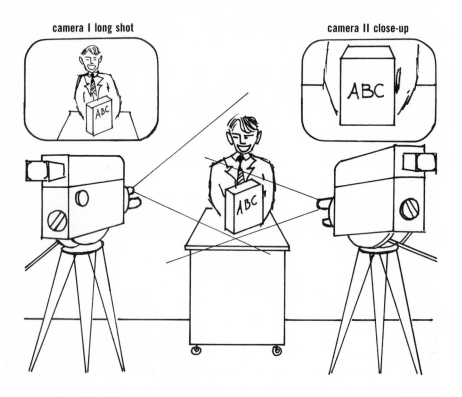

**camera I long shot**                                    **camera II close-up**

### Blocking

Once the show is on the air, you must follow the rehearsed action carefully. This is not the time to change the blocking, just because you think a sudden inspiration may improve the rehearsed staging considerably. If the director has not been warned of your change, the new blocking will always be worse than the previously rehearsed one. The camera has a limited field of view; if you want to be seen, you must stay within that field of view.

Sometimes the director will place you in a position that looks entirely wrong to you, especially if you consider it in relation to the product you are demonstrating. Don't try to correct this position on your own by arbitrarily moving away from the designated spot. A certain camera position and a special lens may very well warrant unusual blocking to achieve a special effect.

### Performer's warning cues

In most nondramatic shows, such as lectures, demonstrations, interviews, and shows of similar nature, there is generally not enough time to work out a detailed blocking scheme. The director will usually just walk you through some of the most important cross-overs from one performing area to the other, and through a few major actions, such as especially complicated demonstrations. During the on-the-air performance, therefore, you must give the director and the studio crew visual and audible warning of your unrehearsed actions. When you want to get up, for instance, shift your weight first, and get your legs and arms into the right position before you actually stand up. This will give the cameraman as well as the microphone boom operator enough time to prepare for your move. If you pop up unexpectedly, however, the camera may stay in one position and focus on the middle part of your body; also, you may hit your head on the microphone, which has been solidly locked into position by the boom operator who has not anticipated your sudden move.

If you intend to move from one set area to another, you may use audio cues. For instance, you can warn the production crew by saying: "Let's go over to the children and ask them . . ." or: "If you will follow me over to the lab area, you can actually see . . ." Such cues will sound quite natural to the home viewer, who is generally unaware of the number of fast reactions these seemingly unimportant remarks may trigger inside the television studio. You must be specific when you cue unrehearsed visual material. For example, you can alert the director of the upcoming slides by saying: "The first picture (or even slide) shows . . ." This cuing device should not be used too often, however. If you can alert the director more subtly yet equally directly, do so. Don't try to tell the director the obvious. He and his crew may only get annoyed with you and may, in extreme cases, even refuse to do what you have asked for. It is the director who runs the show, and you as talent are not the director. An alert director does not have to be told by the performer to bring the cameras a little closer to get a better view of the small object. This is especially annoying to the director if he has already obtained a good close-up with the long lens on the "far" camera. You should also avoid walking toward the camera to demonstrate a small object. Always let the camera come to you, unless you are told otherwise.

## Lighting

Your movements within the studio are also restricted by lighting. You must confine your performing radius to the lighted areas if you want to be seen on the television screen. Never stand too close to the scenery walls or sit on furniture that has been placed too close to these walls. The lighting in these areas is usually poor (no backlight).

Make sure you stand on the floor markings that were made for you in critical lighting areas. Your performing areas in front of a rear screen are usually very carefully marked. You cannot step back close to the rear screen, for instance, because your image would immediately become a silhouette. And don't move set properties that have been carefully placed and lighted.

If you have to demonstrate objects that have a highly reflective surface, be careful not to direct lighting reflections into the camera lens. The best thing to do is to tilt the top part of the object toward the camera and hold the whole object as steady as possible. Ask the floor manager to take some of the glare away by using a dulling spray on the object.

## Audio

As a television performer, you must not only look natural and relaxed but you must also be able to speak clearly and effectively. This part of your job must be learned carefully; it rarely comes solely as a natural gift. A thorough training in voice and diction, interpretive reading, and public speaking are the bare essentials for your job as a television performer. In addition, you must learn to perform adequately for and with the different types of television microphones.

### Television audio procedures

*Opening Cue.* At the beginning of a show, all microphones are dead until the director gives the cue for studio audio. You must, therefore, wait until you receive the opening cue from the floor manager. If you speak before the cue, you will not be heard. Don't take your opening cue from the red tally lights on the cameras unless you are specifically told to do so.

*Audio level.* If you don't handle the microphone yourself, you should not worry too much about the audio level. Since the boom microphone is generally at a distance from the sound source, you must speak with a clear, natural, but fairly loud voice. But don't use affected-sounding stage projection techniques.

In most cases, the audio engineer will take your audio level before you go on the air. Many performers have the bad habit of mumbling or of speaking softly while the level is being set, and then, when they go on the air, of blasting their opening remarks with twice the rehearsed volume. If a level is taken, you must talk as loudly as though you were on the air. You should also avoid extreme volume changes during your performance. Performers who speak softly most of the time and then yell suddenly are not appreciated by audio engineers.

### Microphone techniques

A good television performer must be thoroughly familiar with basic microphone techniques. If he does not handle the microphone himself, he must know what to do to assist the microphone operator and the audio engineer.

*Boom microphone.* 1. Always be aware of boom movements. If a boom swing is involved, don't talk until the boom is above you. But don't be obvious about waiting for the boom. It is unprofessional to say something like "Oh, there comes our friend mike," just to make the audience realize that the long pause was not your fault. The audience cannot see the microphone and will not understand your comments, even though they notice your frantic glances fixed on something invisible above.

2. If the boom rigging breaks, don't panic. A good audio man can pick up your voice even if the microphone is turned in the opposite direction. Again, your audience will not have to know what happened; restrain yourself from making unnecessary remarks about something your viewers may not have noticed.

3. Don't turn too fast. Fast turns involve a great amount of boom movement. If you have to turn, do it slowly. Try not to speak if you have to move fast.

4. Don't speak into the ground. If you talk to a child, for instance, kneel down to him so that the microphone can be brought closer to the child. Try to reduce your voice volume when you speak to someone with a weaker voice.

5. Stay at some distance from hardwall flats. If the microphone gets too close, it may pick up unwanted sound reflections and vibrations.

6. Don't get so close to the boom perambulator that the operator cannot retract the boom any farther.

7. If you get up, do it slowly, especially if your move comes unexpectedly. Give the boom operator a chance to unlock his boom.

8. If you see that a studio traffic jam prevents the boom from following you, stop walking and remain on that spot until you see that the boom has been freed.

*Hand microphone.* 1. Although hand microphones are rugged, they are still highly sensitive instruments. Handle them as carefully as possible. When you have finished using the hand mike, put it down gently. If you drop it accidentally, make sure that the audio engineer checks it out again before air time.

2. When you move with the hand microphone, watch that you have enough cable for the move and that the cable does not get caught while you are walking. If you have both hands free, hold the mike with one hand and pull the cable with the other. If you run out of cable, stop as casually as you can. Don't start pulling as though you were engaged in a rope-pulling contest. Alert the floor manager, if he has not already seen the dilemma.

3. When you use a hand microphone in the studio, don't hold it too close to your mouth. The audio quality will be much better if you hold the microphone only chest high. Outdoors, however, especially if you work in noisy surroundings, you must hold the microphone quite close to your mouth.

4. When you interview someone with the hand microphone, don't push it into your guest's face whenever he has something to say and then withdraw it crudely when you want to get a word in. Leave the microphone in one position, usually favoring the guest, depending on his voice volume. As pointed out in Chapter 3, the guest usually has a weaker voice than the professional performer. If you are outdoors in a noisy place, you might have to move the microphone from one sound source to the other. When doing so, make sure you hold the microphone near the person actually speaking. A veteran television performer once became so thoroughly mixed up during an interview that he held the microphone to his mouth whenever the guest was speaking and pointed it to the guest whenever he was making his own comments. Although the audio pickup was anything but good, the whole production crew roared with laughter at this unrehearsed and completely unintentional comedy routine.

5. When you read off camera, don't change the position of the microphone; hold it steady and in one fixed position.

6. If you need both hands for demonstration, wedge the hand microphone under your arm, with the live side pointing as close to your mouth as possible.

7. If you have to use several hand microphones during your performance, such as on a remote location, for example, make sure you

know where the microphones are located before you get to the new location. Be especially careful in putting down the "old" mike and picking up the "new" one.

*Desk microphone.* 1. Once the desk mike has been placed by the audio engineer, don't move it. You may find in a panel show, for instance, that the microphone is obviously pointing away from you. But this may have been done purposely to achieve better audio balance. Never grab the microphone and pull it closer to you without first checking with the audio engineer.

2. Avoid kicking and banging the table when you work with a desk microphone. These seemingly minor noises sound like heavy explosions over the speaker.

3. Don't lean into the desk microphone in order to be heard. This not only sounds bad but also looks bad.

*Stand microphone.* 1. Try to keep your hands off the stand microphone. Stand mikes are not crutches either in a physical or in a psychological sense. If you intend to bang a stand microphone around the stage for effect, get a prop mike and use another microphone (boom) for the actual sound pickup.

2. Don't change the height of the stand microphone once it is set for you by the audio engineer.

*Lavaliere microphone.* 1. Don't forget to put it on. A talent once discovered that he was sitting on the microphone instead of wearing it at the beginning of a show.

2. Your floor manager or audio engineer can help you to put the microphone on properly. (See wearing techniques in Chapter 3.)

3. If you move with the lavaliere microphone, gently pull the cable behind you to keep the tension off the neck cord. Be sure you have enough microphone cable for your intended move.

4. When you use the lavaliere microphone as a hand microphone, don't hold it too far down in your hand, or you will pick up many annoying hand-rubbing noises.

5. As long as you wear the lavaliere microphone around your neck, you cannot properly pick up someone else's voice. If you intend to interview someone, you must use the lavaliere microphone as a hand microphone.

## Timing

Television operates on split-second timing. Although the director is ultimately responsible for getting the show on and off on time, the performer has a great deal to do with proper timing.

Aside from proper pacing throughout the show, you must learn how much program material you can cover after you have received a three-minute, a two-minute, a one-minute, and a thirty-second cue. You must, for example, still look comfortable and relaxed although you may have to cram a great amount of important program material into the last minute. On the other hand, you must be prepared to fill an extra thirty seconds without appearing to be grasping for words and things to do. This kind of presence of mind, of course, needs practice and cannot be learned properly from a television handbook.

### Floor manager's cues

To pace the show properly, you need accurate cues from the floor manager. His time cues become especially important during the last three minutes of the show.

Different stations may use slightly different cuing signals and procedures. You should, therefore, quickly review the floor manager's cuing system before you go on the air.

React to all cues immediately, even if you think the cue is not appropriate at that particular time. Your director would not give the cue if it were not absolutely necessary. A truly professional performer is not one who does not need any cues and can run the show all by himself; he is the one who can react to different cues quickly and smoothly.

Don't look nervously for the floor manager if you think you should have received a cue. The floor manager will find you and draw your attention to the cue. When the floor manager cues you, don't acknowledge the cue in any way. The floor manager will know whether you have received the cue or not.

The following list will indicate some major cues that are used by most television stations with only minor, if any, variations. Standard time cues, directional cues, and audio cues are included.

## TIME CUES

| Cue | Meaning | Floor Manager's Hand Signal |
|---|---|---|
| Stand by | Show about to start. | Extends arm above his head and points with other hand to camera that will go on the air. |
| Cue | Show goes on the air. | Points to performer or live camera. |
| On time | Go ahead as planned. (On the nose.) | Touches nose with forefinger. |
| Speed up | Accelerate what you are doing. You are going too slowly. | Rotates hand clockwise with extended forefinger. Urgency of speed-up is indicated by fast or slow rotation. |

| | | |
|---|---|---|
| Stretch | Slow down. Too much time left. Fill until emergency is over. | Stretches imaginary rubber band between his hands. |
| Wind up | Finish up what you are doing. Come to an end. | Similar motion as speed up, but usually with whole hand or arm. Sometimes expressed with raised fist. |
| Cut | Stop speech or action immediately. | Pulls index finger in knife-like motion across throat. |
| 5 minutes | 5 minutes left until end of the show. | Holds up five fingers or small card with number painted on it. |
| 4 minutes | 4 minutes left. | Holds up four fingers or card. |
| 3 minutes | 3 minutes left. | Holds up three fingers or card. |
| 2 minutes | 2 minutes left. | Holds up two fingers or card. |
| 1 minute | 1 minute left. | Holds up one finger or card. |
| ½ minute | 30 seconds left in show. | Forms a cross with two index fingers or extended hands. Or holds card with number. Or holds up bent index finger. |
| 15 seconds | 15 seconds left in show. | Forms a cross with extended (and spread) forefinger and middle finger of right hand over extended forefinger of left hand. Or shows fist (which can also mean wind up). |
| Roll film (and countdown) | Projector is rolling. Film is coming up. | Holds extended left hand in front of face, moves right hand in cranking motion. |
| 4–3–2–1– take film | Academy numbers as they flash by on the preview monitor. | Extends four, three, two, one finger; clenches fist or gives cut signal. (Same for roll tape procedure.) |

## DIRECTIONAL CUES

| | | |
|---|---|---|
| Move stage right (or camera left) | Performer must move to his right. | Waves extended left arm to his left. |
| Move stage left (or camera right) | Performer must move to his left. | Waves extended right arm to his right. |
| Closer | Performer must come closer or bring object closer to camera. | Moves both hands toward himself, palms in. |
| Back | Performer must step back or move object away from camera. | Uses both hands in pushing motion, palms out. |
| Walk | Performer must move to next performing area. | Makes a walking motion with index and middle fingers in direction of movement. |

| Cue | Meaning | Floor Manager's Hand Signal |
|---|---|---|
| Stop | Stop right here. Do not move any more. | Extends both hands in front of him, palms out. |
| O.K. | Very well done. Stay right there. Do what you are doing. | Forms an "O" with thumb and forefinger, other fingers extended, motioning toward talent. |

## AUDIO CUES

| | | |
|---|---|---|
| Speak up | Performer is talking too softly for present conditions. | Cups both hands behind his ears, or moves right hand upwards, palm up. |
| Tone down | Performer is too loud or too gay for the occasion. | Moves both hands toward studio floor, palms down, or puts extended forefinger over mouth in shhh-like motion. |
| Closer to mike | Performer is too far away from mike for good audio pickup. | Moves right hand toward his face. |
| Keep talking | Keep on talking until further cues. | Extends thumb and forefinger horizontally, moving them like the beak of a bird. |

## Television Prompting Devices

There are television prompting devices, in addition to direct cues, that are of great help to the television performer who fears suddenly forgetting his lines or who did not have time to memorize a difficult copy that may have been handed to him just before the performance.

The sensitive studio microphones make most audible prompting impossible. Earphones and hearing aid prompting devices have not proved too successful. Most television prompting devices, therefore, are visual.

The visual prompting devices must be designed so that the television viewer is not aware of the prompting device. The performer must be able to read the prompting sheet without appearing to lose eye contact with the television viewer. The prompting device must be reliable, so that the performer can deliver his lines uninterrupted by mechanical failure of the device.

The television performer can make use of four major types of television prompting devices: (1) script reading, (2) hand-held cue cards, (3) idiot sheets, and (4) mechanical prompting devices.

### Script reading

The most simple and also the most obvious prompting device is the television script. Sometimes you can hide the script behind a commercial display; in this situation you would memorize the first few lines and then, as soon as the camera has dollied in, read the rest of the copy from the script. This technique is frequently employed in simple one-camera commercials, where the camera remains for the most part focused on the advertised product. If you are caught reading your script, casually continue reading it. This is much better than appearing embarrassed with nothing to say.

In a lecture performance, it may be convenient and natural to refer to your script of lecture notes.

There are occasions, however, where the free use of a script is directly opposed to the character of the show. At these times you must rely on other memory aids.

### Hand-held cue cards

Another successful prompting device that can be operated by the performer himself is the hand-held 3 × 5 cue cards. Whenever necessary, you can glance more or less secretly at your notes, which are typed or lettered on the cards.

This method has two advantages. (1) The cards are small; they don't show on camera if handled properly. (2) Cards can be handled by the talent himself, who can refer back to previous notes, if necessary.

There are also disadvantages. (1) Too many cards are needed, if the complete copy is written out. (2) If the talent has to read more than just a few major cue lines, the reading becomes quite obvious. (3) The performer's hands are occupied.

### Idiot sheets

This not very flattering expression refers to cue cards generally held by a member of the production crew close to the lens of the on-the-air camera. There are many kinds of idiot sheets, depending largely on what the performer is used to and what he likes to work with. The three most common types of idiot sheets are discussed in the following paragraphs.

1. *24 × 15-inch white horizontal cards.* The copy is handlettered with a black-ink flow pen. The cards must be held close to the lens, preferably on both sides of the camera so that the performer will not be looking at only one side of the camera. Some performers prefer that cards be held below the lens turret or zoom lens. This position allows the performer to keep contact with the lens without looking right or left. Looking down can appear quite natural, since it is a common habit to glance down to collect your thoughts and then look up again. The farther the camera is from the performer, the less obvious the reading becomes. The use of a zoom lens in this connection is quite good, because a close-up can be achieved without changing the distance from performer to camera.

Wrong.
Floorman can't read
along with talent.          Right.
Too far from lens.
Covers too much
of card.

The advantages of these cards are that they are fairly easy to make and to read and the lettering can be quite large. However, the cards have disadvantages. (1) They must be handled by at least two people. (2) The copy is often relatively far away from the camera lens, which makes the performer's reading quite obvious. (3) Many cards are needed for a longer copy. (4) Chances for a card mix-up are great.

2. *Yellow or white paper sheets, 24 × 15 inches, vertical.* The paper sheets are hand lettered with India ink or flow pen. They are held close to the lens by one man, who holds the line to be read parallel to the camera lens.

sheets can
be held          one man
from both        can hold
sides            many sheets

Paper sheets have two advantages. (1) One man can handle as many as twenty sheets fairly easily. (2) Because the copy is comparatively close to the camera lens, the reading is not too noticeable.

They have three disadvantages. (1) There is a great chance of getting the sheets mixed up. (2) Changing the cue sheets is difficult, and there is always the danger of dropping them. (3) The lettering is still too far away from the lens to conceal the reading completely.

3. *Long, thin, vertical strips of paper.* These strips are mounted on small pieces of cardboard (approximately 8 × 36 inches). The strips are handlettered with black grease pencil or a small flow pen. The floor man who handles the cue sheets moves the strips up so that the line being read is parallel to the camera lens.

These strips have three advantages. (1) The copy is close to the camera lens, which camouflages the reading process to a great extent. (2) Several sheets can be attached simultaneously and then torn off one by one. (3) The strips can be easily handled by one floor man.

They have two disadvantages. (1) The amount of copy is definitely limited. (2) The long strips are quite awkward to handle.

*Use of idiot sheets.* When you use idiot sheets, don't stare at them; look at the on-the-air lens as much as possible. Avoid squinting. If you cannot see the cards, have them made larger or, if you have glasses, wear them.

If the floor man forgets to change the cards, snap your fingers to attract his attention; in an emergency you may have to ad-lib until the cue card system is functioning again.

### Mechanical cuing devices

*Cardboard roll.* The simplest semi-mechanical cuing device is a cardboard roll fastened to the front of the camera through which a long sheet of teletype paper is pulled. The teletype paper can be handlettered or typed with an oversized typewriter.

The cardboard roll has four advantages. (1) The copy can be as

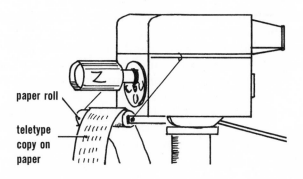

paper roll

teletype
copy on
paper

long as needed. (2) The paper can be pulled continuously over the drum. (3) There is little chance of mechanical failure or cue mix-up. (4) The copy is close to the camera lens.

This roll has three disadvantages. (1) The long strip of paper hangs in front of the camera, which makes that camera fairly immobile (zoom lens is preferred). (2) The lettering size is rather small and requires good eyesight to be read properly. (3) The viewer can still see that the performer is reading.

*TelePrompTer.* The most advanced mechanical prompting device is the TelePrompTer. The TelePrompTer consists of a large box fastened to the front of the camera. The principle of this mechanical device is similar to the paper roll over which the continuous piece of teletype paper is pulled. In the TelePrompTer, the pulling is done mechanically and can be adjusted to the reading speed of the performer. The lettering of the paper is magnified and projected onto a glass plate that is placed directly in front of the camera lens. The projected lettering is clearly visible to the performer, but is invisible on the television screen.

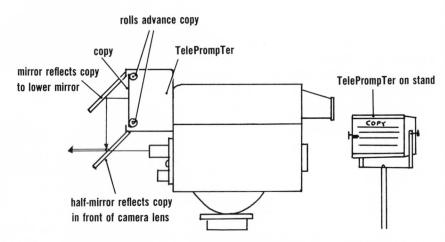

The TelePrompTer has three advantages. (1) The talent can look directly into the camera lens while reading his copy. (2) The lettering is very clear (oversized typewriter) and easily visible. (3) The continuous roll assures proper copy continuity. The TelePrompTer can hold copy for a 90-minute speech or one-hour play, which is enough for most types of television performances.

It also has disadvantages. (1) The rental fees of a TelePrompTer are generally prohibitive in small station operation. (2) The camera with the TelePrompTer attachment is not very flexible, since it must stay on the performer at all times. If frequent camera cutting is intended, TelePrompTers must be placed on all active cameras, which makes this type of prompting even more expensive.

## TYPES OF TELEVISION PERFORMERS

The television performer may be involved in a great variety of television shows. Depending on the type of show he is doing, we can group him into five major categories: (1) the announcer, (2) the interviewer, (3) the host, (4) the master of ceremonies (M.C.), and (5) the moderator. The distinction among these categories is not always clear-cut. Quite frequently the duties of the performer overlap so that a proper definition does not apply. The division into five major performance categories, however, is intended to familiarize you with the basic tasks of the television performer.

### The Announcer

An announcer can be on- or off-camera. The staff announcer is usually off-camera. He works from a special announcing booth and gives station breaks, short commercials and newscasts, and public service announcements over slides, telops, and silent films. The on-camera announcer performs any number of different functions. He can be: (1) commercial announcer, (2) newscaster, (3) sportscaster, and (4) narrator.

*Commercial announcer.* The commercial announcer voices or performs commercials on television. The commercials may range from a simple "straight pitch," such as pointing to a display while reading the copy, to a rather complex demonstration, involving many moves and tricky technical maneuvers.

Performing a commercial is never easy. You must say and do many things within a short time limit. There is no room for error or even for a slight hesitation. Commercials frequently involve more complicated production procedures than most small station shows.

Most commercials are filmed or pretaped before they are telecast. Only very simple commercials are still done live. The video taping of the commercial, however, does not absolve you from doing the best possible job, whether the commercial is taped section by section or in one uninterrupted take.

The key to success for a commercial announcer is, as for any other television performer, careful preparation. The following steps will give you a general idea of how to go about preparing for your commercial presentation.

1. Get to know the product you are advertising.

2. If you have time, memorize your copy verbatim, even if you plan to use some kind of prompting device.

3. Practice your demonstration procedures several times before the actual rehearsal. Watch yourself in a mirror; this will help you to get used to handling the props while maintaining eye contact with the viewer.

4. Take advantage of every free minute during rehearsal to go over your lines. A great amount of rehearsal time is usually taken up by working out technical details, such as lighting adjustments and camera positioning, which will give you enough free time to find a quiet corner and read your lines as often as the time permits. Be sure, however, to tell the floor manager where you are so that he can find you whenever you are needed.

During the rehearsal and the performance you must observe the general rules of television performing. Specifically, pay particular attention to the following points:

1. Make sure you have memorized your copy correctly. Check with the director on specific cue lines, especially if the commercial is only partly scripted. A slight misreading of a cue line may develop into a series of major production crises.

2. Always check whether the demonstration has been set up correctly. The packages should be opened beforehand, bottle caps removed and replaced lightly so that you can operate on the air smoothly and effortlessly.

3. Quickly go through the main steps of your performance. Work the demonstration properties to assure yourself that nothing has been damaged before or during the setup.

4. Check on the order of your idiot sheets. Check also on the order of easel cards that you may be asked to handle.

5. Watch the floor markings that have been made for you. Quickly review the main steps of your blocking.

6. Review the floor manager's cues.

7. Find out what type of microphone you are using. Don't forget to put on the lavaliere microphone.

8. Don't read your commercial to a mass audience; instead, talk about the product to three people seated about ten feet away from you.

9. If something goes wrong, don't let it show. You can be flexible as long as you know what the product you are advertising is all about.

*The newscaster.* The television newscaster reads the news on-camera. His performance is usually supported by ample visual material, such as news pictures and newsfilm. In general, he remains in one position. The newscaster may be on remote location, commenting on important events. He may then be called a television reporter.

As a newscaster, you must read your copy accurately and precisely. There is no time for chit-chat. You must be sincere; you must project authority. Don't appear too pleasant when you read about a tragic accident or too solemn when you have an amusing story to tell. Watch your time and film cues carefully. If the film that accompanies your narration does not come up as planned, keep on reading the film script. You must, however, change all direct references to the film picture. Always have standby copy for emergencies.

*The sportscaster.* The sportscaster is either commenting on a sports event on- or off-camera from remote location or presenting a complete sports show from the studio, similar to the newscaster. If the show is a remote telecast of a sports event, remember that the people can *see* the action. Carefully watch your monitor. As long as the viewers can see what is going on, you don't have to tell them. You should tell the viewers, however, of all happenings that are not visible on the television screen. Be sure to give all scores correctly and to identify the people on the monitor. Don't hesitate to make references to the television screen if it will help to clarify your identification. You can, for instance, refer to the player "on the left of your screen," or "the boxer in the light trunks on the right side of your screen." However, avoid referring to color, such as "the team in the red jerseys," since many people receive color telecasts in black and white.

You must have a thorough knowledge of the event you are describing and a sports vocabulary familiar to viewers. And you should prepare materials, such as identification charts and statistical information, to assist you in effectively presenting the show.

*Narrator.* The television narrator usually narrates over filmed or taped shows of documentary character. His performance is similar to that of a newscaster reading over a silent newsfilm. Factual, authoritative reporting is the keynote of the performance of the television narrator, and precise timing is essential.

### The Interviewer

The interviewer presents people from all walks of life to the television audience. The guest may be seated right next to the interviewer in the studio, or he may be thousands of miles away, connected with the interviewer through the television system.

Before you interview a person, you must familiarize yourself with the person's background, habits, and likes and dislikes. The chief assets of a good interviewer are adaptability and tact. You must be able to listen to what the guest has to say. You are not the star of the show when you interview a guest; the guest is the center of attraction at that moment. Let him talk; the viewer is interested in him and in what he has to say, not in your remarks. Politely direct him to the proper camera, if the director wishes you to do so. Watch your timing closely. When you get a wind up, don't ask another question. If you get a cut and the guest is still speaking, you must interrupt as politely as you can. It is always of great advantage to have your opening and closing remarks thoroughly prepared before each interview. This preparation will help you to set the scene in a precise and interesting manner, thereby avoiding the usually rather uninspiring on-the-air "warm-up period" of interviewer and interviewee. A nice, clean ending to the program is, of course, equally desirable.

## The Host

The job of the program host or hostess is basically to present certain television shows to the viewer at home. Quite frequently, glamorous women act as hostesses for feature films or special half-hour television films. The host usually works in elegant surroundings, trying to make his guests (viewers) feel as comfortable as possible.

As a television host, you must talk directly to your viewers, trying to create a friendly and relaxed atmosphere between you (the host) and the viewer (the guest).

## The Master of Ceremonies

The master of ceremonies, usually called M.C., is a rather pompous title for a performer who presides over entertainment, who ad-libs introductions to different portions of a variety show, or who acts as the show's personality. The viewer is mainly interested in the personality of the master of ceremonies. Many such shows, therefore, are named after the master of ceremonies. You may call your show "The Charlie Dugdale Show," "The Robert Spearman Show," or whatever stage name you think is most impressive.

As a master of ceremonies, you usually work from a show format rather than from a detailed script. You must, therefore, be careful to give very definite cues for your actions or upcoming visuals. But don't be too obvious about it. A cue such as "We now have some pictures to show you," or "Before we interview Mr. X I would like to show you . . ." should be used only when the director has had no way of knowing that you are introducing unrehearsed material. In most cases, an equally direct but less obvious cue will be sufficient warning to the alert director.

### The Moderator

The moderator presides at any kind of panel or discussion show. He usually introduces the members of the panel, asks some of the key questions, and tries to keep the conversation on the subject. He also sees to it that the talking periods among the members of the panel are equally distributed and that the show is properly paced. At the end of the show, the moderator generally summarizes the results of the discussion and closes the show.

As a moderator, you must first of all become thoroughly familiar with the subject under debate. You must be able to judge whether a point has been sufficiently discussed; whether it has been explored and discussed in terms the viewer can understand. Frequently you will have to rephrase questions and answers to clarify the proceedings for the home viewer. Since you deal mostly with people who have little or no television experience, you must be very conscious of the timing element. If there are thirty seconds left, you must be prepared to fill this time with interesting and intelligent remarks concerning the previously discussed subject. Don't stop just because the members of the panel have nothing more to say. It is your job to fill the allotted time and to keep the conversation going.

## TELEVISION ACTING TECHNIQUES

Contrary to the television performer, the television actor always assumes someone else's character and personality.

To become a good television actor, you must first of all learn the art of acting. It is not the objective of this chapter, however, to teach you the basic principles of acting; this discussion will merely point out how you must adapt your acting to the peculiarities of the television medium.

Many excellent actors consider television the most difficult medium in which to work. Television acting has been aptly called "summer stock in an iron lung." The actor always works within a studio full of confusing and impersonal technical gear; and yet he must appear on the screen as natural and lifelike as possible.

It is difficult to establish rigid principles of television acting techniques that are applicable in any situation. Different roles and even different directors may require quite different forms of expression and acting techniques from the actor. The television medium, however, dictates some basic behavior patterns that the television actor must accept if he wants to make the technical medium work for him instead of against him.

## Audience

When you act on television, you have no rapport with the audience —people you can see or at least feel and who applaud and elevate you to your best possible performance. In television, you are acting before constantly moving cameras that represent your assumed audience. Similar to the television performer, you must be camera-conscious, but you should never reveal your knowledge of the cameras' presence. The viewer (represented by the cameras) does not remain in one viewing position, as he would do in the theatre; he moves around you, looks at you at close range and from a distance, from below and from above; he may look at your eyes, your feet, your hands, your back, whatever the director selects for him to see. And at all times you must look completely convincing and natural; the character you are portraying must appear on the television screen as a real, living, breathing human being.

Keep in mind that you are playing not to an audience but to a camera lens; you need not (and should not) project your motions and emotions as you would do when acting on stage. The television camera does the projecting—the communicating—for you. Internalization rather than externalization of your role is a key factor when acting on television. You must attempt to *become* as much as possible the person you are portraying, rather than to *act him out* (in the original meaning of doing, moving). Thus, your reactions are equally as effective on television as your actions.

## Actions

The television camera is restrictive in many ways. It looks at the set and at you mostly in close-ups. This means that your physical actions must be confined to the particular area the camera chooses to select. You must play in quite restricted stage areas, often unnaturally close to the other actors.

The television close-up also limits the extent of your gestures and concentrates on more intimate ways of emotional expression. A close-up of a clenched fist or a raised eyebrow may reflect your inner feelings and emotions better than the broad movements necessary for the theatre actor.

## Emotions

The camera restricts your motions, but not your emotions. Be as genuine as possible in the expression of your feelings. Live the character you are portraying. You should neither overact nor underact. The television camera faithfully reports mugging and faking as well as honesty and real conviction.

If you forget a line, stay in character. Try not to let the camera see your sudden panic.

In television acting, you generally have the chance to build your character more or less continually to the climax. This character building, however, must be done within a rigid time limit that allows little variation in pace; it also must be done within the barely controlled chaos of any television studio production.

## Blocking

You must be extremely exact in following rehearsed blocking. Sometimes mere inches become important, especially if the cameras are set up for special effects. The director may, for instance, want to use your arm as a frame for the background scene or position you for a complicated over-the-shoulder shot. The precise television lighting and the limited microphone radius (especially in small station production) are also factors that force you to adhere strictly to the initial blocking.

The television cameras quite frequently photograph your stage business in a close-up. This means that you must remember all the rehearsed business details and execute them in exactly the same spot in which they were initially staged.

## Speech

Compared to radio, the television boom microphone is generally a good distance away from you. You must, therefore, speak clearly. But speak naturally. Projecting your voice in the theatre tradition sounds very artificial on television.

## Memorizing Lines

As a television actor, you must be able to learn your lines quickly and accurately. You may have only two weeks to memorize a difficult role. A good television actor should not (and really cannot) rely on prompting devices; he must live, not read, his role.

There is no chance for ad-libbing in television drama. The director must rely on your precise delivery of lines; most of your lines are important video and audio cues.

Mechanical prompting devices are sometimes used in daily dramatic shows, such as soap operas. But this is of little importance in small station operation.

## Costume and Make-up Changes

Although almost all television plays are pretaped, you may find that you still have to run from one set area to another and to engage in fast costume and make-up changes. You must be careful never to cross in front of the cameras, and you must do your crossing as quickly and as silently as possible. Sometimes you have literally only seconds to spare.

Often, scene changes require part of the set to be taken down quickly, only a few feet from where you are playing an emotional scene. Pay no attention to such "backstage" happenings. Remain calm and in character, even when you see several engineers frantically working on the camera that is photographing your scene. The picture of this camera might still go out on the air (even if the viewfinder is removed), or another camera from an unrehearsed position may be covering your action.

When fast costume changes are required you may help the costume people by partly unzipping before you get to them. If a make-up change has to be done, keep as calm as possible. Do not project your nervousness, even if only seconds remain for you to get on stage.

### Timing

Your pacing is fairly well established by the time you go on the air. You must, however, be prepared to eliminate certain sections of your role at a moment's notice. Also, you may have to stretch out a fast scene without making the scene appear to drag, or you may have to gain ten seconds by speeding up a slow scene without destroying its solemn character. You must be flexible without getting out of character.

Always respond immediately to the floor manager's cues. Be ready for them and, when cued, start your action without hesitation. Remember that the cues given to you also go to engineering and production personnel.

### Director-Actor Relationship

As a television actor, you cannot afford to be temperamental. There are too many people who have to be coordinated by the director. Although the television actor is important to the television show, other people are important, too: the floor man, the engineer at the transmitter, the boom operator, and the video engineer.

A good television actor is not necessarily the one who is quick in inventing his own stage business and blocking; but he *is* the one who can do quickly and precisely whatever the director asks.

Although you may find little opportunity for acting in small station operation, make an effort to learn as much about television acting as possible. A good actor is generally a good television performer; a television director who has had good acting training will be greatly aided in most of his directing assignments.

## Background for Television Actors

There is much debating about what background is most desirable for the television actor: motion picture acting, radio acting, or acting for the legitimate theatre. But this argument is really insignificant. What you must learn, first of all, are the basic principles of acting, and these are the same regardless of the performance medium.

Many rules that apply to the techniques of television performing are also valid in acting. The most important qualification for the television performer and actor is a thorough familiarity with the basic production principles of the television medium. The better your knowledge of television production, the better your performance will be.

## Talent Unions

Most regular television performers and actors belong to at least one talent union. The most prominent broadcast talent union is AFTRA, the American Federation of Television and Radio Artists. Other talent unions, such as AGMA (American Guild of Musical Artists), AGVA (American Guild of Variety Artists), and SAG (Screen Actors Guild) are usually more concerned with network operations than with local television stations.

There are circumstances under which you can perform on television without belonging to a talent union: (1) if your station is a non-union station—that is, independent of local union stipulation; (2) if you are appearing only once, or rather infrequently, as a guest performer, usually as an expert in your field, such as a scientist; or (3) if you are working for an educational television station, which is often exempt from the usually strict union jurisdiction.

As a television performer, you can be permanently employed by a television station, or you may free-lance—that is, perform on television in a variety of ways without being affiliated with any particular station. Staff announcers, newscasters, and performers who work in similar capacities are generally permanently employed by a station. Actors, on the other hand, often work on a free-lance basis.

If you are permanently employed by a station as a performer, the station will probably draw up a contract stipulating certain working conditions, such as the length of your employment, the nature of your work, and your salary. These station contracts must be in accord with local union regulations. Such union regulations vary greatly from area to area, depending on the television market in which your station operates. Only regional and major networks have uniform salary scales and general working conditions.

When working under contract for a particular station, you are usually not allowed to work for another television station on a regular basis. Sometimes, your contract may even state that if you terminate your employment you will not be able to work for another station lying in the immediate coverage area (signal range) of your old station.

When free-lancing, you do not have a contract with any particular station. However, the local union stipulations regarding minimum wages (scale) and general working conditions must still be honored by the station for which you happen to perform.

Make sure that you are thoroughly familiar with the local talent-union requirements and the station practices before you agree to any kind of talent services.

## SUMMARY

All television talent (people who perform in front of a television camera) can be arbitrarily grouped into two large categories: performers and actors. Television performers play themselves; they are usually engaged in nondramatic activities. The television actor portrays someone else. Television performers and actors must adapt their performance techniques to the characteristics of the camera, to lighting, to audio, and to precise timing. Specifically, the television performer and actor must be familiar with the position of the on-the-air lens, camera switching procedures, and close-up techniques. Accurate blocking becomes essential in television operation. Good television lighting is usually confined to several performance areas. If the talent does not remember the rehearsed blocking, he runs the risk of stepping out of the lighted areas, which may be detrimental to performer as well as performance.

One of the most important parts of the television talent's job is to learn to speak for and work with the different types of television microphones. He must be able to gear his performance technique to the specific kind of microphone used, whether it is a lavaliere microphone, a hand microphone, a desk microphone, or a boom microphone.

Although the director is ultimately responsible for the timing of a show, the television performer or actor must pace himself properly to keep exactly within the allotted time.

Television performers frequently make use of special prompting devices. The four major prompting devices are (1) script reading, (2) hand-held cue cards, (3) idiot sheets, and (4) mechanical prompting devices.

The different television performers can be grouped into five major categories: (1) the announcer, (2) the interviewer, (3) the host, (4) the master of ceremonies, and (5) the moderator.

The television actor must first of all know how to act. He then must adapt his acting technique to the medium of television. This includes, in general, a restriction in bodily movement and gestures and a concentration of more intimate ways of expression. Strict following of the rehearsed blocking and all stage business is essential to the good television actor. Since difficult roles may have to be learned within the very short period of two to three weeks, actors who learn quickly are preferred by directors. Television performers as well as actors must have a clear image of their audience, which may be assumed to be a family of three seated about ten feet away from the performance.

Before you perform or act on television on a more regular basis, make sure you understand the specific requirements of the local talent union and the station.

## EXERCISES

1. Owing to a production oversight, no special audio provisions have been made for the important guest on your news show. Is it possible for you to interview your guest with the lavaliere microphone? If so, how? If not, why not?

2. While you are on the air, your guest refers to some photos that he has brought along. Can you show the pictures although they were not included in the rehearsal? If so, how can you do it?

3. The producer of your educational show asks you to walk up to the rear screen and point out certain pertinent details on the projected map. What is your reaction? Why?

4. The director of a little theatre acting group asks you about some TV acting "rules of thumb" that may help him in preparing his one-act show for television. Can you give such rules? If so, which ones? If not, why not?

5. You are asked to act as the moderator on a panel that will discuss "Television and Juvenile Delinquency." What preparations should you make for this television show?

6. Your director is quite concerned about "stage business" and asks you to perform the business exactly as it was rehearsed. Is the director's concern justified? Why?

7. In your newscast, you have just introduced the next newsfilm for which you are to supply the narration. When you look at the monitor to synchronize your narration with the film, you see yourself. What do you do?

8. Assuming that you have not been specifically told, should you take your cue from the red tally lights or from the floor manager? Why?

9. The cameraman uses a 50mm lens for your close-up during a short spot announcement. He complains that it is quite obvious that you are reading off idiot sheets. What would you suggest, considering that you have good eyesight?

10. The local ratings show that your weekly half-hour variety show is watched by about 100,000 people. What, then, should be your approach as a performer to this mass audience?

# 10

## Make-up and Clothing

### TELEVISION MAKE-UP

The advent of color television and the improvement of mono-chrome camera picture tubes have resulted in a constant change in television make-up requirements and techniques. Some production people think that special television make-up is now mostly a thing of the past, while others still insist on complicated make-up for every person appearing in front of the television camera.

The controversy as to whether special television make-up is nec-essary stems largely from a general confusion in deciding the reasons for applying make-up.

Make-up is always used for three basic reasons: (1) to *improve* the appearance of a person, (2) to *correct* the appearance of a person, and (3) to *change* the appearance of a person. Standard street make-up is used daily by most women to accentuate and improve their features. Minor skin blemishes are covered up, and the eyes and lips are emphasized.

Make-up can also be used to correct closely or widely spaced eyes, sagging flesh under the chin, a short or long nose, a slightly too prominent forehead, and many similar minor faults.

If a person is to portray a specific character in a play, a complete change of this person's appearance may be necessary. Drastic changes of the actor's age, race, and character can be accomplished through the creative use of special make-up techniques.

The different purposes for applying make-up require, of course, different make-up techniques. Improving someone's appearance requires the least complicated make-up procedure. To correct someone's appearance, the make-up job becomes slightly more complicated. And changing an actor's appearance may require involved and complex make-up techniques.

Television make-up is further complicated by the characteristics of the medium itself. Certain electronic and production factors influence television make-up techniques considerably. These factors are (1) reproduction peculiarities of the camera picture tube, (2) television lighting techniques, (3) surrounding colors, and (4) television close-up techniques.

### Make-up and the Camera Picture Tube

The camera picture tubes (image-orthicon, vidicon, and Plumbicon) have a tendency to pick up and exaggerate certain shadow areas. For instance, a boom shadow that is hardly noticeable in the studio may show up clearly on the control room monitor. Dark shadows beneath the eyes, nose, and chin quite frequently distort a person's face unfavorably. A man may be as clean-shaven as possible, but without make-up his beard area may appear as dark, uneven blotches on the television screen.

The monochrome picture tubes tend to photograph warm colors (warm reds, oranges, browns, tans) lighter—that is, the colors appear slightly washed-out—whereas cool colors (blue-reds, blues, bluegreens) photograph darker. Correct make-up colors must be chosen to compensate for these distortions. You must also watch that the make-up colors you choose for color televison are compatible. This means that the particular make-up colors must photograph in a proper gray scale on black-and-white television.

### Television Lighting and Make-up

The customary overhead television lighting creates several undesirable shadows, notably under the eyebrows and beneath the eye, and under the nose and chin area. In some cases the shadows are so objectionable that corrective make-up must be applied. This make-up technique is rather simple. All shadow areas are slightly lightened by lighter-than-normal base make-up. Different studio lighting techniques may call for a slight variation of this particular corrective make-up. Most small station productions, however, do not warrant such extensive and accurate make-up treatments.

In color television, the lighting is necessarily flatter than the lighting in monochrome shows. Some make-up artists, therefore, try to achieve greater face modeling through special make-up. But this takes much time and preparation and is rarely employed in small station operation.

### Surrounding Colors

In general, if the surrounding colors are light (light dress or suit, light background), you should use a rather light make-up color or the skin tones will turn too dark. If the surrounding colors are dark, the make-up should be slightly darker than usual or the face and other skin tones will appear too light.

In color television, the surrounding colors are sometimes reflected in the face and greatly exaggerated by the color television camera. Frequently, such skin reflections are inevitable. But you can keep this reflection problem to a minimum by carefully watching the over-all reflectance of the skin. The skin should have a normal sheen: it should be neither too oily (high reflectance) nor too dull (low reflectance but no brilliance—the skin looks lifeless).

A skin tone of a 35 per cent reflectance (approximately step three on a ten-step gray scale) is considered most appropriate for color television.

### Close-ups

Television make-up must be smooth and subtle enough so that the performer's face looks natural even in an extreme close-up. This is directly opposed to theatre make-up technique, where feature lines and colors are always greatly exaggerated for the benefit of the spectator in the last row.

A close-up of a person's face is always the best criterion for the necessity and the quality of a make-up job. If the performer looks good without make-up, no make-up is needed. Don't forget, however, to have the person move around a little before you make your final decision.

## TELEVISION MAKE-UP TECHNIQUES

In small station operation, make-up is generally used to *improve* a person's appearance. Make-up for *correcting* appearance is rarely needed. And make-up necessary to *change* appearance is almost never required. The latter does not hold true, however, for television operations in colleges and universities, where dramatic television presentations are the rule rather than the exception. Nevertheless, the scope of this handbook does not permit an extensive treatment of all facets of character make-up—that is, make-up techniques that change the actor into a specific character of a particular play. This type of make-up is generally handled by well-trained students and faculty of the theatre departments, who are quick in adapting and refining their stage techniques to the specific demands of the television medium. Most theatre make-up people are sensitive artists who usually learn more about television make-up techniques by taking a good look at an extreme close-up of a television actor's face than by reading long dissertations on the differences between the two media.

We will therefore limit our discussion to only the most basic principles of television make-up, which include (1) make-up materials, (2) make-up application, (3) make-up changes, and (4) removal of make-up.

### Make-up Materials

In general, you can use all types of commercially available make-up on television. Some cosmetic firms, however, have especially developed certain television make-up items that are easier to apply and look a little smoother on television than ordinary cosmetics. Max Factor is probably the major supplier of special television make-up.

#### Base

In television, water-base cake make-up is sometimes preferred to grease-base foundation make-up. Cake make-up is quickly put on and easily washed off. It reduces oily skin reflectance without taking away the normal sheen; additional application of powder is, in most cases, unnecessary.

The Pancake N series, produced by Max Factor, is an excellent foundation make-up for monochrome television. The pancake make-up colors range from a very light pastel pink (TV-1N) to a deep brown (TV-11N). A range from TV-4N to TV-9N is usually all you need for normal make-up. Lighter pancake shades are more often used than darker colors. The pancake series for color television ranges from CTV-1W through CTV-12W.

Any kind of commercially available powder will do for most make-up jobs. Lighter colors are preferred.

Beardsticks are grease-base sticks that help to cover the beard area for general foundation make-up. Excellent beardstick shades are Max Factor's Pan-Stik 4N, 5N, and 6N, or Stein's fairly light color sticks (No. 22) for black and white TV; for color TV, use Max Factor's Pan-Stik CTV-1W to CTV-12W.

### Eye make-up

For eye make-up you will need brown and black eyebrow pencils, eyelash curlers, mascara with roll-on applicator or black cake with brush, and eye shadow in shades of blue-green, green, and sometimes brown. However, you should use eye shadow very sparingly when working in color television.

### Cheek make-up

Cheek make-up is rarely necessary on black and white television. For color television, use Max Factor's TV Light Tech. Dry Rouge for women and TV Dark Tech. Dry Rouge for men. Any other commercially available rouge will also do, so long as the rouge color does not have too much of a blue content.

### Lip make-up

Any commercially available lipstick or lip rouge will do for lip make-up. The most commonly used lipstick color on monochrome television is a deep cherry red. Use a slightly lighter (warmer) red for color television. Max Factor's Moist Lip Rouge TV #2 Special is often used for women, darker colors (burnt sienna brown) for men. Lipstick brushes are necessary for applying lipstick or lip rouge.

In monochrome television, most men can do without lip make-up. In color television, however, lip make-up for men is often necessary.

### Special make-up

*Fingernail polish:* clear, rose-color, or any shade of warm red photographs best on monochrome and color television. Avoid deep blue-reds or purples. These shades turn dark on monochrome television.

*Teeth whitener:* dentine fluid or tooth enamel is sometimes used to make teeth appear evenly white.

*Hair whitener:* most commercially available hair whitener can be used for television make-up.

*Wigs:* theatre wigs made out of coarse materials cannot be used on television. You need carefully prepared hair pieces, especially if you would like to conceal the fact that the actor is wearing a hair piece. Artificial moustaches and side burns must also be carefully manufactured.

*Face masks, artificial noses:* standard nose putty cannot be used on television; instead, rubber and latex masks are generally used for special television make-up jobs. Special make-up paint (Max Factor's rubber mask grease paint) is available, which does not affect the rubber of the masks.

### Miscellaneous items

You must outfit your make-up kit with several miscellaneous items that are essential for any kind of television make-up: tooth and nail brushes, bobby pins, safety pins, straight pins, nail file, scissors, tweezers, razor blades, tape, tissue, cotton, towels, sponges, eraser sticks, make-up adhesives, cold cream, nail polish remover, hair spray, etc.

### TELEVISION MAKE-UP* CHART
### AND
### MAKE-UP CHART FOR PANCHROMATIC FILM TO BE TELEVISED

| Women | Very Fair | Fair | Medium or Dark |
|---|---|---|---|
| Pancake or Pan-Stik | TV-4N | TV-5N | TV-6N |
| Powder | Translucent | Translucent | Translucent |
| Eyebrow Pencil | Brown | Brown | Brown or Black |
| Liner (eye shadow) | 6 or 22 | 6 or 22 | 6 or 22 |
| Eyelash Make-up | Brownish-black | Brownish-black | Black |
| Dry Rouge | TV Light Tech. | TV Light Tech. | TV Light Tech. |
| Moist Rouge (for lips) | TV #2 | TV #2 | TV #2 |
| or | | | |
| Lipstick | Brighter Red | Brighter Red | Brighter Red |

For Film: Pancake or Pan-Stik shades are 7N for Very Fair, 8N for Fair, Medium, or Dark. Lipstick or Moist Rouge is more generously applied. All other make-up requisites remain the same as listed above.

| Men | Fair | Medium | Dark |
|---|---|---|---|
| Pancake or Pan-Stik | TV-7N | TV-8N | TV-9N |
| Powder | TV Tech. | TV Tech. | TV Tech. |

*Television Make-up is a Max Factor trade-mark. Chart courtesy of Max Factor and Company.

| | | | |
|---|---|---|---|
| Eyebrow Pencil | Brown | Brown | Brown or Black |
| Liner (eye shadow) | 22 | 22 | 22 |
| Eyelash Make-up (optional) | Brown | Brownish-black | Brownish-black |
| Dry Rouge | TV Dark Tech. | TV Dark Tech. | TV Dark Tech. |
| Moist Rouge (for lips) | TV T-3 | TV T-3 | TV T-3 |
| Grease Paint or Pan-Stik to cover beard area | TV-6N | TV-7N | TV-8N |

For Film: Pancake or Pan-Stik shades are 11N for Fair and Medium; 665F Pan-Stik or Light Egyptian Pancake for Dark. All other make-up requisites remain the same as listed above.

## COLOR TELEVISION MAKE-UP CHART

| Women | Fair | Medium or Dark |
|---|---|---|
| Pan-Stik Make-up or | CTV-3W or CTV-4W | CTV-4W or CTV-5W |
| Pancake Make-up | CTV-3W or CTV-4W | CTV-4W or CTV-5W |
| Powder | Translucent | Translucent |
| Eye Shadow | CTV Grey or CTV Brown (use sparingly) | CTV Grey or CTV Brown (use sparingly) |
| Creme Rouge (cheeks) | CTV Creme Rouge | CTV Creme Rouge |
| Dry Rouge | Flame (use sparingly) | Flame |
| Lip Pomade or | CTV Light Red | CTV Light Red |
| Lipstick | Pink N. Pretty | Pink N. Pretty |
| Eyebrow Pencil | Light Brown, Brown, or Brownish-black | Light Brown, Brown, or Brownish-black |
| Eyelash Make-up | Brown, Brownish-black, or Black | Brown, Brownish-black, or Black |

| Men | Fair | Medium or Dark |
|---|---|---|
| Pan-Stik Make-up or | CTV-6W or CTV-7W | CTV-7W or CTV-8W |
| Pancake Make-up | CTV-6W or CTV-7W | CTV-7W or CTV-8W |
| Powder | Translucent | Translucent |
| Eye Shadow | CTV Brown (use sparingly) | CTV Brown (use sparingly) |
| Eyebrow Pencil | Brown or Brownish-black | Brown or Brownish-black |
| Dry Rouge (optional) | Light Tech. | Light Tech. |
| Moist Rouge (optional) | T-3 or T-2 (use sparingly) | T-3 or T-2 |
| Lipstick | Natural (warm) | Natural (warm) |

NOTE: There are two series of Pan-Stik Make-ups: CTV-1 through CTV-15 and CTV-1W through CTV-12W. CTV-1 through CTV-15 ranges from pale ivory to very dark brown. Colors contained in this series are sufficient for all skin types. The series CTV-1W through CTV-12W is designed for light to very dark complexions, and is warmer in tone than the former series. This series is preferred for standard use. Pancake Make-up is available in the series CTV-1 through CTV-12 and CTV-1W through CTV-12W.

## Application

It is not always easy to persuade performers, especially men, to put on necessary make-up. You may do well to look at your guests on camera before deciding whether they need make-up. If they do, you must be tactful in suggesting that it may be advantageous for them to put on make-up. Try not to appeal to the performer's vanity, but rather to his desire to contribute to a good performance. Explain the necessity for make-up in technical terms; for instance, telling a bald-headed man that the camera tube will respond better if he puts on some make-up may be more successful than telling him that there are terrible light reflections bouncing off his bald spot.

If you have a mirror available, seat the performer in front of it so that he or she can watch the entire make-up procedure. Adequate, even illumination is very important. If you have to do the make-up in the studio, have a small hand mirror ready.

Most women performers will be glad to apply the more complicated make-up themselves. Putting on lipstick and mascara, for instance, present no problem to the average woman, whereas men may struggle unnecessarily long over such "routine matters." Also, most regular television talent will prefer to apply make-up themselves; they usually know what kind of make-up they need for a specific television show.

### Foundation

*Improving appearance.* Apply pancake base with a wet sponge evenly over the face and exposed skin areas. Make sure to get the base right up into the hair line. Have a towel ready to wipe off excess make-up. If close-ups of hands are shown, you must also apply pancake base to hands and arms. This is especially important to men performers who demonstrate small objects on camera. If an uneven suntan is exposed (especially if the performer wears bare-back dresses or different kinds of bathing suits) all bare skin areas must be covered with base make-up. Baldheaded men need a generous amount of pancake foundation to tone down obvious light reflections and to cover up perspiration. Women should use TV-4N to TV-6N (CTV-3W to CTV-5W), depending on their complexions and on the surrounding colors. Men use darker foundation colors, TV-6N and TV-7N (CTV-6W to CTV-8W).

Be careful not to give your male performers a baby-face complexion. It is sometimes even desirable to have a little beard area show. Frequently, a slight covering up of the beard with a beardstick is all that is needed. If additional pancake foundation is necessary (for

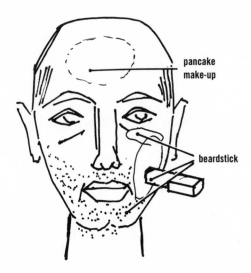

pancake
make-up

beardstick

baldheaded men, for instance), the Pan-Stik around the beard area should be applied first and set with some powder. For color shows, a very light application of a yellow or orange grease paint counteracts a heavy beard quite satisfactorily. Then the whole face, including the beard area, is covered with pancake foundation.

*Correcting appearance.* Lighter base colors can be used for corrective treatment of deep-set eyes and other heavy shadow areas caused by overhead lighting. Be careful, however, not to make this corrective treatment too obvious. It is best to use a pancake foundation that is only two or three N numbers lighter than that used for the over-all base.

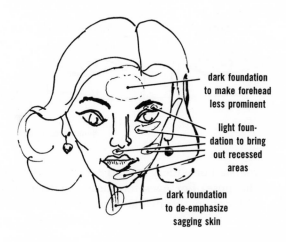

dark foundation
to make forehead
less prominent

light foun-
dation to bring
out recessed
areas

dark foundation
to de-emphasize
sagging skin

You can also make more prominent parts less obvious by applying a somewhat darker foundation color. The general principle for corrective make-up is to use lighter-than-normal foundation on recessed areas and darker-than-normal foundation on areas that you want to de-emphasize.

*Changing appearance.* Very light and very dark foundation colors may be necessary for special effects. If grease-base make-up is used, it must be set with powder. Sometimes you may decide to use no make-up at all, especially when hard and rugged features are desired.

### Eye make-up

You must be careful with any phase of eye make-up. Use too little rather than too much. Unless you have your own method, start with the eyebrow make-up first, then apply the eye shadow, next the lining of the eyelids, and finally mascara on the lashes. This sequence allows you to work freely on the eyes without the constant danger of smearing certain parts of eye make-up over the performer's face.

*Eyebrows.* Most eyebrows photograph sufficiently dark without make-up. Blond women and very blond men, however, need some eyebrow emphasis.

When you darken eyebrows, don't just draw a line along the general direction of the brow, but start directly above the inside corner of the eye and pencil one eyebrow hair at a time. Unfortunately, this procedure takes time, but it is necessary for good eye make-up. The eyebrow should stop about half an inch beyond the outer corner of the eye.

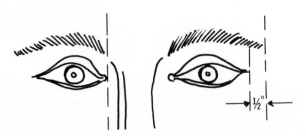

Normal eyebrow make-up

*Corrective application.* For widely spaced eyes, start the eyebrow closer to the base of the nose. For eyes too close together, space the eyebrows slightly wider than the inside corners of the eyes.

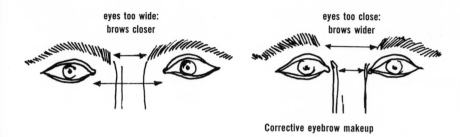

eyes too wide:
brows closer

eyes too close:
brows wider

Corrective eyebrow makeup

### Lip make-up

Apply lip rouge or lipstick with a lipstick brush. Carefully paint the upper lip first and then paint the lower lip. Sometimes you may want to have the performer press the painted upper lip on the lower lip to find the general outline. Always blot dry freshly made-up lips.

*Corrective application.* If the lips are too small, carefully paint the lip rouge beyond the natural lip line. If the lips are too large, cover part of the lips with pancake foundation and paint the lips slightly smaller. Always follow the natural lip line.

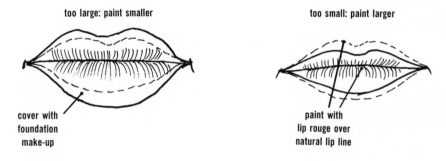

too large: paint smaller

too small: paint larger

cover with
foundation
make-up

paint with
lip rouge over
natural lip line

### Cheek make-up

Cheek rouge is not essential in television make-up. If you use cheek make-up for color television, use a small amount of Max Factor's TV Light Tech. Rouge and blend it into the foundation make-up right along the cheek bone. On monochrome television, cheek rouge is usually unnecessary.

## Make-up Changes

In live television, quick and involved make-up changes are a constant hazard. You may have only one minute in which to change a young girl into an old woman, or an ugly creature into a handsome prince. Costume changes are usually made at the same time, and this does anything but help the make-up man.

Fortunately, the video taping of shows has made such fast make-up changes largely unnecessary. However, if a fast make-up change is required, you can wash off one make-up layer, thereby revealing a second face that had been made up underneath. This procedure, however, requires several professional make-up artists; even then, such changes are always hazardous.

### Removal of Make-up

You can remove oil-base make-up (beardsticks, lipstick, etc.) with cold cream and facial tissues. Pancake foundations can be washed off with soap and water. After you have removed all make-up, you should apply a good skin lotion to avoid unpleasant skin irritations.

More complex make-up that involves special adhesives for beards and hair pieces must be removed with special solvents.

Always have plenty of facial tissues and towels handy.

At the end of each show, check your make-up kit to see which items need replacing. Clean your brushes carefully and disinfect particularly your lipstick brushes.

## CLOTHING AND COSTUMING FACTORS

In small station operation you will be concerned mainly with clothing the performer rather than costuming the actor. The clothes of the television performer must be attractive and stylish, but not too conspicuous or too showy in any respect. The television viewer expects the television performer to be well dressed, in the same manner as employees of banks or other respectable business establishments are dressed.

Naturally, the type of clothing worn by the performer depends largely on his taste. But it also depends on the type of program or occasion and the particular setting in which he works.

There are, however, certain types of clothing that look better on television than others.

The television camera may look at you both from a distance and at close range. If it takes a long shot of you, the lines and the color or gray scale of your clothes are important; if it takes a close-up, the texture and pattern of the material become important. We must, therefore, consider the following factors: (1) materials, (2) color and gray scale, (3) line, and (4) decorative accessories.

## Materials

Good texture is important for all materials worn on television. Sometimes, even if contrasting colors or gray-scale values are not present, you can achieve an interesting variety by using different-textured materials.

Heavy materials are good for table covers and draperies, but not for television clothing. Heavy material makes a suit or a dress look baggy and bulky on camera.

Also, be discriminating in using materials with a high degree of sheen, such as satins and sateen, or any kind of polished material for men's suits. High-gloss suits are all right if worn for "showy" occasions. The master of ceremonies of a flashy variety show, for instance, may look quite appropriate in a highly polished silk suit, but the same suit will probably look out of place if worn by a newscaster or lecturer. Women performers, however, can greatly benefit from such materials: a glossy blouse may look very attractive when contrasted with a skirt of a more conservative material.

Don't use patterns that are too busy and too contrasting. Dresses with dark and light stripes, polka dots, or other closely spaced geometric patterns should not be worn on television. The electronic system of the camera is not capable of handling such extremely contrasting patterns, and these patterns can cause irritating vibrations on the television screen. Sometimes you may notice on the monitor that the stripes extend beyond the dress and bleed through surrounding sets and objects. Color television is especially susceptible to this problem.

Fine detail in a pattern will either look too busy or appear smudgy on camera. If you intend to combine different patterns, the more detailed material should be worn above the waist, since close-ups are focused on the upper half of a person's body.

Furs look better on camera if they are of the short-hair variety.

## Color and Gray Scale

### Monochrome television

Many television people insist that black and white are colors that the television system cannot handle. This is not quite true. Whether white or black can be used depends largely on the surrounding colors and the light reflectance of the material. A woman performer can wear a white dress if it is made out of nonglossy material, such as wool, as long as she wears it in front of a medium- to dark-gray background. On the other hand, a starched white linen dress or a glossy polished cotton dress cannot be worn on camera, even in front of a suitable background. Stark-white, glossy clothes turn exposed skin areas dark on the television screen. Performers who have a dark complexion should definitely avoid wearing white or light yellow. Black can be worn, as long as the performer does not stand in front of an extremely light background. Black velvet, for instance, which has a nice luster in a brightly lighted studio, photographs very well on television.

A pleasant color contrast is desirable, but only to a certain degree. For example, avoid any combination of black and white, whether it is worn by one person or by two performers working next to each other. If you wear a dark suit, reduce the contrast by wearing a pastel-colored shirt. Pink, light green, yellow, and tan all photograph white on monochrome television.

If, on the other hand, the contrast is not great enough, you may run into difficulties. A performer who is modeling a bathing suit must be especially careful to have sufficient contrast between bathing suit color and skin tone, or she may appear to be not properly dressed. The same care must be exercised when evening gowns are worn; beautiful pastel colors may turn into uninspiring and often spotty grays.

In general, choose colors for your on-camera clothes that are not too similar to your complexion and the surrounding set colors, but also not too contrasting. If you have a dark complexion, wear something that is either lighter or darker than your skin color. A blond woman will probably look better in a dark blouse than in a light-colored one. A dark-haired man should probably wear a fairly light suit. Contrasting accents can be achieved by adding different-colored accessories, such as scarves, belts, and jewelry for women, and ties for men.

### Color television

When you choose material for color television, again keep the compatibility with monochrome television in mind. Sometimes you will find that it is simply impossible to make all your costume colors perfectly compatible, and a beautiful color costume may look like a solid, washed-out gray on the black and white monitor.

In deciding on what colors to choose for color television clothing and costuming, you must first answer the following basic questions:

1. Do the colors used for the dress or costume harmonize with each other, and do they televise properly?

2. Are the color combinations kept as simple as possible? (Three different prominent colors in one costume are all you should generally use.)

3. Is the color combination compatible? Is the gray scale value of the color combination too great or not great enough?

4. Do the colors of the costume harmonize with the colors of other costumes on camera at the same time?

5. Do the costume colors harmonize with surrounding set colors? If you have to stage a complicated scene with many color costumes involved, you may ask your dress designer to make up a color chart indicating what costumes are together in what particular setting. In general, this problem occurs infrequently in small station operation. If a college play is staged in color (even if it is only for monochrome television pickup), a costume chart is ordinarily prepared anyway.

Before you make a final decision on whether a certain combination looks good and whether it photographs well on black and white television, check it on camera. Sometimes, different lighting, variations in color temperature, and the specific chemical constitution of certain colors may cause the colors to televise differently, although they may look identical to the human eye.

### Line

The line or silhouette of clothing must also be considered. Unless certain special effects are desired, a slender line always looks better than a stout, hanging line. Unfortunately, television has the tendency to put a few pounds on the performer appearing on the tele-

no    yes    no    yes

vision screen. The slim silhouette of television clothing is designed to combat this problem. Slim dresses and rather tight-fitting suits are, therefore, preferred. If wide skirts are worn, a slim waistline should be emphasized. Avoid any heavy, horizontally striped material, and baggy dresses and suits. The over-all silhouette of your clothing must look pleasing from a variety of angles. It must look slim but comfortable on you. Strapless gowns seldom look good on television, especially in a close-up.

### Decorative Accessories

If the woman performer wears sporty attire, contrasting scarves often add considerably to the charm and character of the outfit. If belts are worn, shiny belt buckles must be sprayed with dulling spray or painted with clear fingernail polish.

Jewelry is an important dressing accessory. The style of the jewelry worn depends entirely, of course, on the taste of the performer. In general, the performer should not overload herself with flashy jewelry; she should instead choose a few distinctive pieces that add rather than distract from the total appearance. Simple, elegant designs, such as pearls, photograph best. In monochrome television, highly polished and sparkling jewelry should be avoided. Rhinestone jewelry and diamonds may cause heavy, distracting glares. If highly reflective jewelry is worn, it must be sprayed with dulling spray or painted with clear fingernail polish. The color camera, however, is much less sensitive to high-gloss reflections; a limited amount of sparkling jewelry is often quite effective on color television.

Neckties should be used to accent the suit in color and texture. If you perform on monochrome television, the particular color of the tie matters little as long as you can achieve sufficient contrast. Avoid wearing a tie clasp. This otherwise decorative and useful item can become a great nuisance when worn on camera. Most tie clasps cause heavy flaring and generally interfere with the wearing of a lapel microphone. If the performer cannot get along without a tie clasp, he must wear it so low that it cannot be seen.

As attractive as a white handkerchief may look sticking out of a dark blue suit pocket, you should not wear it on television. Even the best video engineer cannot properly control such extreme gray scale contrast without getting the over-all picture slightly muddy.

## COSTUMES AND COSTUME CHANGES

The theatre departments of colleges and universities usually have a well-stocked costume room from which to draw standard period costumes. Special costumes can sometimes be rented from special rental services in larger cities. If you use stock costumes on television, make sure that the costumes look convincing even in a tight close-up. Sometimes the general construction and, especially, the detail of theatre costume accessories are too coarse for the television camera. You then have the choice of not using the costume at all or of re-sewing it a little more carefully.

If you use the costumes for a live television show, check whether rapid costume changes are involved and, if so, whether the particular costumes allow quick changing. Hooks and eyes are safe but usually too slow for very quick costume changes. Zippers are the fastest changing device, unless they get stuck; then you may wish you had used ordinary buttons or hooks.

Quite frequently you can achieve a fast costume change by having the actor wear two costumes, or simply by adding or subtracting major costume accessories. Remember to alert your producer or director of any difficult costume change, especially if a proposed show is to be done live.

## SUMMARY

Make-up is always used for three basic reasons: (1) to improve appearance, (2) to correct appearance, and (3) to change appearance. The different purposes for applying make-up require different make-up techniques. Make-up for improving appearance is the simplest make-up procedure; make-up for changing appearance is the most complex job.

Television make-up is also influenced by certain electronic and production factors. These are (1) reproduction peculiarities of the camera picture tube, (2) television lighting techniques, (3) surrounding colors, and (4) close-up techniques. In general, the monochrome picture tubes tend to photograph warm colors lighter, cool colors somewhat darker than they appear to the human eye. On color television, the compatibility of the make-up colors must always be taken into consideration. Also, the surrounding colors are sometimes reflected in the performer's face and greatly exaggerated by the color camera. The degree of skin reflection must, therefore, be controlled by make-up.

The most important principles of television make-up techniques include (1) make-up materials, (2) make-up application techniques, (3) make-up changes, and (4) removal of make-up.

For most nondramatic programs, carefully applied standard street make-up will suffice for women performers, and standard base make-

up (including beardstick make-up) will suffice for men performers.
The final check as to the necessity for make-up or the quality of
make-up application is a careful check of the talent's appearance on
the control room monitor.

Since the television camera looks at clothing from a distance as
well as close-up, four basic factors must be considered: (1) materials,
(2) color and gray scale, (3) line, and (4) decorative accessories.

Good texture is important for materials worn on television. Busy
patterns and closely spaced geometric patterns should be avoided,
however. Light materials are often better looking than heavy materials.

Too much brightness contrast in clothing should be avoided as
much as too little contrast. Surrounding colors play an important
part in choosing the proper color contrast. The colors of the performers' clothing should harmonize but must also be compatible
with black and white reception.

A slender silhouette always looks better than a stout, hanging
line. Horizontally striped, baggy clothing should be avoided. Flashy
jewelry can be worn on color television, but it frequently causes
undesirable reflections on monochrome television.

Costumes for plays must be neat enough to tolerate extreme close-
ups and must have provisions (such as sturdy zippers) for reliable,
fast costume changes.

### EXERCISES

1. What are the three basic reasons for applying make-up?
2. A well-known pianist, who has agreed to appear on your "Meet
   the Artist" show, asks you what he should wear for the occasion.
   He is an elderly gentleman with slightly gray hair. What is your
   answer?
3. An amateur drama group received permission to perform a short
   one-act play on your "Creative Man" series. All actors require
   complicated character make-up. Neither the acting group nor you
   can supply the necessary make-up artists. What would you do?
4. The commercial announcer complains that the floor manager suggested he get rid of his five o'clock shadow before going on the air,
   although he had just shaved before going to the studio. What
   would you tell him?
5. Your floor manager tells you that one of the guest performers, an
   elderly and prominent gentleman, refuses to have make-up put
   on. What would you do?

6. A woman performer cannot understand why you complain about her purple lipstick color, especially since a famous beauty expert has specifically recommended this particular color. How do you justify your complaint?

7. You are asked by a high school group to advise them on the purchase of the most basic television make-up items. They have a very limited budget. What items would you suggest? Why?

8. Your Sunday program will feature a local church choir. The set designer is very much concerned about the color of the choir robes. The choir conductor has told you that the color of the robes is a medium red. The set designer, however, is not satisfied with this answer. He finally insists on seeing the robes personally. How do you explain his great concern about this seemingly minor problem?

9. The new hostess for the Late-Late Show tells you that she has a magnificent gown that would fit the nature of her performance perfectly. What questions would you ask her to find out whether the dress really is suitable for the occasion?

10. The representative of a well-known bathing suit manufacturer would like to incorporate a fashion preview on your morning variety show. She tells you that the suits come in different designs, colors, and textures, from a conservative light-pastel, one-piece bathing suit to a dark-blue polka dot bikini. She assures you that all models are good-looking and deeply tanned. Assuming that you agree to the fashion show, what technical points would you have to discuss with her?

# 11

# The Television Studio
# and Control Centers

Every television program has two program centers: (1) the program origination center and (2) the program control center.

The program origination center is the space in which prepared television shows are put before the cameras. The program control center is the control room in which all activities of the program origination center are properly coordinated.

# PROGRAM ORIGINATION CENTER:
# THE TELEVISION STUDIO

Telecasts can originate anywhere, indoors and outdoors, as long as there is room enough for one camera, power facilities to drive the camera, and enough light so that the camera can see. Most television programs, however, originate in the television studio.

## Physical Layout

The television studio is primarily designed to accommodate television cameras. The studio must allow an unobstructed camera view and maximum camera flexibility.

### Size

The size of the television studio relates directly to the flexibility of programming. The larger the studio, the more complex the programming can become. Complicated shows that involve a multitude of large sets can be produced only in a large television studio. Small studios are forced to restrict the extent and complexity of their shows.

A 40 × 50 foot studio is generally sufficient for most small station operation. But a larger studio is definitely better, even for very simple shows.

### Ceiling height

Since the average television scenery is 10 feet high, a minimum ceiling height of 12 feet is essential. A 15-foot ceiling is sufficient for most small station operation. A higher ceiling (up to 25 feet) is better, however, since it allows some working and cooling space above the lighting grid, which may be anywhere from 12 to 18 feet above the studio floor. A low ceiling is the most serious problem in a room that is to be converted into a television studio.

### Floor

The studio floor must be even and smooth to allow easy and continuous camera movement. The floor must have an extremely hard surface that is not easily marked or scarred by the heavy studio equipment constantly moved about on it. Most studios have concrete floors that are polished or covered with special linoleum or asphalt tile. The color of the studio floor is usually light to provide maximum light reflections.

In some large studios, the studio floors "float"—that is, they are not attached to the studio walls—and outside shocks and vibrations are thus not transferred into the studio.

### Walls

All walls and the ceiling should be acoustically treated. Generous layers of rock wool, held in place by a wire mesh, have proved to be the most practical sound-deadening material.

There must be no windows in the studio, since the outside light would make controlled studio lighting impossible, and the windows would admit sound from outside.

Large, soundproof doors should lead to scene docks and prop rooms, and to an outside loading ramp for the delivery of large properties, such as appliances and cars. Red warning lights on the outside of the studio doors indicate when a television show is in progress.

## Special Studio Installations

### Wall outlets

You will find it convenient to have separate camera and microphone outlets in at least two opposite corners of the studio. These outlets are especially advantageous if your performance areas are spread throughout the studio. Sometimes complicated sets may prevent you from plugging your camera and microphone cables into the usual wall outlet, at which time a second outlet box in a different studio location becomes essential.

Besides outlets for camera and microphone cables, you will need several distribution boxes for the studio monitors as well as many standard A.C. outlets staggered along the studio walls for easy accessibility. Special A.C. outlets are needed for high wattage equipment, such as rear screen projectors and floor scoops.

Several outlets for the floor crew's communication system and for outside telephones must also be provided.

### Studio monitors

You need at least two mobile studio monitors for the average-sized television studio. The coaxial cable for the video signal and the A.C. cable should be long enough so that the monitors can be pushed into every performance area within the studio. The larger the monitor screen, the easier it is for the performer to see. Frequently, the bright studio lighting will wash out the monitor picture and reduce its quality. For this reason, you may want to build a simple detachable shield around the monitor, which will block most of the overhead lighting.

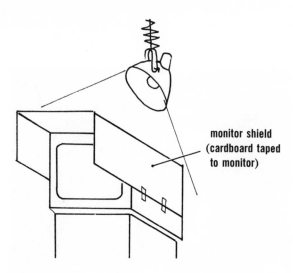

monitor shield
(cardboard taped
to monitor)

The monitor cables are usually suspended from the ceiling so that they can be kept off the studio floor. You can easily make a simple counterweight system for this purpose.

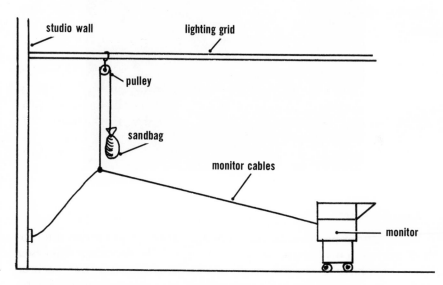

studio wall    lighting grid

pulley

sandbag

monitor cables

monitor

In a small studio, you can hang a studio monitor directly from the lighting grid. A heavy pantograph makes an excellent monitor suspension device. By this means you can lower and raise the monitor according to need.

If you have a studio audience, you will need one or two additional large-screen monitors.

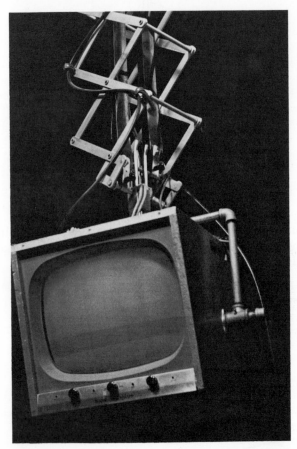

Monitor hung from pantograph

### Studio loudspeakers

Every studio has two speaker systems. One system carries the program sound. This particular system is especially necessary whenever performers have to gear their actions to the program sound, such as dancers or singers who are accompanied by recorded music or who mouth the words to one of their recordings.

The other system is the "talkback system." This system (sometimes called the S.A., or Studio Address, system) is used by the director and the T.D. to give special instructions to people who are not connected with the telephone intercommunication system. The talkback is generally used during rehearsals but not on the air. In case the director accidentally uses the talkback while the studio microphones are turned on, an automatic switch cuts all microphones as soon as the talkback is operated.

### Light control facilities

In large studios, the dimmer control board is often positioned right on the studio floor where the lighting engineer can oversee most of the important performance areas. If the control room is large enough, the dimmer board can also be put there. The patchboard is almost always located in the studio; this location makes patching during the initial lighting setup quite convenient.

### Intercommunication system

All studios must be equipped with a special intercommunication system that permits conversation from control room to studio and from studio to control room while a show is in progress. All members of the production and engineering crews must be in constant contact with the control room personnel during every studio show.

In most small stations, the telephone intercommunication system (intercom) is used. The cameramen have headsets that plug into special intercom outlets on the camera. The floor manager and some of the floor men wear headsets (standard telephone headsets: one earphone and a small microphone for talkback) that are connected with the control room through long, flexible, light-weight rubber cable. The disadvantage of this arrangement is that the cable frequently gets in the way of moving cameras and microphone booms, or becomes tangled up in one of the many pieces of scenery on the studio floor. Although there are provisions on the television cameras for plugging in additional earphones, the production people should not hook up their intercom phones with any of the studio cameras so long as they have separate intercom wall outlets. Tying up with a camera not only limits the operation radius of a floor man, but also interferes with the camera's flexibility.

Larger studios employ a wireless intercommunication system. A small transmitter sends the director's signals into the studio where they are picked up by a small pocket receiver worn by the floor personnel. A special earplug replaces the more cumbersome headset. With this system, the floor personnel cannot talk back to the control room, however.

Frequently it is necessary to supply program sound and control room signals simultaneously. When this happens, a double headset is used in which one earphone carries the program sound, the other earphone the program signals. These headsets are worn by the microphone boom operator and by some studio musicians (usually the orchestra leader) who have to gear their actions to both the program sound and the director's signals.

In most television operations, the director and the technical director (production and engineering crews) use the same intercommunication line, which means that everybody is heard over the same channel. Although in some television stations the engineering and production lines are separate, the one-channel system is much simpler and, therefore, preferred by most television directors.

### Audience area

Some studios have a built-in audience area, but this area is not necessary for small station operation, and it is often inconvenient. If you have an audience-participation show, you can set up collapsible risers directly on the studio floor, leaving one or two aisles through which the cameras can dolly.

If you turn a camera on the audience, you may do well to shut off the monitors during this period, unless you want to put up with the waving and mugging of some people who are eager to see themselves "on television."

## PROGRAM CONTROL CENTER: THE TELEVISION CONTROL ROOM

### Physical Layout

The studio control room is usually adjacent to the studio, on a higher level, and separated by a thick double-glass window. The window is usually 3 to 5 feet above the studio floor.

For simple studio operation, a single-level control room will suffice; for more complicated television operations, and especially for teaching purposes, a two-level or multi-level control room is better.

In a single-level control room, the operators sit next to each other; in a split-level control room, the control room operators sit next to and behind each other.

### Control Room Operators and Equipment

Each control room is divided into three distinct controlling areas: (1) the program control, (2) the video control, and (3) the audio control.

### Program control

The television director is in charge of the program control. He must be able to preview all pictures supplied by the various television

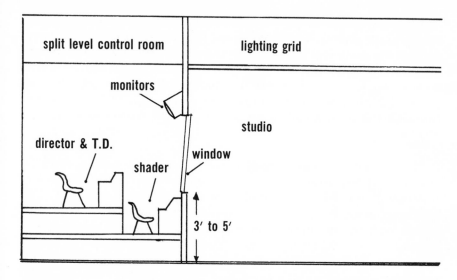

cameras, listen to the program audio, and converse with all members of the production and engineering personnel through the intercommunication system. He must work with the following program control equipment: (1) one preview monitor for each studio camera, (2) the film chain and video tape preview monitors, (3) the master or line monitor (showing the picture that is switched on the air), (4) the intercommunication switches and microphone for the talkback, (5) the speaker with program sound, and (6) a clock.

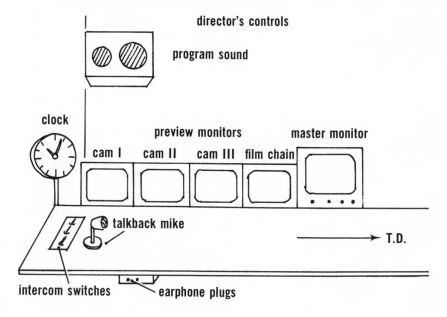

The preview monitors show continuously all pictures supplied by the various cameras. The director can thus choose one of the pictures and tell the technical director to switch this particular picture on the air. Sometimes the director will have to do his own switching, which means that he not only selects the pictures but also works the mechanical button device that puts these pictures on the air. The picture that has been punched up appears on the master monitor.

### Video controls

The video controls are usually in the hands of two people: the T.D. and the video control engineer, sometimes called "the shader."

Although the T.D. is responsible for every technical aspect of a live television show, his primary job while the show is on the air is to switch from one picture source to another according to the director's signals.

Because the T.D. and the director work closely together, the T.D.'s switching panel must be located next to the director's control table. In some operations, however, the switching panel is located one level down from the director, or in a different corner of the control room. This separation of director from T.D. is unfortunate and often results in rather sloppy, or at least impersonal, mechanical switching.

### Video switcher

Depending on the complexity of electronic equipment, the video switching panel may be relatively simple or extremely complicated. Even a simple video switcher should provide at least three switching possibilities: (1) program monitoring and previewing, (2) switching between studio cameras, and (3) special effects, such as fading and dissolving.

The individual rows of buttons are called "banks" or "buses." Bus 1 and bus 2 are switching buttons for different program sources: studio cameras, slides, telops, film, etc. Bus 3 is a preview bus that permits the T.D. to preview other program sources while one program is already on the air. The fading levers enable the T.D. to fade *from* or *to* black, to dissolve, and to super. The last button is the "black" button, which releases the switcher and produces a black image on the screen. This button can also be used for an extra program source. You may, however, find many switchers with one button, labeled "film," which handles all originations from the film projection chain, including film, slides, and telops. In addition to that, there may be a separate film chain switching unit that allows you to start and stop the film projector, turn on and advance slides and telops, and operate the video tape machine on this remote control.

line or off-the-air monitor button    preview program
switch

fading levers

black

g

f

e

d

bus 3 ⇒    c

bus 2    b

bus 1    a

(a) button for camera one; (b) button for camera two; (c) button for camera three; (d) arbitrary (depending on the station's wiring); generally: slide; (e) film; (f) telop; (g) auxiliary buttons for remote program sources.

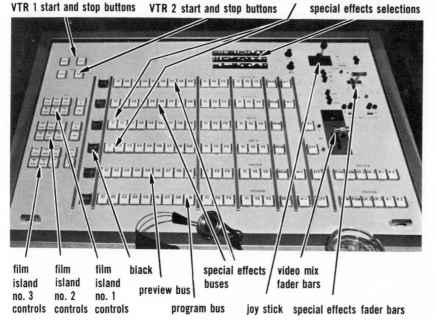

mix buses (for regular switching)

VTR 1 start and stop buttons    VTR 2 start and stop buttons    special effects selections

film
island
no. 3
controls

film
island
no. 2
controls

film
island
no. 1
controls

black

preview bus

program bus

special effects
buses

video mix
fader bars

joy stick    special effects fader bars

Large video switcher with special effects buses and vtr, film, and slide remote controls (Studio 1, San Francisco State College)

397

More complex switchers have special-effects buses, faders, and a joy stick. Also, remote film, slide, and video tape controls are usually incorporated into the more complex switching system.

*Operation.* In the type of switcher illustrated below, the left fading handle activates bus 2 (upper bank); the right fading handle activates bus 1 (lower bank). If both fading handles are pushed up (away from you), you must switch on bus 2; if both levers are down (toward you), you must switch on bus 1.

**levers down: bus 1 active**        **levers up: bus 2 active**

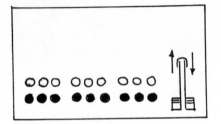    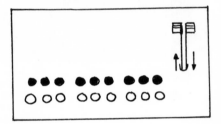

*Cut.* Let us assume that bus 2 is active and you have pressed the camera one button on bus 2: camera one is on the air. If you want to cut from camera one to camera two, simply press the camera two button on the same bus (upper bank). In order to cut back to camera one, you press the camera one button again. If you want to put a slide on the air, you punch up the slide button on the same bank.

**camera I on air (bus 2)**    **cut to camera II**    **camera II on air (bus 2)**

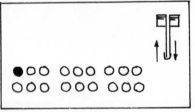    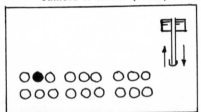

*Dissolve.* For a dissolve from camera one to camera two, punch the camera two button on bus 1 (lower bank) while camera one is already punched up on bus 2 (upper bank). Then move both fading levers from the upper bank to the lower bank. The speed at which you pull the levers determines the speed of the dissolve.

camera I on air

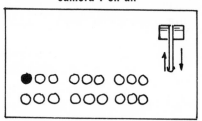

dissolve to camera II preset

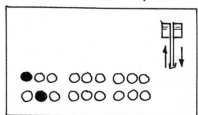

dissolve in progress (super effect)

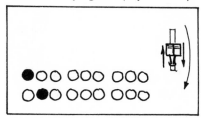

dissolve finished; camera II on air

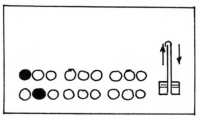

*Super.* You can accomplish a superimposure two different ways: (1) You can preset the buttons in the same way you would preset a dissolve and then move the fading handles halfway between bus 1 and bus 2. Both banks will be activated, each delivering a picture with exactly half the picture strength. This supering method is quite satisfactory. (2) A better super, however, can be achieved by operating only one of the two fading levers. If both levers are pushed up, activating bus 2, for instance, take the right lever only and pull it down, in the direction of the lever arrow. This will gradually activate bus 1 and put the punched up camera on the air, too. The advantage of this method is that the intensity of the superimposure can be better controlled.

*Fade.* You can fade in on either bank by moving one of the fading levers to its corresponding bank.

In a fade to black, the levers are split against the arrows. This means that you pull bus 2 lever to bus 1 and push bus 1 lever to bus 2. Both banks are thereby blocked from putting out any video signal. You can also fade to black by punching the release button on the inactive bank (which releases all previous connections) and then bringing up both levers from the active bank to this inactive bank. What you are doing, in effect, is dissolving to black.

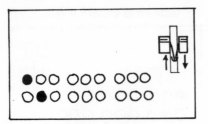

super method one: both buses are active; levers are half-way

method two:
camera I on air (bus 2)
camera II preset for super

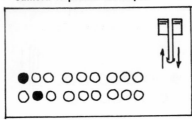

bring bus 1 fader down:
bus 1 is activated for super

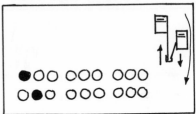

fade-in camera I on
bus 2 (move left lever up)

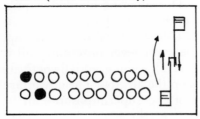

fade in camera II on bus 1
(move right lever down)

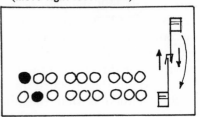

fade to black:
split levers against arrows

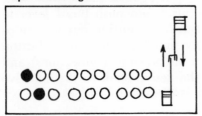

fade to black:
move both levers to activate
release button

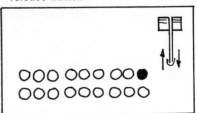

Other special effects can also be controlled with the fading levers. A great amount of auxiliary equipment, however, is needed for special effects switching. (See Chapter 7.)

### Picture control

The quality of the television pictures, as they are supplied by the cameras, is constantly controlled by the video control engineer. His main concern is the proper shading of the picture, which means that he is constantly controlling the black and white contrast and the color levels while watching the special video control monitors.

In small station operation, the T.D. must often take care of the shading in addition to his switching job. This puts a very great burden on the T.D., especially when he is engaged in a fast three-camera show.

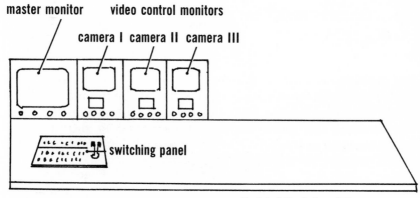

Technical director's controls

This switcher-shader combination is only possible, however, if the video control monitors are installed next to the switching panel (single-level control room) rather than on the lower level (double-level control room) or in master control.

In a split-level operation, the director and the T.D. work on the upper level, the video control engineer on the lower level. Large preview and master monitors are usually placed in front of the director's desk or hung above the control room window for the program control operation.

### Audio control

The audio control facilities are usually separated from the video controls. The audio control facilities can be considered a small radio station attached to the television control room. Frequently, a sliding

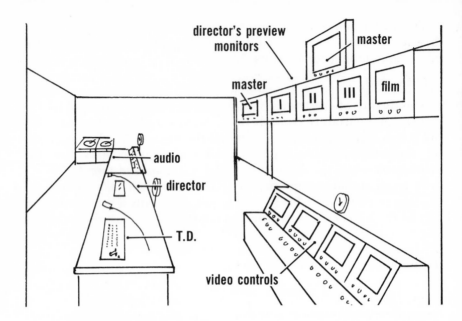

glass door connects the audio control room with the video control room. The reason for this separation is that the audio man must be able to work undisturbed from the seeming confusion in the video control room. The audio engineer is connected to the intercommunication system by earphones or by a small loudspeaker hooked up with the director's intercom line.

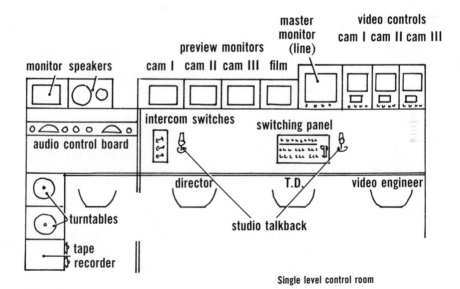

Single level control room

The audio control room usually houses two turntables, one or two tape recorders or cartridge systems, the audio control board, and a line monitor for the master monitor picture. The audio booth itself is connected with the television studio by a large double-glass window, like that of the video control room, which allows the audio engineer to observe the manipulation of the different studio microphones.

The audio engineer controls all facets of television audio, including (1) all studio microphones, (2) recorded music and sound effects, (3) film audio, (4) video tape audio, (5) audio tape, (6) video tape beeper, (7) telephone beeper, (8) audio playback level, and (9) talkback level and level of intercommunication system.

## MASTER CONTROL

Master control is the nerve center of a television station. Generally, the master control room houses the complete film chain and often the video tape machines. Most of the electronic camera control equipment, such as all the synchronizing generators, are also located in the master control room. And sometimes all camera video controls are put into master control, too. A switching control enables the two operators (who are on duty during the whole broadcast day) to receive the programs from the studio, from remote location, or from

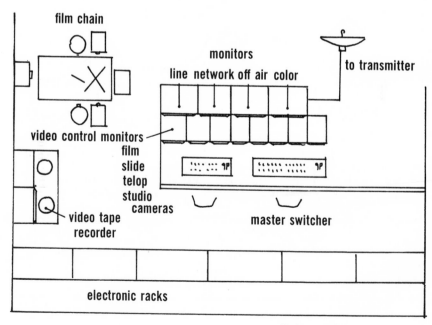

Master control room

the network. Any of these signals can be switched to the line that carries it to the transmitter, where it is actually telecast.

The master control panel looks much like the studio control board, except that it is a little more complicated. In addition to the usual preview monitors, there are the film chain monitors, the video tape monitors, the network line monitor, and the off-the-air receiver (which acts exactly like a home receiver, taking the picture "off the air").

## ADDITIONAL PRODUCTION SPACE

In addition to the studio and control room facilities, you must have adequate space for prop storage, scene storage and construction, and make-up and dressing rooms for men and women. Ideally, the additional production space should be at least two to three times as large as the studio space.

All these rooms should be located as close as possible to the main studio or studios. This is especially important for the property and scenery storage rooms. Hallways and doors must be large enough to permit easy movement of heavy and bulky properties and scenery.

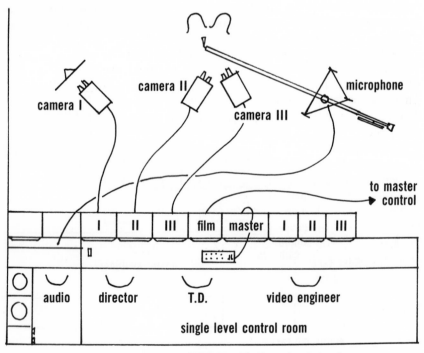

Television origination and control centers

Make-up and dressing rooms must have proper mirrors and good, even lighting that is of the same color temperature as the studio lighting.

## SUMMARY

There are two program centers for every program origination: (1) the program origination center (usually the television studio) and (2) the program control center (usually the television control room).

The size of the television studio directly influences the flexibility of programming. The larger the studio, the greater the programming potential. Two of the most important factors of a television studio are the ceiling height and the studio floor. A minimum ceiling height of 12 feet is required for hanging the lighting instruments. The studio floor must be smooth and even to permit easy and smooth camera movement.

Special studio installations include a variety of wall outlets, studio monitors, studio loudspeakers, light control facilities, and an intercommunications system.

Some studios have special audience areas that accommodate a studio audience; the audience can, if desired, become part of the show.

The program control center—the control room—is usually adjacent to the television studio, separated by a thick, soundproof double-glass window. In small studios, the control room facilities are installed on a single level; for more complicated television operations, and especially for teaching purposes, a two- or multi-level control room is preferred.

The control room is divided into three distinct controlling areas: (1) program control (director, associate director, and producer), (2) video control (including the switching panel and the camera control monitors), and (3) the audio control.

Master control is the nerve center of a television station. It houses the complete film chain or chains and often the video tape recorder. Master switching controls with necessary monitors and camera control equipment are also housed in the master control room.

## EXERCISES

1. The school official asks you to look at different rooms and tell him which one you think is most suitable for remodeling into a tele-

vision studio. What would you look for? On what factors is your decision based?

2. You are asked to design a simple control room. What factors would you have to consider? What basic control equipment must you install for a three-camera chain?
3. How do you preset a dissolve?
4. How do you preset a super?
5. Can you cut from one camera to another (from camera two to camera one) while supering a slide? If so, how?
6. Can you dissolve from one camera to the other while supering a slide? If so, how?
7. How can you fade to black?
8. What is the function of a preview bus?
9. Design a good setup for a studio audience area, including seating arrangements and audio and video monitor locations.
10. What are the basic functions of master control?

# 12

## Producing and Directing

In small station operation, the producing and directing jobs are usually handled by one person acting as producer-director. This combination seems to work out quite well, since many duties of small station producing and directing overlap. Nevertheless, this work combination puts an extra burden on each job.

For the sake of better clarification, we will discuss the duties of the producer and the director separately.

# THE PRODUCER'S DUTIES

The television producer is the organizer of a show. He frequently creates show ideas and then prepares the necessary material for on-the-air production. He takes care of all financial matters, contracts, and material clearances. He knows what technical facilities are available and what the potentials and limitations of these facilities are. The producer coordinates rehearsal and performance schedules and sees to it that his show receives the necessary publicity and promotion.

The specific duties of the television producer naturally change with each different show idea. Sometimes a show has to be developed from scratch; at other times, the television producer may receive a television script in which most of the production details have already been worked out. In spite of diversified subject matters, there are certain production procedures that can be applied to almost every television production job.

# PRODUCTION PROCEDURES

Every television show starts with an idea. Once the idea has been conceived, it will have to undergo, first of all, a short investigation of its validity for television presentation. If the investigation shows positive results, the idea must then be expanded, developed, and converted into a logical, effective series of visual and audible elements. The steps necessary to convert the original idea into a series of audio-visual elements are usually called production procedures, or, in short, production.

As a producer, you must have good judgment. You must know what is good and what is bad. This knowledge depends largely on the extent and depth of your education. In addition, something else is required: showmanship. You must have the ability to present certain show material to the public in the most exciting, convincing, and effective manner possible.

The following outline of production techniques should serve as a guide to (1) the investigation of the validity of an idea for television production and (2) the actual production procedures.

### Investigating an Idea

1. Does the idea seem particularly exciting? If so, why? If not, why not?

2. What are the potentials of this idea? Is the idea *per se* sound enough to justify further investigation?

3. If the idea were developed into a television show, what, if anything, would the viewer gain by it?

4. Why would you like to present this idea? What are your objectives?

5. If you develop this idea into a television show, what obvious production problems must you consider?

## Producing the Show

### Material

1. *Audience.* What type of audience do you want to reach—men, women, family, teen-agers, college graduates, children?

2. *Time.* In general, a specific type of audience determines a specific telecasting time—morning, noon, afternoon, late afternoon, evening, weekend. What time would be ideal for your purposes? What are your extreme time limits? What compromises are you prepared to make?

3. *Selection of material.* Always put emphasis on good content of material. Does the proposed material convey your original idea? Has your material good literary content? Good visual content? Will the chosen material be interesting to your television audience?

4. *Research.* Availability of material must be considered. Do you have the time for necessary research? If not, do you have skilled people to do the job for you? (There is a great opportunity for small stations to call upon the research facilities of local high schools, colleges, and universities. Radio and television students generally appreciate every chance to work with an actual show, even if the job only involves research in the school's library.) Have you explored all possible research facilities, such as libraries, museums, art galleries, schools, newspapers, chambers of commerce and other civic and state institutions, professional organizations, and film libraries? Give some thought to what properties and other visual material the show will require.

5. *Method of presentation.* What is the intended style of the presentation? What type and number of performers and actors do you need? Ask yourself whether the proposed method of presentation will hinder or aid the original idea. Try to make the presentation as exciting as possible, yet try to keep it as simple as possible. In most cases you will find that effectiveness and simplicity go hand-in-hand. What is the proposed length of your show? If you can express an idea quite thoroughly in fifteen minutes, don't try to expand the show into a ninety-minute spectacular. Where does your show originate? Studio?

Remote? Are you familiar with the technical potentials and limitations of the particular studio or remote location?

6. *Production conference.* Call your first production conference as soon as possible. The following people should be called into the first conference: producer, assistant producer, director, associate director, art director, technical director, and floor manager. Frequent production conferences with production and technical people are very important and, in the end, save time. Don't attend the conferences unprepared, thinking that everything will work out all right. It won't. Be specific about all production problems.

### Cost

What is your available budget? Do you know who pays whom? Make a rough cost estimate, considering: (1) writer, (2) talent, (3) other performers, such as musicians and dancers, (4) standard production rates, such as studio costs, (5) scenery, graphic material, and properties, and (6) special production items, such as film and audio and video tapes.

If your show is sponsored, you must make proper arrangements with the specific advertising agency and/or sponsor. In general, your sales representative should work closely with you on these arrangements.

### Script

In most cases, you will have to write your own script. If someone else writes the script, be discriminating in the choice of the writer. The quality of the writer is not always proportionate to the amount of money he requests. Be sure the writer understands fully every detail of your proposed show. If your writer disagrees with your original idea (without coming up with a much better one) don't use him. The script he will produce may be technically quite efficient, but will probably lack inspiration and enthusiasm. Watch for clear video and audio instructions. Make sure that the format of the script is consistent throughout. If you have to make script changes, change *all* copies of the script. The script is your only means of production coordination from this point on.

### Talent

In most instances, you will have the talent in mind when you write the script. However, if you have to cast the talent, consult the director of the show. In general, you can always rely on professional television talent, but don't be afraid to give newcomers a chance, at least in the audition. Frequently, young talent will surprise you with excellent, inspiring performances. Quick learners are important for television work. Make sure the performers belong to a proper television union (see page 413).

### Technical facilities

The technical problems are usually worked out by the director of the show. You must, however, know what to check so that you can keep control over the show preparations.

1. *Sets.* The availability of stock scenery often dictates the style of presentation. The sets should never dominate the show, however. Scenery is strictly a supporting element. The scene designer must attend the preliminary production conferences; he may have valuable suggestions concerning the whole presentation technique. Make sure the sets are designed for the television camera and not for the studio audience.

2. *Graphic materials.* All graphic materials, such as slides, studio cards, telops, credit crawls, maps, charts, and mounted pictures, are usually ordered in connection with the set plan. Watch for unity of style in all visual (and audio) material. Observe art department deadlines.

3. *Properties, make-up, and wardrobe.* In general, the art director is responsible for obtaining the necessary properties. But you must cover the expense of shipping (delivery and pickup) and the insurance of valuable objects. Make sure that dressing and make-up rooms are available for rehearsal and show times, or that you provide adequate make-up and wardrobe facilities.

4. *Cameras.* The director will decide on the number of cameras, special camera pedestals, lens complements, and special effects items.

5. *Audio.* The director also decides on necessary audio equipment: the number and type of microphones and their placement for desired radius and flexibility; music, live and recorded; and special audio effects.

6. *Lighting.* The lighting engineer will take care of normal studio lighting. He must be informed of the exact amount and direction of action, location of sets, and desired special effects. Make sure your script allows enough time for complicated light changes.

7. *Special production facilities and effects.* You must inform the engineering department of any special requests for video and audio tape facilities, telephone beeper hookups, special films, etc. The director will take care of special effects, mechanical and/or electronic.

8. *Show origination.* Be sure to check with the production coordinator (sometimes called production manager or operations manager) about

the availability of studios and equipment for rehearsals and on-the-air performances.

### Commercials

Is your show sponsored? If so, how will the commercials be presented—live, film, or video tape? Check with the sales department and advertising agency on the what, when, and how of the commercial presentation. Double-check on each commercial item. Even a ten-second spot announcement involves large sums of money. Make sure the commercial properties are delivered in time.

Do you have too many commercials or other interruptions scheduled for your show? Do you comply with the time standards for "non-program material"? The NAB (National Association of Broadcasters) Time Standards for Non-Program Material indicate certain restrictions on length and frequency of commercials and other non-program material.

The old Television Code definitions of "commercials" and "class AA, B, C, and D times" (most valuable down to least valuable time) have been replaced by the concepts of "non-program material" and "prime time."

*Non-program material* includes regular commercial announcements ("Buy brand X"), billboards ("brought to you by . . ."), credits in excess of 30 seconds (directed by, produced by, written by, etc.), and promotional announcements ("see our special color spectacular next week on this channel").

Public service announcements ("support your local Girl Scouts") are not considered non-program material, so they don't fall within the non-program material time standards.

*Prime time* is defined as a continuous period of not less than three evening hours per broadcast day, as designated by the station, between the hours of 6:00 P.M. and midnight.

According to the time standards, all non-program material in prime time must not exceed 10 minutes in any 60-minute period. In non-prime time, non-program material cannot exceed 16 minutes in any 60-minute period.

In prime time, there can be no more than four program interruptions by non-program material within a 60-minute show, and no more than two interruptions within a 30-minute show. In non-prime time, four interruptions are permitted within a 30-minute show.

There are some exceptions to these interruption standards. Five instead of four interruptions are permitted within a 60-minute prime-time variety show. News, weather, sports, and special events are entirely exempt from the interruption standards. The reason for these exemptions is that variety shows, news, sports, weather, and special-events shows generally consist of a series of separate presentations whose continuity will not necessarily suffer from frequent interruptions.

For programs of 15 minutes or less in length, the following interruption standards apply in prime time and all other time: 5-minute program: 1 interruption; 10-minute program: 2 interruptions; 15-minute program: 3 interruptions.

Stations should keep in mind that despite NAB's caution against frequent program interruptions, a series of short spots within each program interruption may still lead to an annoying commercial cluttering.*

### Union affiliations and material clearances

*Unions.* Make sure you understand all union contracts. Are your performers members of a television union? If not, is their appearance cleared by the union as well as your station? Do you have the proper contract forms? Check again with your station on the money arrangements concerning union fees. The following are the most important television unions:

*Talent Union:*
American Federation of Television and Radio Artists (AFTRA). Most television talent belongs to AFTRA.
American Guild of Musical Artists (AGMA).
American Guild of Variety Artists (AGVA).
Directors Guild of America, Inc.
Screen Actors Guild (SAG). Screen Extras Guild (SEG). Important only when film commercials are produced.

*Engineering Unions:*
International Brotherhood of Electrical Workers (IBEW). Studio and master control engineers; may include floor men.
National Association of Broadcast Employees and Technicians (NABET). Studio and control room engineers; may include floor men.
International Alliance of Theatrical Stage Employees and Motion Picture Machine Operators (IATSE).

In small station operation, some members of the production crew may belong to engineering unions also. Directors sometimes belong to AFTRA, especially when they double as announcers.

Always be careful, when you ask a studio guest to do anything but

---

*Time standards are subject to change. Up-to-date information is available from the Director, NAB Code Authority, 1812 K Street, N.W., Washington, D.C. 20006.

answer questions during an interview. As soon as the guest gives a short demonstration of his talents, he may be classified as a performer and become automatically subject to AFTRA fees. Also, don't request the floor crew to do anything that is not directly connected with their regular line of duty, or they may collect talent fees. Cameramen usually have a contract clause that assures them a substantial amount of money if they are willfully shown on camera.

*Music Clearances.* You need proper clearances for recordings as well as the performance of written music. All published music is subject to performance royalties. Only after 56 years do music copyrights become public domain and require no special royalty payments. There are three major organizations that hold most of the music copyrights: (1) ASCAP, the American Society of Composers, Authors and Publishers; (2) BMI, Broadcast Music, Incorporated; and (3) SESAC, The Society of European Stage Authors and Composers. If the licensing society is not indicated on the label of the recording, check the society in one of their large music catalogues. Larger stations have standing contracts with these organizations. The station usually pays a lump sum once each year which covers the royalty fees for all musical presentations during that time. You must, however, report each individual number that you have played on the air. If such a contract does not exist between your station and the music organization, you must pay for each performed piece individually. There are additional problems when the program that uses music recordings is recorded on either film or video tape. This constitutes a recording of a recording and may need an additional release.

*Copyright.* Is your script violating possible copyrights? Have you incorporated any kind of copyrighted material? Be sure to get proper clearances from authors, publishers, literary agents, photo agencies, etc., for all copyrighted reproductions of paintings, prints, and photographs, as well as copyrighted plays, stories, and other program material.

*Code.* Before you go into rehearsal, make sure the material is well suited for television presentation. Sometimes a script reads well but may become objectionable when presented in a certain manner. Is your program in good taste? Does it comply with the NAB Television Code? Remember that your program is viewed by a great variety of people from all walks of life. The beginning of the preamble of the NAB Code points specifically to you and your relationship with the viewer:

> Television is seen and heard in every type of American home. These
> homes include children and adults of all ages, embrace all races and

all varieties of religious faith, and reach those of every educational background. It is the responsibility of television to bear constantly in mind that the audience is primarily a home audience, and consequently that television's relationship to the viewers is that between guest and host.

Read the television code carefully. It gives you explicit information on the following subjects: (1) advancement of education and culture; (2) responsibility toward children; (3) community responsibility; (4) general program standards; (5) treatment of news and public events; (6) controversial public issues; (7) political telecasts; (8) religious programs; (9) general advertising standards; (10) presentation of advertising; (11) advertising of medical products; (12) contests; (13) premiums and offers; (14) time standards for advertising; and (15) interpretations of the television code.

One code interpretation that is especially important is that commercials involving beer and wine must not show any on-camera drinking.

### Production coordination and rehearsal schedules

1. *Script distribution.* Your script must be properly distributed to all persons concerned; copies must go to master control, announcer, art director, technical director, lighting engineer, floor manager, floor men, associate director, assistant producer, all talent, and the director. Keep at least three copies for your file. In a medium-sized station, you will need at least fifteen script copies. It is always better to have a few copies too many than not enough.

2. *Facilities request and log information.* The log, like the script, is an essential means of production coordination. (We will discuss the log in more detail later in this chapter.) Before the traffic department can issue an accurate log, it must receive accurate information from several departments. This information is based on facilities requests issued by the producer or director.

Depending on the complexity of the television operation, facilities requests may contain various information arranged in a variety of ways. Some facilities-request blanks have most of the standard studio facilities printed on them (such as camera 1, 2, 3; lenses: zoom, normal turret, special), and these items are then checked off by the producer or director and distributed to the various departments involved. Other blanks are merely coded to indicate production areas and facilities, such as ST (studio only), SF (studio and facilities), P (properties), and R (remote). You can then fill in the detailed information. For example, under SF you may indicate two TK-60 with normal lens complements, a big boom with a BK-5A, and normal lighting.

```
Feb. 15                         R-TV-F TELEVISION REQUEST                    114
  DATE                                                                      NUMBER

Production Title    Creative Man                    Single X   Series      Length  28:30

Director    Hamilton              Producer   Smith        Sub. by    Smith

Class   RTVF 141        Instructor     Dart              Studio   1      Area

Air Time and Date   10:00 a.m.   March 5                  Contact   Smith or Dart

CODES:  S studio only        ST sets           PR properties      SF studio and facilities
        G graphics           F facility only    L lights
        P personnel          R remote           D distribution

                        (Be sure to attach necessary forms, sketches and added information to complete request)

                                         Type or Print

  SF         Four cameras, TK-60, normal lens complement on cameras 2, 3, 4.
  CODE       Verotal V zoom on camera 1.

             Big and medium booms, both with EV 242.

  CODE
  L          Normal lighting facilities (will have three pre-set scenes --
             see attached lighting plot).

  ST         Three space modulators in three set areas (see attached floor plan).

  CODE
  P          See attached prop list.

  CODE
  G          Five super slides (use 36 pt. Univers).


             Slide 1:  Directed by Bob Hamilton
             Slide 2:  Produced by John Smith
  CODE       Slide 3:  Written by Bill Bishop
             Slide 4:  An RTVF 141 Production
             Slide 5:  Creative Arts, San Francisco StateCollege

  D          On Channels 3 and 6
  CODE

  CODE

  CODE

  CODE

  CODE

  CODE

  CODE


Instructor                      Operations                 Engineering

Date                            Date                       Date

Orig. Pink: Operations
```

Since several key departments must receive the same information, several carbon copies are necessary. Usually, the copies are of different colors, each of which is assigned permanently to a specific department. For example, engineering may get the yellow copy, blue may go to the art department, pink to the originator of the facilities request, and so on. The departments that generally get copies of the facilities request are (1) production, (2) engineering, (3) film editing, (4) traffic, and (5) art. In large network operations such as CBS, the facilities requests go to so many departments and consequently have so many different colored carbons that the blanks are called "rainbows."

Make sure that the facilities requests reach the various departments *before* each department's deadline.

3. *Rehearsal schedules.* Your director will determine the rehearsal schedules. Make sure the schedule is posted as early as possible. Indicate the type of rehearsal and whether it is a script reading, dry run,

or camera rehearsal. Check again with the production coordinator on the availability of studios and other technical facilities for your rehearsals.

### Publicity and promotion

The functions of the publicity and promotion departments are to minimize the gap between the potential and the actual television audience. In other words, publicity and promotion are designed to inform all set owners of upcoming television programs and to stimulate them to tune in these programs. The higher the number of actual television viewers in relation to set owners, the higher the rating figure will be. Although the quality and success of your show are not necessarily expressed by high ratings, it is still desirable to reach as many viewers in your desired audience as possible. Be sure, therefore, to inform your publicity and promotion people of exact data concerning your show.

### Rehearsals and performance

From now on, the director of the show takes over. He will conduct the necessary rehearsals and direct the on-the-air performance. As producer, however, you should (without interfering) watch over all rehearsals and the on-the-air performance.

## THE DIRECTOR'S DUTIES

### Responsibilities

The efforts of all personnel in a television station finally culminate in the director's performance. As a director, you are responsible for editing the program material and putting it on the air, thus making it available to the television audience. Your first responsibility, then, goes to the television audience. You are dealing with the feelings and emotions of people—a much more delicate job than dealing with their physical health. You must fulfill not only their wants but also (and especially) their needs. Always remember that you are dealing with human beings.

You also have great responsibility toward your station—toward the people who have put their trust in you to use their efforts for successful on-the-air presentations.

And you have responsibility toward yourself. Like any other artist, you must always try to do your best possible job, no matter how trivial the job may seem at times.

## Background

As a television director you need a good and varied education. It is not enough for you to know how to get a particular shot; you must also know why you want to get it. This means that you need some background in the creative arts—music, drama, painting, and dancing. You must also be familiar with at least the basic forms of literary expression.

Like the producer, you must know when a picture, sound, or movement is good or bad, and you must know *why* it is good or bad. You must be decisive. You cannot afford to try one specific setup three or four different ways before you finally decide which is best. You must be able to judge something as being good and right without having to try the bad and wrong first. But don't let these strong injunctions inhibit experimentation; sometimes even the most experienced director *must* try out several different ways of presentation in order to find out which way will be the most effective.

Your job is considerably complicated because you have to make a highly technical medium work artistically for you. This means that you have to know the potentials and limitations of all television production elements before you can use them properly. Also, you must know the potentials and limitations of the people with whom you work. You must be able to make the people work not only *with* you but *for* you. You must realize that the engineers and the floor personnel are all experts in their particular fields. A good director is not the one who knows everything better than the people he works with; but he *is* the one who can stimulate his associates to do their best and who can coordinate their efforts into a unified whole, the final television show.

### Coordination of Production Elements

As a beginning director, you will find that the proper coordination of the different production elements within a rigid time limit seems to be the most difficult aspect of your job. During a simple two-camera show, you are engaged in the following activities:

1. Talking and listening to studio engineers and production crew: cameramen, microphone boom operator, floor manager, floor men.

2. Conversing with the people in master control and control room: T.D. (technical director), audio engineer, master control engineers (operating video tape, slides, etc.).

3. Watching at least three monitors at all times: two camera monitors, master or line monitor, and, if you have film or tape inserts, the film preview monitor.

4. Watching the time: the control room clock for the over-all running time, the stop watch for individual show segments.

5. Listening to the audio (usually the most difficult job for the beginning director).

6. Following the script.

7. In some stations, doing your own switching.

But this is only a small part of your job as a television director. You must know not only when to talk to whom and when to watch a particular monitor; you must know first of all *what* to say to these people and *what kind* of picture to watch in the different monitors. In other words, you should learn the "what" and "why" before the "when."

Before we step into the control room, therefore, we will consider briefly the two main elements with which you have to work as a television director: (1) pictures and (2) time. Sound, another essential television element, requires at first considerably less coordination than pictures and time. We will therefore purposely neglect this aspect in this chapter.

## THINKING IN PICTURES

When you consider directing a television show, or more specifically, when you read a television script, you must think in pictures. You will probably find it easier to think first in individual images that are not necessarily connected with each other, and then of a picture sequence that will tell the story. The first process we call visualization, the second picturization. Let us define these important terms once more. Visualization is the translation of ideas and words into individual pictures. Picturization means putting these individual images into a proper order so that their continuity conveys a particular meaning.*

### Visualization

#### Purpose

In small station operation, you will be primarily concerned with nondramatic presentations. Your main purpose in these shows is to show persons, objects, actions, and reactions as *clearly* as possible. Your television camera becomes basically a reporter.

In dramatic presentations, you must frequently show an object in a special way so that it takes on a particular meaning. In this connection, a close-up of a girl's eyes may become a pictorial means to

---

*This definition of picturization is not to be confused with Alexander Dean's in his *Principles of Directing*.

suggest love rather than to demonstrate the anatomy of the human eye. You may want to show a close-up of a tape recorder to indicate mechanization rather than to advertise a particular manufacturer.

In your visualization process, then, you must try to show things as clearly as possible, and at times present them so that they convey meaning and thought.

### Television picture composition

Television pictures are, like any other pictures, subject to the conventional aesthetic rules of picture composition. But there are factors peculiar to the television medium that influence your visualization process to a certain extent.

1. The size of the television screen is small. To show things clearly, you must show them relatively large within the frame of the screen. In other words, you have to operate more with close-ups (CU) and medium shots (MS) than with long shots (LS) and extreme long shots (XLS).

2. You must always work within a fixed frame, the television aspect ratio of 3:4. If you want to show something extremely tall, you cannot change the aspect ratio into a vertical framing.

3. The pictures on the television screen are two-dimensional pictures. You must create the impression of a third dimension through a special arrangement of objects within the frame and the demonstration of relative size: objects closer to you are bigger, objects farther away seem smaller. Overlapping planes and special lighting effects can also contribute to the illusion of a third dimension. A good three-dimensional effect always needs a clear picture division into (a) foreground, (b) middle ground, and (c) background.

4. The camera (which is a substitute for the viewer's eyes) and the object in front of the camera generally move about. This means that you must consider motion as well as static arrangement of objects within the frame. About ten per cent of the picture area gets lost through the television transmission and reception process. (See discussion on essential area in Chapter 6.) You must compensate for this loss by framing somewhat looser than what you have visualized. Some directors draw black lines on their line monitor to indicate the essential framing area.

5. The extreme time limitations in all phases of television production prevent you from paying careful attention to every minute detail of picture composition and motion within the frame. In small station operation, you will rarely find enough time to run through even one complete camera rehearsal. Picture compositions therefore, often

studio monitor                                          home receiver

depend on the creative ability and fast reflexes of the television cameraman. All you can sometimes do is correct certain framing factors,
rather than determine them. But lack of time should not invite you
to forget about composition altogether; on the contrary, you need a
thorough knowledge of picture composition to be able to correct
quickly the pictures that the cameramen are getting for you.

You are probably already familiar with the basic principles of picture composition. You can probably tell, for example, whether a color
photograph is well balanced, whether it has good contrast (either in
color or in black and white; the black and white contrast is sometimes called by its Italian name: chiaroscuro), and whether the lines,
planes, and volumes are artistically arranged. Learn how to look at
a picture from a design point of view. Even a well-drawn cartoon
strip in the newspaper can teach you a great deal about composition
and staging within a small frame (which is quite similar to your television screen).

In the following discussion on television framing, no attempt is made
to teach you the basic rules of composition; nevertheless, the framing
examples should give you an idea on how to stage and show objects
within the television frame most advantageously.

### Some major staging and framing techniques

*Balance.* Always arrange your objects within the frame so that they
balance properly. Balance means roughly that one picture area does
not completely outweigh the other, either in mass, color, or movement. If you have distinct horizontal and vertical lines, place them
slightly beyond the centers. Division ratios of 2/5 to 3/5 or 1/3 to 2/3
are the most common framings.

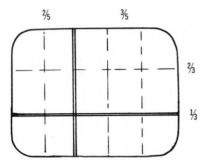

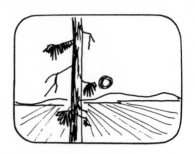

*Symmetry.* If you place an object in the exact middle of the television screen, you divide the picture area symmetrically. This type of balance is generally not very interesting. If you want to show or emphasize a single object as directly as possible, however, a symmetrical arrangement is quite satisfactory.

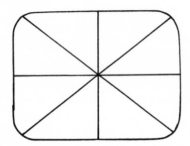

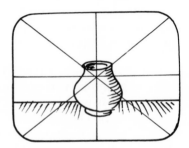

*Equilibrium.* Every picture has a certain equilibrium. It can be (a) stabile (stable), (b) neutral, or (c) labile (unstable).

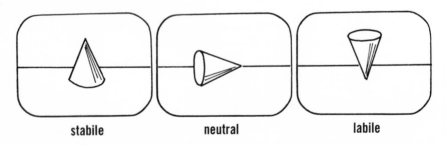

**stabile**              **neutral**              **labile**

Sometimes you may want to disturb the picture equilibrium for dramatic effects. This you can do with a canted shot, which you can obtain by tilting the camera to its side or, much better, by shooting into a specially hung mirror. (See Chapter 7.)

**Staging and framing for single performer or object**

1. If you have only one performer talking directly into the camera, frame him rather tightly and place him directly in the symmetrical center of the screen. This framing will put great emphasis on the speaker without giving the viewer a chance to become distracted by unnecessary picture elements.

**not so good**

**better**

If you show one commercial product, such as a single bottle or can, frame it right in the middle of the screen.

**bad**

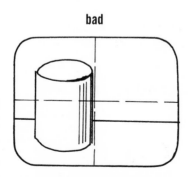

**good**

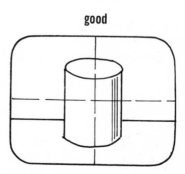

2. If your performer looks in a direction other than the camera, leave some space in the direction he is looking. For example, if your

performer is looking toward the left edge of your screen, place him in the right half of the frame.

**good**                               **good**

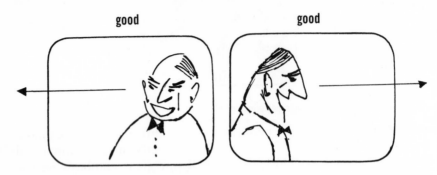

The space in front of the performer (sometimes called "nose room") suggests the other person or object at which he is looking. You should not frame the performer in the half of the screen into which he is looking. The performer should not touch the edge of the screen with his nose, for example.

**bad**                               **bad**

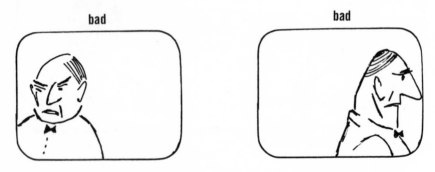

For special dramatic effects, however, framing the performer close to the screen edge at which he is looking can suggest that something is about to happen behind him.

**good only if** ———————→ **something happens behind**

3. Avoid extreme high or low angle shots, unless you want to achieve special effects. High angle shots frequently foreshorten legs unfavorably, and low angle shots distort body and face. Be especially careful of high angle shots during any kind of dance performance. In a dramatic presentation, a high angle shot can suggest smallness and humbleness of an object or person; a low angle shot can make a person look huge and powerful, often brutal.

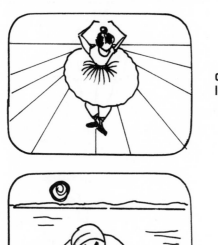

camera is too high:
legs are distorted

high camera position:
looking down

low camera position:
looking up

4. Watch for odd juxtapositions of performer and set areas or props. Don't have lamps or flower pots growing out of the performer's head.

bad

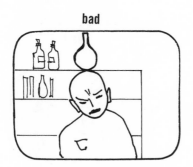

bad

5. In your framing of a person, concentrate on the upper part of the body rather than the lower part. A medium shot, for example, should not chop off a person's head so that large areas of the studio floor can be shown. Leave enough headroom.

bad good

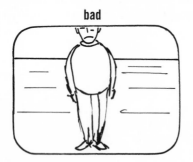 

6. If you take an extreme close-up (XCU) of a performer's head, cut the upper part rather than the lower part of the head.

bad better

### Staging and framing two performers

1. You must stage two performers to get an interesting group shot (two-shot) as well as good close-ups. This job is not as easy as it sounds. If you stage them side-by-side in front of the camera, you will

not so good better

have no trouble getting two-shots and close-ups; the majority of your shots, however, will show the often unflattering profiles of the performers.

2. In any television staging, downstage-upstage (toward and away from the camera) arrangements are generally better than lateral positionings. A good arrangement for an interview between two people, for instance, is to seat the people slightly diagonal to the cameras or to put them in a direct upstage-downstage position. Your guest must always face downstage—that is, into the cameras.

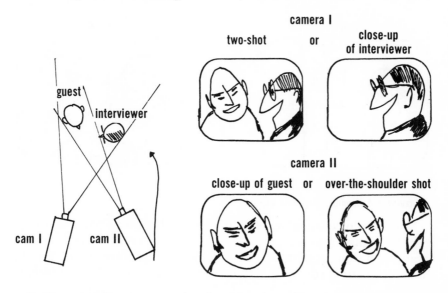

3. You can also get over-the-shoulder shots from both directions, if you like. Be careful to keep both cameras on one side, or the per-

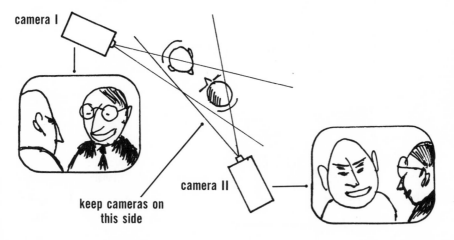

formers will seem to jump from one side of the screen to the other. And remember that over-the-shoulder shooting takes valuable time, especially since you need additional pieces of scenery to prevent overshooting on either side.

4. You must make certain compensations for an awkward difference in height. If you have a very tall man talking to a child, for example, either the man should stoop down to the child or the child should be put on a riser. Don't just frame the child, thereby chopping off the man's head and feet.

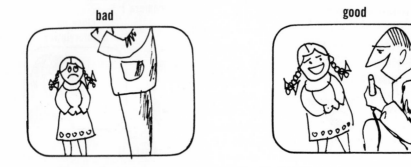

**Staging and framing groups and objects**

Make use of triangular, semicircular, and circular patterns whenever you stage a group of people or display several objects. Avoid straight-on shots of groups, unless you want to achieve certain effects. In group staging, you must keep everyone as close together as possible.

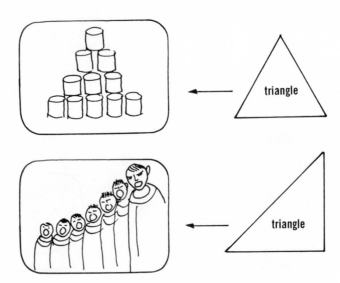

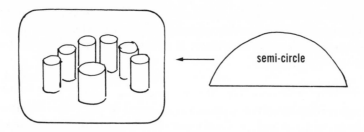

### Depth staging and special framing

Depth staging for three-dimensional effects, which means placing objects at different distances from the camera, provides a good opportunity for creative framing. You can make good use of the discussed characteristics of lenses (the short lens exaggerates relative size and depth, the long lens reduces feeling of depth, enlarges objects, shrinks distance) when you want to emphasize and de-emphasize objects within the frame. But don't depth-stage merely for depth-staging's sake. You must have proper motivation for every picture, whether it is for good composition or for achieving some psychological effect. In framing a depth-staged set, always show a prominent foreground piece, which pushes the other objects farther back in the frame. Use any person or inanimate object that bears some relation to the essential picture area and to the essential happening within the frame. You can use a globe as a foreground piece for a study set, or a telephone or a water cooler for an office set. Don't become too obvious in the selection of foreground pieces, however, or you will destroy the purpose and meaning of the shot.

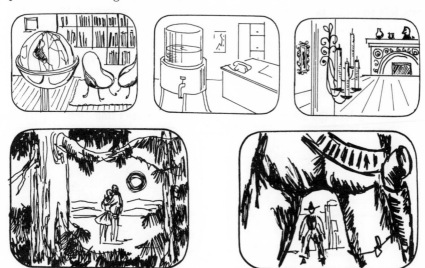

You can achieve special framing effects by shooting through foreground objects, such as the spokes of a wagon wheel, the legs of a chair, or even the legs of a man. But beware of using this effect too often.

## Picturization

Picturization involves a proper succession of television pictures or, in television language, a succession of shots. Picturization therefore needs movement: the movement in front of the camera, the movement of the camera itself, and the movement achieved by adding one picture to the other, the picture sequence. One type of movement changes the pictures smoothly (dolly, pan), the other more abruptly (cut, dissolve, fade). We can divide the movements necessary for picturization into three types: (1) primary movement, which is the movement in front of the camera, mainly the movement of the performers; (2) secondary movement, which is the movement of the camera itself (pan, dolly, tilt, truck, pedestal, zoom); and (3) tertiary movement, which is the movement created by the more or less rapid succession of shots from different cameras (cut, dissolve, fade). The three movements are additional means for you to emphasize the important and de-emphasize the unimportant, and to show action and reaction.

### Primary movement

Movement toward or away from the camera (upstage and downstage) is much stronger than any type of lateral movement. Therefore, you can achieve more emphasis by having the performer walk toward or away from the camera than by having him walk from camera left to right or vice versa. Exits and entrances become impressive when they happen from or toward the camera. Again, such strong movements must be properly motivated to become artistically valid.

If you frame lateral movement, you must *lead* the moving object with your camera. The viewer wants to know where the performer is going, not where he has been.

lead the subject

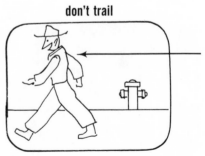

don't trail

### Secondary movement

Secondary movement, the movement of the camera, includes pan, tilt, dolly, zoom, truck, and pedestal. You may have to use secondary movement out of necessity to follow primary movement or to adjust composition; or you may want to use it to emphasize or dramatize an object or happening. All secondary movement must be properly motivated. Don't use it just to keep the cameramen entertained or the viewer awake. The "how" of the secondary movement has already been described in Chapter 1. The following paragraphs briefly describe the "why."

*Pan.* When you pan, you turn the camera horizontally. The primary reason for the pan is to follow action. When you pan past several stationary objects, watch that there is not too much "dead space" between one object and the other. Diagonal staging is better than lateral and will bring the objects closer together. It also allows a better, more interesting pan.

**too much dead space**    **minimum dead space**

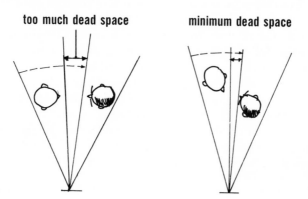

In general, your panning will be as fast as the movement you have to follow. When you pan stationary objects, you must pan slowly enough for the viewer to see the objects. If you must pan several widely spaced objects, you can pan slowly while you have the object in your frame, and then pan rather fast to the next object. This helps to bridge the empty space.

A swish pan is a very fast pan, generally used for idea-associating effects. You can, for instance, indicate some kind of connection between two locales or happenings by swish panning from one set area to the other. This is primarily a motion picture technique, however. News photographers (film cameramen) use the swish-pan technique frequently to indicate that two events happened simultaneously in different locations. For example: Show street sign—Jones and Market. Show fire. Swishpan to another street sign—Third and Mission. Show new fire in this location.

The director's signal for the pan is *pan left* or *pan right.*

*Tilt.* Tilting is pointing the camera up or down. This movement is frequently called panning up and panning down. The motivations for tilting are very similar to those of the pan. You can tilt to follow action or to create dramatic effects. For instance, you can reveal the great height of an object by gradually tilting up on it. Or you can create considerable suspense by slowly tilting down for a terrible discovery, such as tilting down on a staircase to discover the body at the foot of the stairs.

The director's signal for the tilt is *tilt up* or *tilt down,* or *pan up* or *pan down.*

*Dolly.* Dollying is moving the camera toward or away from the object. A dolly-in will gradually enlarge an object on the screen. You can dolly in to see something more clearly or to draw special emphasis to one particular picture detail. A dolly-back (or dolly-out, or pull-back) will do the reverse. In a dolly-back you go from a detail to the over-all; in a dolly-in you go from the general to the specific. You must also dolly to follow action toward and away from the camera, as well as lateral action, through widening of the field of view.

Depending on the dolly speed, you can make a strong point (fast dolly) or a more subtle point (slow dolly). Sometimes you have to "creep" in and out (dolly very slowly) in order to change a shot without making the viewer aware of the change.

The director's signal for the dolly is *dolly in* (*push in*) or *dolly out* (*dolly back, pull back*).

*Zoom.* Although the camera does not move during a zoom, the zoom can be called a secondary movement. A zoom-in and zoom-out looks like a dolly except that perspective of objects in relation to the camera does not change as it does during a dolly. A zoom is often, though not always appropriately, used instead of a dolly. You can also use a zoom for dramatic effects, especially when you want to emphasize a particular picture detail quickly and emphatically. Standard examples for studio zooming are a fast zoom-in on the telephone while it is ringing (indicating a very important call), or on the villain who has suddenly been exposed (surprise, shock). Use fast zooming sparingly and carefully; too many images that seem to crash through the television screen can be very annoying to the viewer.

The director's signal for the zoom is *zoom-in* or *zoom-out* (or back).

*Truck.* A truck is a lateral movement of the camera and camera mount. To show several laterally staged objects straight-on, you can truck the camera along the objects. Or you can use a truck to follow lateral action without changing the angle or the distance from the moving object. In a one-camera show, for example, you may have to truck to follow the performer from one set area to the other.

A truck shot looks especially impressive and effective if you move the camera past the foreground pieces of a depth-staged setup. The foreground pieces seem to move slowly past the screen (temporarily blocking out the picture) while the background objects seem stationary. This adds greatly to the three-dimensional effect.

The director's signal for the truck is *truck left* or *truck right.*

*Pedestal.* To pedestal up or down means to lower or raise the whole camera on the studio pedestal. Most frequently, the studio pedestal is adjusted simply to compensate for tall and short cameramen. But the pedestal can be used to change the perspective of a scene: pedestalling up enables the viewer to look down on the scene, pedestalling down makes him look up on the scene.

The director's signal for the pedestal is *pedestal up* or *pedestal down* (or *raise your camera, lower your camera*).

The movements of the studio crane are not discussed here, because they are simply an extension or combination of any of the discussed movements.

It must be pointed out that you should use secondary movement only when the situation calls for it. A pan that does not fulfill a specific need is obviously unnecessary. In general, the viewer should not become conscious of camera movement. There is one exception to this rule, however. When the camera is used subjectively, the viewer can and may very well become aware of the camera. A subjective camera assumes the role of a person moving around the set and among other performers and actors. The viewer sees everything through the eyes of the subjective camera, representing the "other" person. Use this technique, however, only if the form or story content makes such an extravagant camera handling feasible.

### Tertiary movement

The tertiary movement is created by a sequence of shots from two or more cameras. When you work with more than one camera you have an opportunity to edit the picture sequence. You can select from a variety of pictures and determine a particular picture to go out on the air. Tertiary movement is the strongest point in the picturization process. Through the use of two cameras you can easily emphasize and de-emphasize, show action and reaction in rapid or slow succession. The different transition methods from picture to picture (switching devices from camera to camera) become very important.

There are three standard transition devices: (1) the cut, (2) the dissolve, and (3) the fade. (Other transition devices have been discussed in Chapter 7.)

*The cut.* The cut is an instantaneous change from one image to another. Television cutting is sometimes (and more accurately) called switching. The two basic reasons for cutting are (1) to show the viewer what he *needs to see* and (2) to show the viewer what he *wants to see.* For example, if the instructor writes something on the blackboard, you can cut to a close-up of the board to show what the viewer needs to see. Then, after the instructor has been obviously distracted by someone the viewer cannot see, you can cut to a shot of the other person (or a wider shot) to show the viewer what he wants to see.

The cut is the most common transition device. It is the fastest and, if done properly, the least obvious transition. It resembles most closely the changing of fields of view by the human eye. Try to look from one object to another, both located in different corners of a room. You will notice that you don't look at things in between (as you could in a pan) but that your eyes "jump" from one place to the other, similar to a cut.

*Standard cutting techniques.* Although the do's of many present television techniques may become the don'ts of tomorrow, certain established production techniques will probably prevail unchanged for some time to come. You should therefore familiarize yourself with some of the most frequently used cutting techniques.

*Cutting on action and movement.* 1. If you cut on action, cut during the action, not before or after it. If you have a close-up of a performer who is just preparing himself to rise from a chair, you should cut to a wider shot just after he has started to rise, but before he stands.

2. Don't cut from a pan to a stationary camera. If you must cut from a panning camera, have the other camera pan in the same direction before cutting to it.

3. Don't cut on lateral action from opposite sides; the direction of the movement will be reversed on the screen (see page 435).

4. Don't over-cut. A series of fast, meaningless cuts will not condense the action as it does in motion pictures. On live television, time cannot be expanded or condensed. An event will take just as long on the screen as it takes in the studio. A fast pace, however, may very well call for fast cutting; a slow pace for slow cutting.

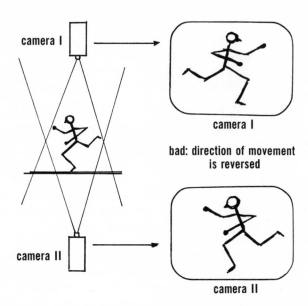

camera I

bad: direction of movement
is reversed

camera II

*Identification cutting.* 1. If you cut to identify an object or person more closely, don't cut from an extreme long shot to an extreme close-up unless you want to achieve a particular dramatic or comic effect. If you are too wide, you must dolly in before you cut to the close-up. This rule also applies in reverse: don't cut from an extreme close-up to an extreme long shot.

2. Don't cut to extreme angles. If one camera shows you a long shot of a performer with his back to the camera, don't suddenly cut to an extreme close-up of the face of that person. Such a jump cannot be comprehended easily by the viewer who has no idea of camera positioning and other such production matters. You may have visualized and framed the two shots quite well, but the picturization of such a combination is bad. The shots do not cut together.

3. Try to keep close-ups of objects in the same screen position in which they appear in the long shot (see page 436).

4. Don't cut to a nearly identical shot unless you want to repeat a certain picture sequence for special effects or unless you must free a camera unexpectedly. If you cannot vary the shot, don't change it. Don't be afraid to stay on one camera, even for a long period of time, if you have no reason for changing the shot. If you direct a straight television address by your home town mayor, for example, one camera is all you need, even though you may have three cameras available. There is no reason for cutting blindly. If the speaker is interesting, he will hold the attention of the television audience without

camera I        camera II        camera II

a ———→ b     b •———————— b

bad             good

your pictorial maneuvers; if he is not good, frequent and fancy cutting will not make the speech any better.

*Cutting on dialogue and music.* 1. In general, cut at the end of a sentence or a phrase. This is fairly simple as long as the dialogue is fully scripted. In an ad-lib show, however, where you must outguess the performers most of the time, exact cutting is not always that easy. Listening to the audio portion in this situation becomes extremely important. Important reaction shots can, however, be cut in anytime during a sentence.

2. If someone moves while in the middle of delivering a speech, you must cut on the action. Don't wait until he has finished a sentence. Action is always a stronger factor for cutting than audio.

3. In musical performances, shots should be cut only at the end of a musical phrase. The pace for cutting is determined by the pace of the music. Fast, rhythmic cutting, however, is not possible in live television. No cameraman or director can find all the material and variety of shots that fast cutting requires.

4. If the music being performed is continuous and not definitely phrased, you should not cut at all; instead, use another transition method, such as the dissolve.

The director's signal for the cut is *take one* (depending on the number of the camera). In general, you must ready the camera before you take it: *ready one, take one.* On your ready signal, the T.D. puts his finger on the switching button and, if you have a preview bank, puts the upcoming shot on the preview monitor; on the take signal, he presses the button, putting the camera on the air.

*The dissolve.* The dissolve (also called a lap dissolve, or lap) is a smooth transition from one image to another. In a dissolve, the image of the first camera is gradually faded out while, simultaneously, the image of the second camera is gradually faded in. At one point, the dissolve shows both images at the same time, similar to a superimposition. (See Chapters 7 and 11.) A superimposition effect is nothing more than an interrupted dissolve that is "frozen" when the images show approximately equal strength. A dissolve can be used as a smooth bridge for action, change of locale, or change of time, or to indicate a strong relationship between two images.

For an interesting and smooth transition from a wide shot of a dancer to a close-up, for instance, simply dissolve from one camera to the other. The movements will temporarily blend into each other and indicate the strong association between the two shots. The action is not interrupted at all.

Where the mood or tempo of the presentation does not allow hard cuts, you can use dissolves to get from a long shot to a close-up or from a close-up to a long shot. A close-up of a soloist, for instance, can be dissolved into a long shot of the whole choir, which may be more appropriate than an instantaneous cut.

Matched dissolves are used for decorative effects or to indicate an especially strong relationship between two objects. For instance, a decorative use would be a sequence of two fashion models hiding behind sun umbrellas. Model one closes her sequence by hiding behind an umbrella; model two starts her sequence the same way. You can now match-dissolve from camera one to camera two. Both cameras must frame the umbrellas approximately the same way before the dissolve. An example of an associative use is a close-up of a door in a very expensive dwelling match-dissolved to a close-up of a door in an old shack.

You can use a dissolve during continuous music or during a long speech or commentary. This is a way to change cameras in the middle of phrases when it would be awkward to cut.

You may prefer to indicate a change of locale by dissolving rather than cutting to the new set area. A change of time can also be suggested by a slow dissolve (long time lapse, slow dissolve; short time lapse, fast dissolve).

You can vary the speed of the dissolve according to the mood of the presented material. In general, use dissolves sparingly. Don't dissolve if you can cut.

The director's signal for the dissolve is *ready two for a dissolve, dissolve to two;* or *ready two, dissolve to two.* The T.D. will generally feel the speed of the dissolve. If not, you may indicate the speed of the dissolve either by saying, "diiiiisssssooooooolve" (long dissolve), or by giving him a brisk "dissolve" (short dissolve). Many directors indicate the speed of the dissolve also by arm movement.

*The fade.* You can fade both to or from black. You can also fade to white (but this is rarely done).

In general, start each program by fading in the camera picture from black. The fade *from* black always indicates a beginning.

The fade *to* black suggests a complete separation of program elements. It usually indicates that one program element has come to an end. You should end every program by taking it to black. If you have to insert a commercial message in your program, you may do well to go to black before the commercial, not so much to warn the viewer of the upcoming distraction as to tell him that this is a segment not directly connected with the material of the show.

If you fade one of the pictures of a superimposition to black, you have a split fade. To accomplish a split fade, tell the T.D. to *take out one* or *take out two;* or to *go through to one* or *two.*

You can also use a fade to black in an emergency. Rather than showing the viewer all the details of a collapsing set, take the picture to black until the emergency has passed or until you have put up a "one moment, please" standby slide.

The director's signal for a fade is *fade in slide* or simply *up on slide; fade to black* or *to black.* A fade to black immediately followed by a fade-in is sometimes called a "dip to black" or, borrowing from radio terminology, a "cross-fade."

Be careful not to go to black too often; your program continuity will be interrupted too many times by fades that all suggest final endings. The other extreme is the "never-go-to-black" craze. Some directors won't dare go to black in fear of giving the viewer a chance to switch to another channel. If a constant dribble of program material is the only way to keep a viewer glued to the set, the program content, rather than the presentation techniques, should be examined.

### General Visualization and Picturization Factors

Unless your show is completely scripted, you cannot visualize and picturize your show in every detail. You *must* visualize and picturize the most important phases of your show, however. You must preplan enough to know, for example, which camera will open the show and which camera will shoot the closing credits. You must also know which camera takes most of the close-ups from what particular angle and which camera covers certain cross-overs from set area to set area. In general, then, you must observe the following points:

#### Visualization

1. When you take a close-up of a person, the close-up should not distort the person's appearance. Don't capitalize on physical defects, especially for humorous purposes.

2. Account for the loss of the picture margins through transmission when framing a shot.

3. Avoid effects for their own sake.

### Picturization

1. No matter how many cameras you have for your show, you can work with only two at a time. So don't become nervous if, on special occasions, you are called upon to direct a five-camera remote.

2. Employ secondary and tertiary movements only when necessary or properly motivated. Don't be afraid to "sit on a shot" so long as the shot is meaningful.

3. Preplan as much as you possibly can before going into rehearsal or on the air.

## TIME AND THE DIRECTOR

Correct, split-second timing is essential in all television operations. Every second of a day's telecast is preplanned and properly logged. All television stations work on a similarly tight time schedule. In television, time is money. Your Standard Rate and Data Book will tell you how much your station's time is worth in actual dollars and cents.

Good timing is also important for keeping your show well paced, which means that it should have a feeling of speed appropriate to the theme and mood of the story.

As a television director, you must learn to operate within two kinds of time: (1) actual time, expressed in minutes and seconds, and (2) psychological time, expressed in relative speeds, depending on the character of the show. In general, it is easier to learn to work with "actual" time than with "psychological" time. All aspects of psychological time cannot be learned from a production handbook. You must develop this sense of timing through practice in a variety of art forms, including music, dance, drama, and poetry. Only the main factors of psychological time that become important in television directing will be mentioned briefly.

*Pace.* Pace is the speed of the over-all performance: slow, fast, moderate, dragging.

*Tempo.* Tempo is the speed of the individual program segment. Both a slow segment and a fast segment may be part of a slow pace, for example.

*Rate.* Rate refers to the speed of the individual performance. One actor has a slow part, the other a fast part.

We can compare these three aspects of psychological time with the structure of an essay. Pace is the whole essay; tempo is the paragraph;

rate is the individual sentence. The interrelation of pace, tempo, and rate provides the rhythm of the show.

But before you can adequately learn psychological time, you must first of all learn how to work within the limits of actual time.

## Television Log

The schedule that tells you exactly when your program starts and ends is the television log. The television log is issued daily, usually one or two days in advance. The log will give you, in general, the following information:

1. Origin of program (network, local, which studio).
2. Scheduled time: When does the program start? When does the next program start?
3. Length: How long is the spot or program? 20 seconds? 90 minutes?
4. Title of program or announcement (sponsor identification): What is the name of the program? What is the name of the scheduled commercial?
5. Code (optional): What is the code of the commercial film? (Usually of value only to the film department.)
6. Video: How does the video portion originate—live, film, or tape?
7. Audio: How does the audio portion originate—live, E.T. (electrical transcription), film, or tape?
8. Type or class (optional): What type of announcement is it? Public service? Local spot announcement?
9. Special information: What should the director know about the program? Are live introductions to be scheduled for ten seconds unless otherwise noted?

Check your master log daily for possible corrections before you start computing your show timing.

## Timing Methods

There are two methods of timing: (1) front-timing and (2) back-timing.

### Front-timing

If you are responsible for commercial or noncommercial inserts in a feature film (directing "residue"), for instance, you should know the exact time (running clock time) when the breaks occur. You can time the individual segments with your stop watch. The advantage of knowing the actual time at which each break should occur is that you have good control over the over-all timing; you know exactly how much over or under the scheduled time you are at each specific break. If you run over on the first two breaks, you can speed up the next breaks by keeping the film rolling at all times and by keeping the live introductions down to the ten seconds of the academy leader roll-through. If you are way behind time, you may have to stop the end of the first reel of film slightly early so that you can start the second reel on time; or you may be able to "dry run" (start but not put on the air) the second reel on time and switch to it as soon as you are through with the film commercial at the end of the first reel. Both methods, however, are strictly emergency procedures and should not become standard practice, especially for the director who does not take the trouble to pretime his film programs.

In front-timing, you simply add the running times of all the program segments. Let us assume that your film starts at 5:00:40. Your opening is 0:15. You have 14:28 of feature film before you come in with a one-minute live commercial. At what running times does your live commercial come up? Your live commercial must start at 5:15:23 and must be finished by 5:16:23. Your stop watch times are given in the right-hand column.

| running time | segment | stop watch time |
|---|---|---|
| 5:00:40 | OPENING | 00:15 |
| 5:00:55 | FEATURE | (14:28) |
| 5:15:23 | LV COMM | 01:00 |
| 5:16:23 | FEATURE | (13:16) |

When you compute time, always remember that you are working with a sixty scale and not with a hundred scale. In subtracting time,

$$5:00:55$$
$$+ \quad 14:28$$
$$\overline{5:14:(83)} \longrightarrow \underline{\underline{5:15:23}}$$

it helps to take one minute from the minute column and convert it into seconds, especially when you have to subtract a high number of seconds from a small number.

$$5:15:23 \quad \text{convert to:} \quad 5:14:83$$
$$- \quad 14:28 \qquad\qquad\qquad - \quad 14:28$$
$$\qquad\qquad\qquad\qquad\qquad \overline{\underline{5:00:55}}$$

### Back-timing

You must back-time every live program so that you can properly pace the show in order to close on time. For back-timing, you take the time of the program segment that is logged to follow your program and count back the number of minutes and seconds that you deem necessary for your pacing. In any event, you must back-time at least three minutes, two minutes, one minute, and the last thirty seconds for every program that runs five minutes and longer.

Assume your log indicates that your "Sunday Sports Program" is followed by a Salvation Army Public Service Announcement at 4:29:30. Your talent for the sports show would like to have a five-minute cue and the standard cues from three minutes on. When do you give him the five-minute cue and what are the times of the standard cues? Your sports show format should show the following times:

$$4:24:30 \quad - \quad 5 \qquad \text{back-time to here}$$
$$4:26:30 \quad - \quad 3$$
$$4:27:30 \quad - \quad 2$$
$$4:28:30 \quad - \quad 1$$
$$4:29:00 \quad - \quad \tfrac{1}{2}$$
$$\boxed{4:29:30} \quad - \quad BLACK \longrightarrow \text{start with this}$$

### Desired times—must times

Some directors like to indicate "desired times" and "must times." The desired times indicate at what point the show should be (ideally) at a particular time; the must times indicate where the show *must* be at that time.

### Cushions

Always have some timing safeguards in case the program runs over or short. These safeguards, called cushions, consist of program material that can be either inserted or deleted, according to available time. For example, cushions can be closing announcements of different lengths, or fast or slow credit crawls.

## Timing Tools

The director's timing tools are the control room clock and the stop watch. The clock is used to time the over-all program length. Don't time the entire program with your stop watch, especially if a network program follows your show. The network people will not have your stopwatch time, but only the synchronized clock time. In addition to that, stop watches can be as much as five seconds off in a half-hour program.

The stop watch is used to time show segments, such as film commercials, video tape inserts, or special interviews. Don't neglect to start your watch at the beginning of the insert. Inexperienced directors often have difficulty in remembering to start their watches after the countdown of the film leader.

The stop watch is also used to time entire shows or show segments that are video taped. Lack of time does not allow you to wait with your video recording until the clock shows a favorable time (easy to compute). If you have a film insert in your video taping, you must use two stop watches or read the insert off the control room clock. The timer on the VTR will help you with accurate over-all timing.

## THE SCRIPT

A television script contains all the necessary audio and video information for a complete show. The script generally shows the video instructions on one half of the page, the audio instructions on the other. The only exception to this practice is the form of the dramatic television script, which, similar to a motion picture or stage script, lists video and audio in one row. In every television script you must write the text that is spoken in upper and lower case letters, and all other audio instruction in upper case (capital) letters. For video instructions, you can use both upper and lower case letters.

Basically, there are four types of show scripts: (1) the fully scripted show, (2) the semi-scripted show, (3) the show format, and (4) the fact sheet or run-down sheet.

### The Fully Scripted Show

A complete television script indicates every word that is spoken during a show, as well as detailed audio and video instructions. Dramatic shows, comedy skits, news shows, and most major commercials are fully scripted. There are advantages and disadvantages in directing a fully scripted show. The advantages are that you can visualize and picturize the complete show before going into rehearsal. You have definite cue lines, and you know where the camera goes at what time. You know what lens you need for a particular shot. The disadvantages are that you are tied down to following the script very carefully, and this is an additional burden to the many things you already have to do during a performance. Also, if the actor or performer forgets to give you the exact text as indicated in the script, your shooting procedure may be seriously affected.

EXAMPLE OF A FULLY SCRIPTED SHOW

| VIDEO | AUDIO |
|---|---|
| 2-SHOT | HERALD: |
| | If this end clings to the ocean floor, what keeps the upper part of the plant off the bottom? |
| CUT TO<br>CU of pod | LIMBAUGH: |
| | At the base of each leaf-like structure, there is a bladder, or float attachment. This small bulb is hollow and filled with gas. These bulbs hold the plant upright. |
| DOLLY BACK<br>HERALD breaks pod | HERALD: |
| | I see that these float bulbs grow all the way to the end here. What is an average length for one of these strands of kelp? |
| | ETC. |

In the preparation of a news script, you may find it convenient to use white pages for all straight news items, yellow pages for all film and tape copy. This way you will know when a film or tape is coming up and it will be easier for you to pull a particular film or tape copy if you have to eliminate a prerecorded news item.

EXAMPLE OF A FULLY SCRIPTED DRAMATIC SHOW

JOHN:

What else do you want me to say?

PHYLLIS:

Tell me that you really love me.

          JOHN (NOT CARING):

I love you.


(PHYLLIS LOOKS AT JOHN.  SHE SLOWLY TURNS AWAY FROM JOHN
AND STARTS CRYING)

          JOHN (PUTTING DOWN NEWSPAPER):

Oh, for pity's sake! Stop it, will ya?


(PHYLLIS SLOWLY WALKS INTO KITCHEN.  JOHN GETS UP AND FOLLOWS
HER)

          JOHN:

Why the hell do you always have to make a scene on my day off.

Can't you leave me alone?  Can't you understand that I am

tired?  (ANGRILY):  I love you, I love you, I love you!

Now, isn't that good enough for you?  What the hell else shall

I do?  (HE WALKS OVER TO THE HI-FI SET AND TURNS ON THE RADIO)

          PHYLLIS:  etc.


## The Semi-scripted Show

A show is only semi-scripted if the dialogue is indicated but not completely written out. In general, the opening and closing remarks are fully scripted, while the bulk of the dialogue or commentary is only generally indicated, such as "Dr. Hyde talks about Aristotle; Dr. Marsh replies."

This type of script is almost always used for programs of an educational nature, for variety programs, and for other types in which a great amount of ad-lib commentary or discussion occurs.

The important part in semi-scripting a show is to indicate specific cue lines that tell the director when to roll a film or when to break the cameras to another set area.


## The Show Format

The show format lists only the order of particular show segments, major set areas, and major running and segment times. A show format is frequently used in shows that have established performance routines, such as daily morning shows and variety shows. Most panel discussion shows, for instance, are directed from a show format.

EXAMPLE OF A SEMI-SCRIPTED SHOW

| VIDEO | AUDIO |
|---|---|
| | DUNN:<br>Tell me, Dr. Crane, how far has the operation progressed? |
| COVER SHOT of operation team | CRANE:<br>REPLIES THAT DR. GALANTE IS WORKING ON THE TUMOR AND WILL HAVE IT OUT VERY SOON. |
| | DUNN:<br>Then he will give it to you for examination? |
| CU of CRANE | CRANE:<br>EXPLAINS THAT FIRST THE GENERAL SHAPE AND APPEARANCE OF A TUMOR MAY POINT TO THE CORRECT DIAGNOSIS. THIS MUST BE CONFIRMED BY MICRO-SCOPIC EXAMINATION. |
| | DUNN:<br>How long will that take? |
| | CRANE:<br>REPLIES A FEW MINUTES |
| LS OF SURGERY | GALANTE:<br>CALLS DR. CRANE, COMMENTS ON APPEARANCE OF TUMOR, HANDS SPECIMEN TO HIM. |
| | Etc. |

EXAMPLE OF A SHOW FORMAT

| RUNNING TIME | SEGMENT TIME: | SEGMENT: |
|---|---|---|
| 11:42:47 | 3:00 | SHORTY PARSONS AND HER WONDERFUL DOGS |
| 11:45:47 | 1:00 | FRITOS LIVE |
| 11:46:47 | 10:00 | LIFE MAG'S INTERVIEW ON THE WEST... |
| 11:56:47 | 1:00 | MCKESSON AND ROBBINS SOF |
| 11:57:47 | 0:30 | SLIDES: "O'COPPER."  ET: THEME UP AND BG |
| 11:58:17 | 0:43 | FORTUNE BIDS ALL BYE BYE FROM AUDIENCE AREA |
| 11:59:00 | 0:30 | CREDIT SUPER SLIDES |
| 11:59:30 |  | TO BLACK |

## The Fact Sheet or Run-down Sheet

A fact or run-down sheet lists the items that are to be shown on camera. It also indicates roughly what should be said. No special video and audio instructions are given. The fact sheet is usually supplied by the advertising agency that likes to have a particular performer ad-lib its commercials.

Generally, the director must rewrite the fact sheet into a show format so that he and the talent know what they are supposed to do. Directing solely from a fact sheet is not recommended, since ad-libbing by both director and talent rarely works out satisfactorily.

EXAMPLE OF A FACT SHEET

FRITOS CORN CHIP COMMERCIAL          DATE: XXXX  TIME: XXXX.

PROPS:  Fritos Corn Chip Bag with Header.  Lone Ranger Tattoos

(four sets).  Display of Fritos Corn Chip Bags.  One

Soft Sheet Poster.

OFFER:  1.  FREE: four Lone Ranger Western tattoos

2.  FREE: with every 29 cent bag of Fritos corn chips:

GOLDEN CHIPS OF CORN: Best munching ever. High in

Protein energy. Great for after-school snacks.

Tastes like fresh-roasted corn!

3.  FREE: Lone Ranger Western Tattoos: Look real, but

wash off easily. Use for your hands and arms. Use

on stationary. T-shirts.

4.  HURRY GROCER'S SUPPLY LIMITED.


## Marking the Script

Before you can mark a script, you must first of all carefully read it. Second, you must visualize individual shots indicated in the video column. Third, you must relate these shots to the floor plan and set in which the show is going to take place. This is the beginning of your picturization process. Fourth, you must look for special audio instructions and edit the commentary or dialogue so that it fits the style and time allotment of the show. This involves, fifth, a rough timing of the script.


AUDIO CUES:

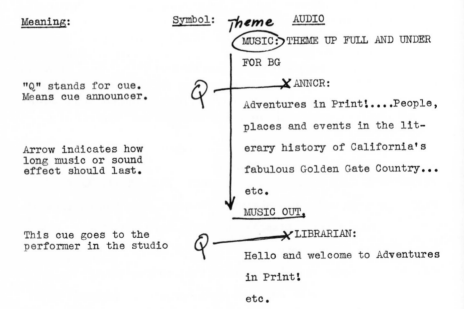

Meaning:                         Symbol:   *Theme*    AUDIO

                                          MUSIC: THEME UP FULL AND UNDER

                                          FOR BG

"Q" stands for cue.                       ANNCR:
Means cue announcer.

                                          Adventures in Print!....People,

                                          places and events in the lit-

Arrow indicates how                       erary history of California's
long music or sound
effect should last.                       fabulous Golden Gate Country...

                                          etc.

                                          MUSIC OUT.

This cue goes to the                      LIBRARIAN:
performer in the studio
                                          Hello and welcome to Adventures

                                          in Print!

                                          etc.

After you have edited the script properly, you must mark it with all the necessary audio and video cues. Although there are some standard marking symbols, you will probably devise some special script markings that seem to work best for you. When marking a script, watch the following points:

1. Your marking symbols must be clear and easily comprehensible.

2. Once you have arrived at a workable system, don't change it from show to show. Standardize your symbols as soon as possible.

3. Don't overmark your script. Too many confusing symbols are worse than none at all.

4. Your cue markings must precede the desired action.

Whenever the shot or the camera directions are given in the video column by the writer, you don't have to rewrite these instructions with your own symbols. A simple underlining or circling of the printed video instructions will generally do.

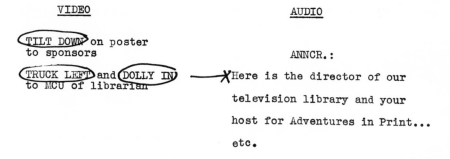

If such specific video instructions are not given, you can simply pencil them in.

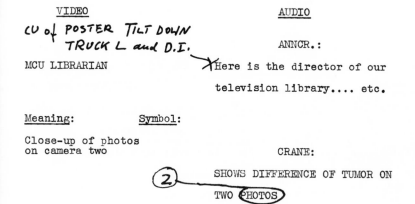

| Meaning: | Symbol: | |
|---|---|---|
| Take camera one | ① ————→ | DUNN: |

Thank you, Dr. Crane. Now, there
are other types of cancer afflict-
ing women. To learn about these,
let us look in on Dr. Steiner,

| Dissolve to camera two | DISS ② | talking with a patient. |

              Etc.

              DUNN:

Here, as in other parts of the body,
he emphasizes that surgery and radi-
ation are the standard forms of

| Roll film, means start film projector | ROLL FILM | treatment. Let's see how a radiolo- |

gist uses X-ray in the treatment of
cancer.

              Etc.

              DUNN: (contd)

In another hospital radioactive
cobalt is used to treat cancer.

| Roll tape. Start tape machine. Appr 4 sec. start. | ROLL TAPE | Focused on the tumor, the machine rotates over this spot as the treatment is given. |

              Etc.

              CRANE:

Under the microscope, the normal

| Take slide Change slide | SL | cells look like this. And the can- |
| | SL | cer cell looks like this. |

| Take Telop | T | Here is a cell with especially |

              large nuclei.

              Etc.

Meaning:                    Symbol:

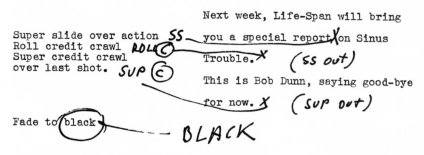

DUNN:

Next week, Life-Span will bring

Super slide over action **SS** — you a special report on Sinus
Roll credit crawl **ROLL** Ⓒ
Super credit crawl Trouble. ✗ *(ss out)*
over last shot. **SUP** Ⓒ
This is Bob Dunn, saying good-bye

for now. ✗ *(sup out)*

Fade to ⟨black⟩ — — — **BLACK**

The marking symbols illustrated on the following two pages include only the most frequently used cues, which have become more or less standardized throughout the industry.

When you mark a fully scripted drama, you may want to indicate some of the more difficult blocking maneuvers and specially framed shots. Since there is rarely enough room on your script for extensive markings, you can put the script into a ring binder with blank paper on the opposite side of the script page.

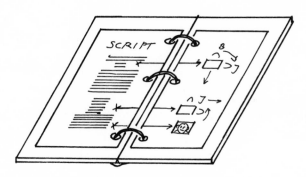

Most blocking maneuvers and special shots are best explained by small thumbnail sketches (see page 454).

## THE REHEARSAL

Lack of adequate rehearsal time is one of the most serious production problems in small station operation. Rehearsal time is rarely scheduled, and when it is made available, it is usually too short. How can you combat this problem? Only with very careful preparation before you get to the rehearsal.

| MEANING | SYMBOL | |
|---|---|---|
| | |  |
| Extreme long shot (cover shot) | *XLS* | |
| | |  |
| Long shot (full shot) | *LS* | |
| | |  |
| Medium shot | *MS* | |
| | |  |
| Medium close-up | *MCU* | |
| | |  |
| Close-up | *CU* | |
| | |  |
| Tight close-up | *TCU* | |

452

| MEANING | SYMBOL |
|---------|--------|

Extreme close-up     *XCU*

Knee shot     —

Bust shot     —

Two-shot (two people in frame)     *2-shot*

Three-shot     *3-shot*

Over-the-shoulder shot     *O. shoulder*

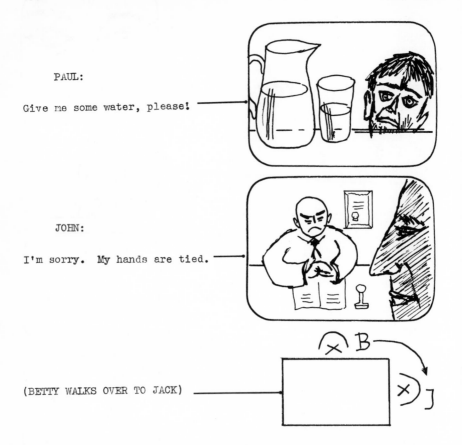

PAUL:

Give me some water, please!

JOHN:

I'm sorry. My hands are tied.

(BETTY WALKS OVER TO JACK)

Before you call for a script reading, be thoroughly familiar with all aspects of your script. Know what everyone has to say and do, and where everything is going to take place in a specific setup. Have your script marked, at least temporarily, before you start reading it with the talent and before you discuss special production problems with the production and engineering people. Ideally, your show preparation should consist of (1) director's preparation, (2) script reading with talent, (3) dry run with talent, (4) walk-through with technical and production personnel and with talent, and (5) camera rehearsal.

### Director's Preparation

1. Read the script.
2. Get a floor plan as soon as possible.
3. Work out rough blocking, the most important cross-overs, and the major camera and microphone positions.
4. Decide on the number and type of microphones needed.
5. Mark and roughly time the script.

6. Check whether all scripts have been properly corrected, if corrections are needed.

## Script Reading

1. Issue a call for the reading.
2. Explain the purpose of the show, the general production procedures, the mood of the show, etc.
3. Read segments. If it is a semi-scripted show, have the talent ad-lib all the sections.
4. Time the script carefully.
5. Set a date and place for the dry run.

Devote much care and time to the script reading. Most major problems should be worked out here.

## Dry Run

1. Hold the dry run preferably in the studio or a rehearsal hall (usually not available in small station operation) or, if not possible, in any other available place. Use tables, chairs, and chalk marks on the floor for sets and furniture.
2. Work out all blocking problems.
3. Always keep microphone movement and camera movement in mind.
4. Call out all cues aloud, if it will help.
5. Go through the complete script, including major actions and the entire dialogue or commentary.
6. Time each segment and the over-all show. Allow time for long camera movements, music bridges, announcer's introduction and close, etc.
7. Set a time for the walk-through, the camera rehearsal, and the checking-in time for the on-the-air performance.

## Walk-through

All people directly involved with the studio operations must participate in the *technical walk-through:* the associate director (if you are fortunate enough to have such valuable help), the technical director, the cameramen, the audio engineer, the lighting director, the boom operator, the floor manager, and all floor men. Consider and explain the following problems:

1. Basic blocking and action of talent.
2. Camera locations and basic camera traffic.
3. Special shots and special framings.
4. Special lenses used.
5. Microphone placement, microphone boom traffic.

6. Basic cuing.
7. Scenery and prop changes; prop placement.
8. Easel positions.
9. Major lighting and special lighting effects.

In the *talent walk-through,* explain again to all performers or actors their major actions, positions, and crossings.

1. Show the performer how to hold a particular object so that you can get the desired shot.
2. Explain to all talent what is going on so that everyone knows the continuity of the show.
3. Explain briefly the major visualization and picturization aspects.
4. If possible, have the performers or actors walk through the action (with the microphones live).
5. Have each person go through his opening lines and then skip to his individual cue lines.
6. Give everyone enough time for make-up and dressing before the camera rehearsal.

### Camera Rehearsal

In small station operation, camera rehearsal and final dress rehearsal are almost always the same rehearsal. Frequently, your camera rehearsal time (which is scheduled too tightly anyway) is cut short by technical problems, such as minor or major lighting adjustments and camera adjustments. There is one attribute you must have as a television director—patience. You may get nervous when you see most of the technical crew working frantically on your key camera five minutes before air time. There is nothing you can do, however, except realize that you are working with (1) an extremely skilled group of technicians who know just as well as you do how much depends on a successful performance and (2) a highly complicated technical machine which, like all machines, sometimes works and sometimes doesn't.

Basically, there are two methods of conducting a camera rehearsal: (1) the stop-start method, and (2) the uninterrupted run-through (similar to a dress rehearsal). Both methods of rehearsal are conducted from the control room.

With the *stop-start method,* you interrupt the camera rehearsal whenever you find something wrong; then you go back to a logical spot in the script and start all over again, hoping that the mistake is not repeated. This is a thorough but time-consuming method.

The *uninterrupted run-through* usually gets interrupted, too. But you should call for a "cut" (stop all action) only when a grave mistake has been made, one that cannot be corrected at a later time. All minor mistakes are corrected *after* the basic run-through.

The camera rehearsal is your last chance to get a fairly accurate timing on the show.

Even after the most careful script preparation, you must frequently change certain camera directions and blocking procedures. Be open-minded to suggestions from the production and engineering crews, but don't be indecisive. Once you have made a change and it seems to work out, stick to it.

In complicated, fully scripted shows your task as a director will be considerably aided if you supply the cameramen with *shot sheets*. A shot sheet lists every shot a particular camera has to get. As soon as a camera is free (momentarily off the air), the cameraman can look at his shot sheet and frame up his next shot without your specific instruction. Some of the newer cameras have special shot-sheet holders directly below the viewfinder. Some shot sheets are quite detailed, telling the cameraman what to get, how to frame it, and what lens to use. Here is an example of the way a shot sheet may be written:

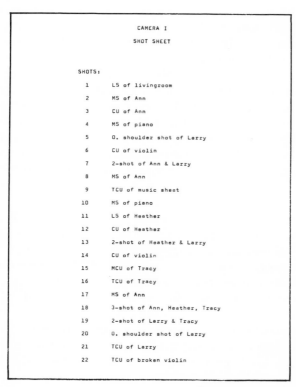

CAMERA I

SHOT SHEET

SHOTS:

| | |
|---|---|
| 1 | LS of livingroom |
| 2 | MS of Ann |
| 3 | CU of Ann |
| 4 | MS of piano |
| 5 | O. shoulder shot of Larry |
| 6 | CU of violin |
| 7 | 2-shot of Ann & Larry |
| 8 | MS of Ann |
| 9 | TCU of music sheet |
| 10 | MS of piano |
| 11 | LS of Heather |
| 12 | CU of Heather |
| 13 | 2-shot of Heather & Larry |
| 14 | CU of violin |
| 15 | MCU of Tracy |
| 16 | TCU of Tracy |
| 17 | MS of Ann |
| 18 | 3-shot of Ann, Heather, Tracy |
| 19 | 2-shot of Larry & Tracy |
| 20 | O. shoulder shot of Larry |
| 21 | TCU of Larry |
| 22 | TCU of broken violin |

**Example of a shot sheet**

In the final camera rehearsal, you rehearse the complete show, including all video and audio elements, such as film, tape, sound effects, slides, and telops. Be sure to finish the rehearsal early enough to allow time to reset the rehearsed production elements. Films must be rolled back and rethreaded, tape must be cued up again, slides have to be brought into proper order, etc.

## Walk-through Camera-rehearsal Combination

Necessary as the above-mentioned rehearsal procedures seem, they are rarely possible in small station operation. For a half-hour show you may have only a 40-minute camera rehearsal. In this situation, you must combine walk-through and camera rehearsal.

A successful walk-through camera-rehearsal combination includes the following procedures:

1. Always conduct this type of rehearsal from the studio floor. If you try to do it from the control room, you will waste valuable time trying to explain your shots and moves through the inadequate intercommunication system.

2. Get all personnel into their opening positions. Cameramen are ready for their opening shots, microphone boom is being operated, floor manager is ready for cuing, T.D. and audio engineer are ready for action in the control room.

3. Walk the talent through all the major parts of the show. As soon as a performer demonstrates an object, tell the cameraman how you want the shot framed. Call your shots over the hot microphone into the control room and have the T.D. put the particular camera pictures on the studio monitors, so that everyone (including yourself) can watch and see how everything looks.

5. As soon as the performer knows how to go on from there, skip the middle of his performance and have him introduce the next segment.

6. Rehearse all major cross-overs on camera. Look frequently through the cameraman's viewfinder to check framing (especially the camera in off-position, getting ready for the next shot).

7. Give all cues for music, sound effects, film clips, tape inserts, etc., but, to save time, don't have them executed (except music).

8. Have all key positions for the talent marked with paint, chalk, or masking tape.

9. Rehearse some of the most important parts of the show (opening, closing, and cross-overs) again from the control room.

10. Be courteous, even though you are terribly pressed for time.

11. Allow everyone at least five minutes before air time to get ready for the on-the-air presentation.

The major drawbacks of this rehearsal method are: (1) No one, including you, ever has a chance to go through the whole show continuously. (2) You don't have the opportunity to see and call all your shots from the control room and to see complete studio traffic develop. (3) You cannot accurately time the whole show.

## THE ON-THE-AIR PERFORMANCE

Directing the on-the-air performance is, of course, the most important part of your job, as important as all the preparations may have been.

### Stand By

1. Check with the floor manager to make sure everyone is in the studio and ready.

2. Announce the time remaining before the telecast over the intercommunication system.

3. Alert everyone to the first cues.

4. Check with the audio engineer about the theme music, and with master control about the opening film, slides, and VTR.

5. Tell the floor manager who gets the first cue.

6. Line up the opening shots.

### The Show

"Thirty seconds. Fifteen seconds. Stand by to roll film, stand by music, stand by to cue announcer. Ten seconds; STAND BY. Roll film. (*On air*) Up on film. Music. Fade music, cue announcer. Ready slide. Super slide. Super out. Music out. Slowwwwly. Stand by to cue Bob (*the performer*). Ready one. First cue (*film cue*). Cue Bob, take one. Two, get a close-up of what Bob is holding. Ready two; take two. One, hold the cover shot. Ready one; take one. Two, on the easel. Tighter; good. Ready two for a dissolve. Dissolve to two. (*By now you are well into the show. Don't forget to watch the time. After the three-minute cue you must prepare for the closing. Are the closing slides and the closing crawl ready? Watch the time carefully.*) Thirty seconds. Wind him up. Cut. Cut him. Good. Ready music. Closing theme, yes. Ready two; take two. Music. Fade music under. Cue announcer. Ready crawl. Roll crawl. Super crawl. Super out. Music up and out. To black. Right on the nose. Hold. O.K., all clear. Thanks very much. Good job, everyone."

Unfortunately, it does not always go as smoothly as that. You can contribute greatly to a smooth performance, however, if you pay particular attention to a few important on-the-air directing procedures.

These are:

1. Give all your signals clearly and precisely. Appear relaxed but alert.

2. Cue your talent before you come up on him with the camera. By the time he starts to speak, you will have faded in the picture.

3. Don't tell the floor manager just to cue "him," especially when there are several "hims" in the studio, awaiting cues sooner or later.

4. Don't give a ready cue too far in advance, or the people will not be ready by the time your take cue finally arrives (after everyone has forgotten about it).

5. Don't pause between the "take" and the number of the camera. Do not say: "Take____(*pause*)____two." Some T.D.'s will punch up the camera before you say the number.

6. Keep in mind the number of the camera that is already on the air, and don't call for a cut or dissolve to that camera.

7. Don't ready one camera and then call for a take of another camera. In other words, don't say: "Ready one; take two." If you change your mind, nullify the ready cue first and give another ready cue.

8. Talk to the cameras by number and not by the name of the cameraman. What would you do if both your cameramen were called "Bob?"

9. Call the camera first before you give instructions. For example: "Camera two. Give me a close-up of the display. Camera three, cover shot. Camera one, dolly in."

10. After you have put one camera on the air, *immediately* tell the other camera what to do next. Don't wait until the last second to inform your free camera what to do.

11. If you have one camera tight on an object, put the other camera on a cover shot. Always protect yourself with a wide angle shot. But don't become a slave to this rule. If you need both cameras on tight lenses, use them.

12. If a camera goes "soft" (impaired picture quality) or fails completely while on the air, keep calm. Continue your show with one camera on a dolly lens (50mm). If the remaining camera gets caught on a long lens, go quickly to black, have the cameraman change over to a dolly lens, fade up again and continue your show. With a zoom lens you will have no problems changing the field of view of the remaining camera.

13. If you make a mistake, correct it as well as you can, and then forget it. Don't meditate on how you could have avoided this particular mistake while neglecting the rest of the show.

14. Don't get hung up on little details; keep the whole show in mind.

15. During the show, speak only when necessary. If you talk too much, people will stop listening carefully and may miss important instructions.

16. If you are fortunate enough to work with an A.D. (assistant or associate director), you must be sure about each other's particular functions. Usually, the A.D. sets up the shots and you as the director ready them and take them. For example, your A.D. will tell camera three to get a close-up of Phyllis, while you simply follow at the right moment with a "ready three—take three." As soon as camera three is on the air, your A.D. will tell cameras one and two what to do next. Some assistant directors set up *and* ready the shots so that all the director has to do is to correct the framing whenever necessary and to snap his fingers when he wants to take the shot. The "finger snapping" can be an effective directing device if you do it precisely and consistently; however, it often develops into a meaningless habit, especially when it merely duplicates your voice signals.

## Post Show Duties

After the show, give thanks to crew and talent. If something went wrong, don't storm into the studio blaming everyone but yourself. Wait until you can think objectively about the situation. Then don't just criticize, but instead make suggestions on how to avoid similar mistakes in the future.

Don't forget the necessary production reports, music lists, and union contracts (if you act as producer-director). File your marked script for future reference.

## SUMMARY

In small station operation, the producing and directing jobs are combined and handled by the producer-director. This combining of tasks is desirable, since many of the producing and directing duties overlap.

The producer is the organizer of television shows. He creates show ideas and prepares the necessary material for on-the-air production. The director edits the material and puts it on the air. The producer, then, must be concerned with the investigation of the validity of an idea for television presentation and with television production procedures. These procedures include, in general, the following steps:

1. Material, with considerations about audience, time of telecast, selection of material, research, method of presentation, and production conferences.

2. Cost, including budget considerations for talent, scenery, writer, and special production items.

3. Script.

4. Talent.

5. Technical facilities, including sets, graphic materials, properties, make-up and wardrobe, cameras, audio, lighting, special effects, and show origination facilities.

6. Commercials.

7. Union affiliations and material clearances.

8. Rehearsal schedules.

9. Publicity and promotion procedures.

The director is mainly concerned with the coordination of all production elements, including talent, engineering, and production crews. A television director must think in pictures. Visualization and picturization are two essential concepts for the television director. Visualization is the translation of ideas and words into pictures, and includes such concepts as picture composition and major staging and framing techniques. Picturization means putting these individual images into a proper order so that their continuity conveys a particular meaning. The picturization process can be achieved by primary movement (movement of objects in front of the camera), secondary movement (movement of the camera: pan, tilt, dolly, zoom, truck, pedestal, boom), and tertiary movement (sequence of shots through editing: cut, dissolve, and fade).

Since every second of a telecasting day is preplanned and properly logged, split-second timing is essential to all television operation. The television director must learn to work with two kinds of time: (1) actual time, as expressed in minutes and seconds, and (2) psychological time, which is expressed in relative speeds, and stems from an understanding of timing. Psychological time includes the over-all pace of a show, the tempo of the individual segments, and the rate of the individual performances within each segment. Timing methods for actual time (the director works with clock and stop watch) include front-timing and back-timing.

The television director must be familiar with the different forms of the television script: the fully scripted show (indicating every word spoken and all necessary video instructions), the semi-scripted show (showing only the major parts of the dialogue and some video instructions), the show format (listing only the order of the particular show segments), and the fact or run-down sheet (listing the items to be shown on camera or to be talked about). The director should develop a special script-marking system, which will aid him considerably during the on-the-air performance.

The preparation for the on-the-air show involves, in general, a script reading; a dry run (without cameras); a walk-through with the production crew, technical crew, and talent; and a camera rehearsal, including all technical facilities. The walk-through camera-rehearsal combination can be used when adequate rehearsal time for all previously mentioned rehearsal procedures is lacking.

The most important job of the television director is the on-the-air coordination of all production elements. Simultaneously, the director must (1) talk and listen to the studio engineers and floor men, (2) talk and listen to the people in the control room (T.D. and audio engineer), (3) watch at least three monitors, (4) watch the control room clock and a stop watch, (5) listen to the audio, (6) follow the script, and (7) in some stations, do the actual camera switching. For all these tasks, a proper command of standard television terminology is mandatory.

The producer-director must always realize that he is producing his program for many people, not just an audience but individual human beings who will accept both bad and good programming material, but who will benefit greatly from good material and be equally harmed by bad material.

## EXERCISES

1. Set up a simple two-man interview and find the most workable staging and camera arrangements.
2. Stage three people in many different ways so as to shift emphasis from one person to the other. Experiment with secondary and tertiary movements.
3. Take a few objects and display them in a variety of ways for the camera. Watch the different setups on the monitor and pick out the most workable combinations. Say *why* you prefer one particular setup to the rest of the displays.
4. What production procedures would you have to consider in the production of a half-hour television show, featuring (1) the Budapest String Quartet and (2) the latest fashions?
5. You are to direct three live commercial cut-ins during the afternoon movie. The first cut-in is supposed to go on the air only five minutes after you have received the script from the agency representative, who is terribly sorry for being so late. He tells you, how-

ever, that the talent knows the "pitch" perfectly well. Unfortunately, you cannot camera rehearse the commercial since the film runs through the studio control board. Should you go through with the commercial? If so, what can you do to ensure an adequate commercial presentation?

6. Due to extreme lack of space, your key monochrome camera in your remote pickup of a public hearing is confined to one designated spot. You are able to pan and tilt but not dolly the camera. What lens, or lenses, would you probably use on this camera?

7. Your weekly "Modern Ballet" show has been temporarily moved into a very small studio. What would you suggest to (a) the choreographer, (b) the art director, and (c) the television engineers to create the illusion of a large studio?

8. At the end of your farm program, you decide to super the closing credits over the prize chicken the farmers had proudly displayed in your studio. You have just started with your first credit super when the chicken suddenly decides to break loose and run out of camera range. What do you do?

9. You are to direct another show of your "Creative Man" series, featuring the Budapest String Quartet. Unfortunately, you don't read music. Do you think you can properly direct this show? For instance, since you are not familiar with the quartet's first selection, the "First Bagatelle" by Anton Webern, how can you tell when the movements are coming to an end?

10. Professor Wilhelm Wente is your guest scientist on your panel program "Modern Technology." Unexpectedly he calls for a closer camera view of his newly developed rocket model. Your free camera is in such a position that it will have to shoot off the set to get the desired shot of the rocket. You want to give the viewers a good look at the model as soon as possible, but you don't want to distract the viewers' attention by showing all the ladders and microphone stands that are in camera range behind the rocket model. How can you get the desired close-up of the rocket without shooting off the set? How can you quickly give the desired close-up without changing camera positions?

# 13

## Remote Telecasts

When a television pickup is made outside the studio, we speak of it as a remote telecast, or simply a remote.

During a remote telecast, the cameras are generally looking in on an event that has not been staged specifically for television. The event is merely reported by the cameras, not created for them. Remote telecasts transmit actuality.

As a director of remote telecasts, you have a rather difficult assignment: you must show the event as realistically as possible, and yet, since you cannot show everything at once, you must edit the event carefully to show certain sections of the event that are characteristic of the whole. The only visualization factor to keep in mind is to show everything as clearly as possible; the important picturization factor is to show the event in a realistic continuity. For instance, don't be afraid to show pauses as well as action. A director who constantly cuts to "cute shots" of spectators during lull periods of a baseball game does not understand the production technique of television reporting. The viewer at home is not really interested in what certain spectators look like; what he wants to do is watch the game with its fast *and* its slow periods.

## REMOTE EQUIPMENT

Every television remote requires as a minimum the setup of a small television station. The television performance center, the studio, may be indoors or outdoors, wherever the event is taking place. The television control center, however, must be set up specially. In general, all television remote equipment is housed in a large truck or bus built or adapted for this purpose.

The specially manufactured television equipment located in the remote truck includes (1) auxiliary camera equipment for up to five cameras (portable power supplies and sync generators); (2) camera control monitors, which are sometimes used by the director as pre-

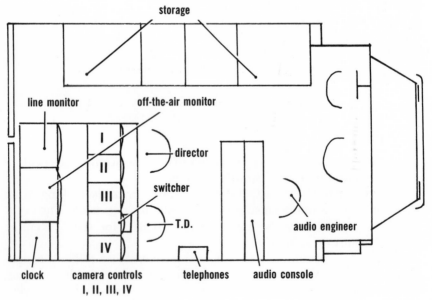

Remote truck

view monitors, and master monitor; (3) switcher; (4) off-the-air monitor and antenna; (5) remote audio equipment (amplifier with volume controls and mixer); (6) power distribution box; (7) microwave dish with small transmitter attached (usually outside the truck); and (8) intercommunications equipment between remote crews and studio (transmitter) crews.

Remote cameras and microphones are generally standard studio equipment. Constant efforts have been made by the manufacturers of television equipment to design a television camera and the necessary recording or transmission facilities that are light and flexible enough to be carried and operated by one man. Such flexible equipment is especially important for the coverage of news, sports, and special events.

The Ampex Corporation has developed two "camera-backpack" combinations. One such combination consists of a monochrome camera and a video tape recorder; the other of a color camera and the necessary electronic accessories. The camera and video tape recorder combination consists of a monochrome camera and a standard broadcast video tape recorder. The 13-pound Plumbicon camera has an

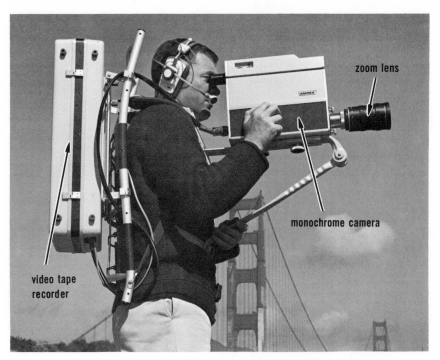

zoom lens

monochrome camera

video tape recorder

VR-3000 video tape recorder

electronic viewfinder, a 4 : 1 zoom lens, and controls for the camera as well as for the video tape recorder. The backpack video tape recorder is the 35-pound VR-3000, which permits up to 20 minutes of continuous recording. Camera and recorder are battery powered. Since the VR-3000 is a standard broadcast recorder, its 2-inch tapes can be played back immediately on any other standard broadcast recorder, such as the Ampex 1100 or the RCA TR-22.

The Ampex color camera backpack consists of the BC-100 Plumbicon color camera, which is carried on the operator's shoulder, and the backpack, which contains the necessary electronic accessories. The camera weighs 35 pounds and has an electronic viewfinder and a 6 : 1 zoom lens. The color signal is relayed from the backpack to a base station through a thin cable (up to 2,000 feet in length), or a small microwave relay. At the base station, the color signal is processed—that is, it is changed into a signal that can be broadcast and then is fed to the television station.

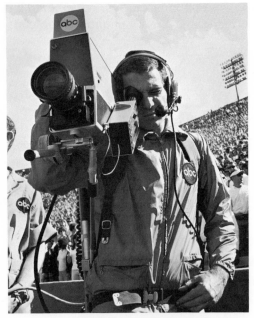

Ampex color camera and back-pack color accessory equipment

The Sony Corporation has also developed a camera and video tape recorder combination, consisting of a very small monochrome camera that can be handheld, similar to a 16mm motion picture camera.

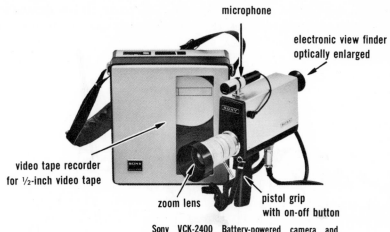

Sony VCK-2400 Battery-powered camera and video tape recorder

The television camera has a small, one-inch electronic viewfinder and pistol grip controls that activate the camera and the video tape recorder. The recorder and batteries are worn on a belt. The narrow video tape cannot be played back on standard broadcast recorders.

## REMOTE SIGNAL TRANSMISSION

The video signal is usually microwaved from the remote location to the transmitter. The audio signal can be sent either with the video signal via microwave (multiplexing), or to the transmitter by telephone wires.

You can send the signal by microwave only if you have a clear, unobstructed line of sight from the point of origin to the transmitter.

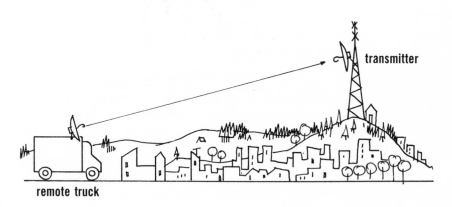

If you do not have a clear line of sight, you must employ one or several microwave links between the point of origin and the transmitter.

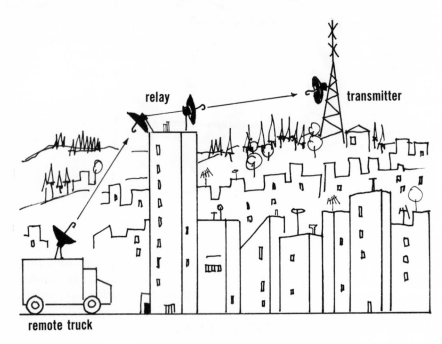

These microwave relay stations are generally supplied by the telephone company, a service that is appreciated by the individual television stations, in spite of the rather extensive additional cost. The video signal can, of course, also be sent by special cable.

## REMOTE SURVEY

Thorough advanced preparation is essential for every remote telecast. The failure or success of a remote is frequently a direct result of the extent of the preceding survey.

### Survey Participants

Every remote telecast must be surveyed from (1) a production point of view and (2) a technical, engineering point of view. Every remote location must, therefore, be surveyed by at least one member of the production department and one member of the engineering department—preferably the director and technical director of the telecast. Frequently, the director and T.D. are joined by one or several production and engineering supervisors, especially when the remote involves the coverage of an especially important event.

You can solve many problems by inviting a person who is responsible for, or at least thoroughly familiar with, the exact proceedings of the event. This person can usually arrange for necessary parking facilities, for example, and many other important production details. He can also give you an accurate run-down of events in their sequence, and may even provide spotters who can help you with the identification of personnel and other important details of the event.

## Survey Method

Many production and technical problems must be considered during a remote survey and possible solutions worked out. In general, the production part of the remote telecast is determined first; engineering then tries to make the planned production procedures technically possible. Depending on the complexity of the remote telecast, extensive compromises must often be made by production people as well as engineers.

As a director, you can make such compromises only if you know what the particular technical setup and pickup problems are and what changes in your production procedures will help to overcome these technical problems. You must, therefore, familiarize yourself with the production problems as well as the engineering problems of television remotes. Although many of the production and engineering survey questions overlap, we will, for better clarification, consider them separately.

### Remote survey: production

*Place and time.*
1. Where is the exact location of the telecast?
   *a.* address; *b.* telephone number.
2. Who is your contact for the event?
   *a.* name; *b.* address; *c.* business phone; *d.* home phone.
3. When is your remote telecast?
   *a.* date; *b.* time.

*Camera placement.*
1. What is the exact nature of the event? Where does the action take place? What type of action do you expect? Consult the person or persons responsible for the event.
2. How many cameras do you need for a proper pickup? Try to use as few as possible.
3. Where do you need the cameras?
   *a.* Never place your cameras on opposite sides of the action. In general, the closer the cameras are together, the easier and less confusing the cutting will be.

*b.* Shoot with the sun, never against the sun. The sun must remain in back or to the side of the cameras for the entire telecast. The press boxes of larger stadiums are generally located in the shadow side of the stadium.

*c.* Always survey the remote location during the exact time of the scheduled telecast, from 2:00 to 4:00 P.M., for instance, so that you can observe the exact location of the sun and the prevailing lighting conditions. If it is not a sunny day, try to determine the location of the sun as closely as possible.

4. Are there any large objects blocking the camera view, such as trees, telephone poles, or billboards? Will you have the same field of view during the actual time of the telecast? A stadium crowd, for instance, may block the camera's field of view, although at the time of the survey the view was unobstructed.

5. Can you avoid large billboards in the background of your shots, especially when the advertising competes with your sponsor's product?

6. Do you need special camera platforms? How high? Where? Can the platforms be erected at this particular point? Can you use the remote truck as a platform?

7. If competing stations are also covering the event, have you obtained exclusive rights for your camera positions?

*Camera movement.*
1. Do you intend to move certain cameras?
    *a.* Where do you want the cameras to go?
    *b.* Is the camera on or off the air during the dolly?
    *c.* What kind of floor do you have? Can the camera dolly on the floor or do you need to build special plywood pathways?
    *d.* What kind of camera dolly do you need?
    *e.* How wide are the hallways and doors? Can the camera get through? Measure the halls and doorways, if necessary.

*Camera lenses.*
How close do you have to get to the action? What lenses do you need? List each camera and state the desired lens complement. This will be only a tentative line-up, since you may want to change lenses once the cameras are set up. If you have only one zoom lens, you should determine the location of the zoom camera as early as possible.

*Lighting.*
1. Do you need additional lighting? If so, what kind and where?
2. Can the lighting instruments be hung conveniently, or do you have to make special lighting arrangements?
3. Do you intend to shoot against windows? If so, the windows must be covered to block out undesirable light.

*Audio*

1. What type of audio pickup do you need? Where do you need it?
   a. Microphone booms, even small ones, are generally too cumbersome to take on remote location.
   b. Hand microphones, which can also be used as stand and desk microphones, are used almost exclusively for remote telecasts.
2. What is the exact action radius as far as audio is concerned?
   a. How long must the microphone cables be?
   b. How many microphones do you need?
   c. Where are the microphones located? (You may want to hang microphones over the crowd or over an orchestra pit, for example.)
   d. Do you need any long-distance microphones for special sound pickup?
3. Do you need speakers to carry the program sound? If so, how many? Where do they have to be located?

*Intercommunication.*

1. Do you need special intercommunication lines for your production personnel or can these people (floor manager, floor men) plug their earphones into the cameras? If you need special lines, where do they have to go? This is especially important if your off-camera announcer must take direct cues from you rather than the floor manager, who may have something else to do at that time.
2. Do you need double headsets to carry both program sound and the director's signals? How many do you need? Where do you need them?
3. Check with the engineer on the availability of one or more outside telephones to keep you in touch with studio and transmitter.

*Miscellaneous production items.*

1. Where are card easels and small commercial setups located?
2. Do you need a special clock? Where?
3. Do you need program monitors, especially for the announcer? How many? Where do you need them?
4. Do you need a slate for video tape recording?

*Permits and clearances.*

1. Have you secured proper clearances from the police and fire departments for the telecast?
2. You must obtain special parking permits for the remote truck and other station vehicles.
3. You need special passes for all engineering and production members, especially when the event requires special admittance fees.

4. Have you made arrangements with the police department to assist you in keeping onlookers at a safe distance from all television equipment?

*Special performers.*

Be sure to explain the proceedings of the telecast to all people who are directly involved in the program. Check with these people again concerning the exact line-up of events.

### Remote survey: engineering

In this section, only the engineering survey points that have a direct influence on production procedures and, ultimately, on your portion of the remote survey will be listed. Technical points that have already been mentioned in the production survey, such as cameras and microphones, will not be indicated again. You will note that most of the points below concern the engineering department rather than the producer-director. However, you should be thoroughly familiar with the major aspects of the engineering survey so that you can, if necessary, gently remind the engineers of their particular survey duties.

*Power.*

1. If you don't have your own generator, is there enough electricity available? Where? You will need anywhere from 60 to 125 amp. for the average remote operation, depending on the equipment used. Color generally needs more power than monochrome equipment. Most service entrance cables into houses carry at least 100 amp., enough for the average remote operation.

2. Contact the person who is in charge of the house power (electrician, janitor). Talk to him about the necessary connections. Make sure he is available at the time of the remote setup and at the time of the telecast.

*Location of remote truck or equipment.*

1. The location of the remote truck depends on the availability of power and the location of the cameras. Avoid long cables. Maximum length of camera cables without loss of picture quality: 1,000 to 1,500 feet (usually 500 to 1,000 feet for vidicon cameras).

2. The truck should not block normal traffic. Get proper clearances and protection from the local police department.

3. In some special cases, you may have to take the equipment out of the remote truck and set it up elsewhere, in a room, basement, or tent. Make sure that the new "control room" is dark enough so that the pictures can be properly shaded.

*Location of microwave dish.*

1. Look for a good microwave location, as close to the truck as possible. Good locations generally are tall buildings, fire escapes, hillsides, tops of sports arenas, etc. Check carefully on the direct line of sight with your transmitter.

2. Watch possible sources of video and audio signal interference, such as nearby X-ray machines, or any other high-frequency electronic equipment.

*Routing of cables.*

1. Figure the approximate lengths of all camera and audio cables. Overestimate rather than underestimate.

2. Route your cables in the shortest possible distance from camera to remote truck, without, however, blocking important hallways or doors. Try to route the cables above doorways and hallways. Tape all loose cables to the floor so that the danger of someone tripping is at least minimized.

3. If you have to cover a great span with free hanging cable, relieve the tension by tying the cables on a strong rope stretched over the same distance.

*Lighting.*

1. Are there enough A.C. outlets for your lighting instruments? Are the outlets fused for your lamps? Don't overload ordinary household outlets.

2. You should have enough extension cords and distribution boxes (or simple multiple wall plugs) to accommodate all your lighting instruments. Don't forget the A.C. line for the announcer's monitor.

*Telephone lines.*

1. Do you have access to telephone wires for your audio lines?

2. You need at least one working telephone that connects you with the studio and the transmitter. Make special arrangements with the telephone company.

### Survey memoranda

You may find it advantageous to work out a list indicating the major points you must cover on a remote survey. Check each point on the list as you go along. Also, it may help to draw a sketch of each new remote survey. Indicate the locations of performance areas and major equipment:

1. Performance areas.
2. Major action.
3. Surrounding buildings, trees, etc.

4. Cameras.
5. Remote truck.
6. Power source and telephone lines.
7. Microwave dish.

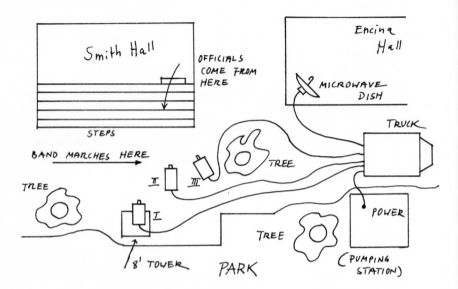

## REMOTE SETUPS FOR MAJOR SPORTS COVERAGE

Most remote operations involve the coverage of major sports events. A good remote director must know the major sports thoroughly. He must know not only the basic rules of the game but also the different techniques of a particular team. Frequently, the remote director gets cued in on major tactics of the home team and, as much as possible, of the guest team also. This helps him and his cameramen to anticipate certain plays and game maneuvers.

The cameramen and all members of the production crew must also be thoroughly familiar with the particular sports event to be covered. There is usually little time to preset shots during a fast game; the cameramen must react automatically and show the right thing at the right time.

As a director of a sports remote, it is extremely important that you standardize your shooting procedures and cues as much as possible. The crowd noise (and possible bands playing) make communication anything but easy. Give your signals loudly and clearly. Be as brief as possible, so that your cameramen don't have to listen for ten seconds before they find out what you really mean.

There are no "rest periods" for anyone during a remote telecast. Each camera must be prepared to go on the air at any time, with no or very little warning. In a fast play, you may have to cut between three cameras without once giving the customary "ready" signal.

## Major Setup Methods

There is no complete agreement on the methods of covering major sports. Not even something as basic as camera placement has been satisfactorily standardized. Available budget and equipment, different physical environments, and the personal taste of the producer or director make such a standardization rather impractical, if not impossible.

The networks often have twice as much equipment and manpower available as a local station for the same job. For example, a network generally uses at least seven cameras for a football pickup: one camera in the locker room, one in the press box for the announcer, three high in the stands for general field coverage, one on the field, and at least one "isolated" camera for instant replay of key plays. (We will discuss instant-replay techniques later in this chapter.) A local station may have to get by with only two cameras in the stands for field coverage and a third camera on the field. One of the two cameras in the stands is also used for the announcer.

Although an abundance of cameras for a remote pickup will provide you with a great variety of pictures from which to choose, it does not necessarily follow that the remote that uses the most cameras is always the most effective one. In fact, some remotes done with very few cameras have proved to be exceptionally effective in continuity and style.

In the following discussion, we will be concerned with some basic remote setup techniques that have worked fairly well under a great variety of conditions. The number of cameras, their basic location, and their major functions will be discussed from a point of view of local station operation.

In all remotes, you must show the viewer enough so that he will be able to follow the over-all game; and you must also show him enough detail so that he can observe special playing techniques.

In general, try to move your cameras as close to the event as possible without losing the over-all view and without blocking the view of spectators. The closer you have your cameras, the shorter the focal lengths of the lenses can be for your close-ups. Long lenses have two major disadvantages, especially when used over a relatively short distance, as in a boxing arena: (1) Fast action is difficult to follow on a long lens. (2) Long lenses reduce the distance on the television screen; the space between two people seems drastically reduced and, in certain cases, may be considerably misleading to the home viewer. The same disadvantage holds true for zoom lenses, of course, if zoomed in to a long focal length.

If possible, you should use zoom lenses on all remote cameras. When your pickup is in color, your cameras come with zoom lenses anyway. However, if you have only one zoom lens available for a monochrome remote pickup, be sure to place your zoom camera in the key coverage area. The lens complements of the other cameras will depend entirely on the location of the cameras in relation to the event.

In the following diagrams, the zoom camera is specially indicated.

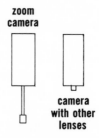

**Baseball**

*Number of cameras:* Three.

*Locations:* On first base line or on third base line. First base line is preferred because most action happens there. Camera one: directly behind home plate (possibly shooting through special break-proof glass window). Camera two: in middle of first base line or next to camera one. Camera three: next to camera two, a little higher up, if possible.

Baseball setup

*Functions:* Camera one (wide and tight lenses): follows balls and strikes; acts as another umpire; observes pitch; sees back of catcher and umpire. Camera two (zoom camera): follows ball. Camera three (wide and tight lenses): follows double plays, covers second base, etc.; gets most "color" shots.

### Football

*Number of cameras:* Four.

*Locations:* Three cameras in the stands, as close to the 50-yard line as possible. All on one side of the stadium (press box, shadow side). Camera one: close to the announcer. Camera four: on the field, at the same side as the other three cameras; camera four should be mobile; it can be mounted on a special field dolly.

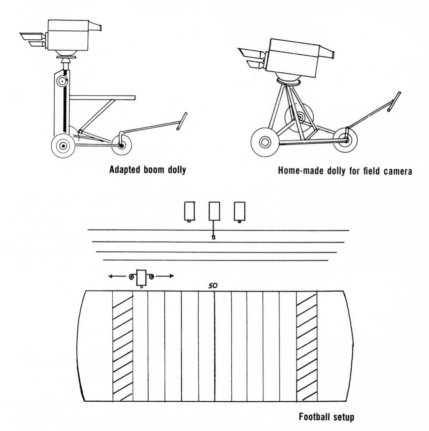

Adapted boom dolly       Home-made dolly for field camera

Football setup

*Functions:* Camera one (wide, medium long, and long lenses): wide lens establishes shots of ball field; medium long lens covers announcer with commercial product, easel cards, scores, etc.; long lens covers field action. Camera two (zoom): field action. Camera three (medium long and long lenses): field action. Camera four (medium and long lenses): gets "color" shots, players on bench, huddles, etc.

### Track

*Number of cameras:* Three (or four).
*Locations:* Similar to football setup. Two (or three) cameras in stands (shadow side). One camera on field.

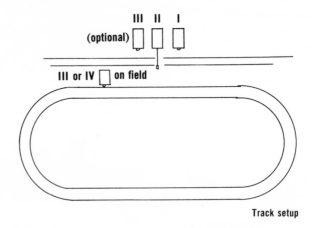

Track setup

*Functions:* Camera one (wide, medium, and close lenses): covers announcer, easel cards, etc., gets establishing shots; picks out action. Camera two (zoom): follows field and track action. Camera three (medium and long lenses): covers action and gets "color" shots. If there is a fourth camera, camera three concentrates on action, camera four supplies "color" shots.

### Basketball

*Number of cameras:* Three.
*Locations:* Two cameras in stands at the middle of the court, opposite officials and benches. Camera three: at end of court, behind and to one side of the basket.
*Functions:* Camera one (medium and long lenses; if high and if enough light is available, use zoom): follows ball. Camera two (wide and long lenses): covers announcer and title cards, follows game; also looks at players and officials in benches. Camera three (short and medium lenses): covers foul shots; gets "color" shots.

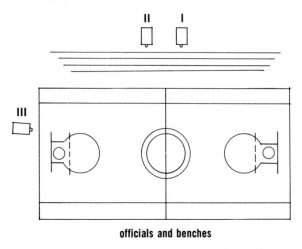

officials and benches

**Basketball setup**

### Tennis

*Number of cameras:* Two (or three).

*Locations:* Both cameras at one end of the court, shooting with the sun. Camera two higher than camera one. Possible third camera at the side of the court, opposite officials.

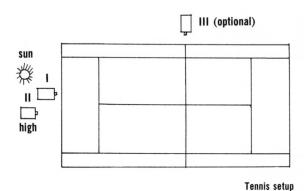

**Tennis setup**

*Functions:* Camera one (medium and long lenses): follows ball. Camera two (wide and medium lenses): gets establishing shots; follows ball; gets color shots. Camera three (optional; medium and long lenses): gets "color" shots.

### Boxing

*Number of cameras:* Two.

*Locations:* Both cameras close to the ring, without blocking spectators; about ten feet apart. Cameras should be slightly higher than the ring to shoot over the ropes.

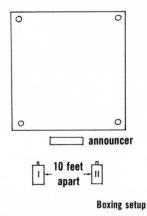

Boxing setup

*Functions:* Camera one (wide and long lenses): gets establishing shots, covers announcer, easel cards, close-ups of action. Camera two (medium and long lenses): gets medium and close-up shots of action.

### Wrestling

*Number of cameras:* Two.

*Locations:* Similar to boxing setup. Fairly close to ringside, about ten feet apart. Camera one: slightly above the ring, shooting over the ropes. Camera two: can be rather low, almost level with ring mat.

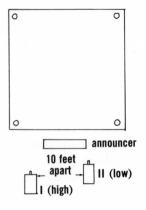

Wrestling setup

*Functions:* Camera one (wide and long lenses): gets establishing shots, covers announcer, easel cards, close-ups of action. Camera two (medium and long lenses): shoots from below (be careful that camera two does not shoot into the overhead lights); gets close-ups and medium shots of action.

The setups for other sports events are very similar to those mentioned above. Your main objective in any sports coverage must be to report the event as faithfully as possible. During the whole telecast, you must not only show your viewers as much important detail as possible, but also keep them sufficiently oriented to the over-all developments.

## Instant Replay

Instant replay means that a key play or other important event is repeated for the viewer, often in slow motion or stop motion, immediately after the event has happened. Instant-replay operations are quite complex and need several additional pieces of television equipment: (1) an isolated camera, (2) an instant-replay switcher, and (3) an instant-replay video tape recorder.

### Isolated camera

When watching an instant replay of a key action, you may notice that the replay either duplicates exactly the sequence you have just seen or—more frequently—shows the action from a slightly different angle. In the first case, the picture sequence of the regular game coverage—that is, the line output—has been recorded and played back; in the second case, the pickup of a separate camera, which was not involved in the general coverage, has been recorded and played back. This separate camera is called the "isolated camera." The sole function of the isolated camera is to follow key plays and other key action for instant replay. It is never used for the general coverage of the event. The isolated camera is generally placed high up in the stands near the middle of the field. When two isolated cameras are used, however, they are placed directly on the field at each end.

### Instant-replay switcher

Since the instant-replay operation is largely self-contained and independent of the general coverage, it frequently uses separate switching facilities. A small switcher is usually installed right next to the main switcher, enabling the T.D. to feed the instant-replay tape recorder, or recorders, with either the isolated camera picture or the line-out picture of the regular coverage. If large enough, the preview bus of the main switcher is sometimes delegated for the instant-replay switching.

### Instant-replay video tape recorder

In order to be maximally effective, the replay of the key action must, indeed, be almost instant—that is, it must follow the action as soon as possible. Also, the replay of the action should permit the viewer to analyze the action somewhat more critically than was possible during the normal coverage. The video tape recorder used for instant playbacks must therefore permit extremely fast recuing and also slow and stop motion. Special video tape recorders have been developed to fulfill these requirements to some degree, although not without sacrificing picture quality. Since the rewinding and cuing of video tape is relatively time consuming, a disc recorder has been developed; it operates somewhat like a disc dictaphone machine. No rewinding is necessary with the disc recorder, since the video pickup "arm" can be reset to the beginning of the recorded action very quickly. Special attachments to the tape recorder allow the action to be replayed either in a form of slow motion (which looks like a rather jerky series of several frames) or in stop motion (which shows each frame individually). Depending on the instant-replay requirements, one or more video tape recorders are used.

The instant-replay operation is often guided by the producer rather than the director, for the following reasons: (1) the director is much too occupied with the regular coverage of the event to worry about which actions should be replayed; (2) the producer usually knows when key plays occur and which ones he would like to have replayed; hence he can pay full attention to the replay procedures.

Instant-replay operations are very expensive and complicated and are, therefore, rarely attempted by small stations.

## SUMMARY

A remote telecast is any television pickup made outside the studio. Every television remote requires the setup of a small television station. In general, all television remote equipment is housed in a large truck or bus built or adapted especially for this purpose. The remote truck usually houses (1) auxiliary camera equipment for up to five cameras (portable power supplies and sync generators), (2) camera control monitors and master monitor, (3) switcher, (4) off-the-air monitor and antenna, (5) remote audio equipment, (6) power distribution box, (7) microwave dish with transmitter, and (8) intercom equipment.

The video signal is usually microwaved from the remote location to the transmitter or sent by special cable. The audio signal is either multiplexed with the video signal or sent through telephone wires.

The success of a remote depends largely on a careful remote survey by the director and the responsible engineer. The major points of the production survey are (1) place and time of telecast, (2) camera placement, (3) camera movement, (4) camera lenses, (5) lighting, (6) audio, (7) intercommunication, and (8) permits and clearances.

The major points of the engineering survey are (1) availability of power (minimum of 60 amp.), (2) location of remote truck and equipment, (3) location of microwave dish, (4) routing of cables, (5) lighting facilities, and (6) telephone lines.

For instant replay, special equipment is required: an isolated camera, special switching arrangements, and a video tape recorder that permits fast recuing and slow motion.

| Sport | Number of Cameras | Zoom | Location |
|---|---|---|---|
| Baseball | Three | Yes | Behind home plate and along first base line. |
| Football | Four | Yes | Three in shadow side on top of stadium; one on field. |
| Track | Three or four | Yes | Three in stands (shadow side); one on field. |
| Basketball | Three | Not essential | Two in stands opposite officials and benches; one behind basket. |
| Tennis | Two or three | Not essential | Two at end of court, shooting with sun; third on side opposite officials. |
| Boxing | Two | Not essential | Close to ring, ten feet apart. |
| Wrestling | Two | Not essential | Close to ring, ten feet apart. |

## EXERCISES

1. What major production problems must you consider in a remote coverage of a parade moving through a very narrow downtown street?

2. You are to cover an exclusive fashion show from the middle of the city park. What particular problems must you consider in your remote survey.

3. In your program series on medical problems, you are to originate several remote telecasts from different hospitals. The first program deals with radiology. Although the basic camera layout is simple,

your T.D. is rather concerned about the telecast and speaks of possible trouble. Why is he so concerned?

4. Your program manager asks you to provide the viewer with immediate repeats of the key plays of the high school homecoming game. Considering that your station has only standard remote equipment (three cameras, Ampex 1100), what would you tell him?

5. A boat race official tells you that the two best observation points are on each side of a particular river bend. He suggests you set up cameras right at these points. Do you agree with the setup? If so, why? If not, why not?

6. You are asked to televise a rather difficult heart operation. The doctors would like you to have the cameras look at the operation directly from above. How can you achieve this? What special arrangements would you have to make?

7. You are asked to survey a remote location at the county fair grounds. The fair official in charge tells you that he can participate in the survey only if it is very early in the morning. He assures you, however, that he will be available during the whole afternoon the day of the telecast. What is your reply? Why?

8. Your program manager and the harbor official have agreed to televise the last ferry boat run. They plan not only to cover the event from shore, but also from the ferry boat itself, televising interviews with captain, crew, and passengers. How can you do this? Offhand, what are your main production problems? What technical problems must you take into consideration?

9. The tennis coach tells you that the best place to watch the game is from the shadow side of the court, right next to the net, about half way up in the stands. He tells you that he can have some camera platforms built if you cannot set up your cameras in the bleachers. What is your reaction? Why?

10. In a very rugged remote location, you must pull all the equipment out of the truck and set up the control center in the open. What are some of the production and technical points you must discuss with the T.D.?

# 14

## Station Personnel

The type and number of station personnel differ considerably with the size of the television station. In network operation, for example, a fairly simple show may involve at least two writers, a producer, an assistant producer, a director, and an associate director. In small station operation, the same show may have to be written, produced, and directed by one man, the producer-director.

There is, however, very little difference in the basic organization of large and small stations. Every television station must have certain key people and departments to enable the station to operate professionally.

The basic organization of a television station consists of four major departments: (1) business, (2) sales, (3) programming, and (4) engineering.

These major departments are subdivided into several minor departments, the degree of division depending entirely on the size and scope of the station.

The general manager heads all departments. He determines major station policies and is ultimately responsible for the entire station operation. He usually hires all key management personnel.

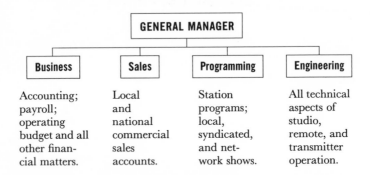

| **Business** | **Sales** | **Programming** | **Engineering** |
|---|---|---|---|
| Accounting; payroll; operating budget and all other financial matters. | Local and national commercial sales accounts. | Station programs; local, syndicated, and network shows. | All technical aspects of studio, remote, and transmitter operation. |

Listed in this chapter are the most important departments of a medium-sized television station. The types and functions of these departments and their most important interactions with each other are discussed briefly.

## BUSINESS

*Head:* controller or treasurer. Sometimes the controller is also called the business manager. He is in charge of all money matters and frequently assists in legal matters, especially if a company attorney is not available.

*Departments:* (1) accounting, in charge of collecting accounts, distributing the operating budget, handling sales contracts, etc.; and (2) payroll, which handles the weekly payroll for all station employees.

## SALES

*Head:* sales manager. He is in charge of the entire sales department. He frequently supervises the traffic, promotion, and publicity departments.

*Functions of sales department.* (1) Salesmen are responsible for all local accounts; they sell station time to local advertisers and sponsors. (2) Salesmen for national accounts are responsible for selling program time to national advertisers and sponsors; they handle all network accounts.

*Interaction:* with the traffic department about proper scheduling; with producer-directors on the possibility of selling new program material; with the business department about all money matters; and with the continuity department about commercial acceptance policies and, sometimes, about preparation of copy for programs.

## Promotion

*Head:* promotion manager. He is in charge of publicity and promotion departments. In small stations, the promotion manager is the only employee in both departments; he takes care of all station promotion jobs himself. He is directly responsible either to the general manager or (more often in small stations) to the sales manager.

*Functions.* The promotion department promotes the station as well as individual programs. It also promotes certain sales, and it supplies agencies with sales and programming information. The promotion department does extensive merchandising.

*Interaction:* with the sales department about available air time and accounts; with the publicity and programming departments about new programming features; and with the art department about special promotional art work, such as photos, posters, and mail pieces.

## Publicity

*Head:* publicity director. He is usually responsible to the promotion manager. Frequently, especially in small stations, the publicity director handles all publicity assignments himself.

*Functions.* The publicity department publicizes the station as well as the station's programming. The publicity director is in constant contact with the radio and television desks of all local newspapers and magazines. He supplies these agencies regularly with annotated program schedules and feature stories about new shows and new station personnel. He also organizes special show preview luncheons for the press, as well as special press conferences concerning certain new station policies.

The promotion and publicity departments are largely responsible for creating a "station image" for the public.

*Interaction:* with all departments, but especially with programming about program schedules and with management about key personnel changes and station policies.

## Traffic

*Head:* traffic manager. He oversees all traffic operations. He is usually directly responsible to the sales manager.

*Functions.* The traffic department collects and orders all programming data for each telecasting day and issues the daily log.

*Interaction:* with programming about local and network program schedules; with sales and continuity about commercial and public service announcements; and with film editing about certain film program times. The traffic department is the central point of all program information; it must, therefore, interact with every department in the station.

## PROGRAMMING

*Head:* program manager (or program director). He is in charge of all station programming, local or network. He usually acts as chief film buyer. He is also responsible for a number of people and departments that are directly involved in the station programming: (1) assistant program manager, (2) production manager, (3) continuity department, (4) education and public affairs department, (5) news department, (6) film department, (7) art department, (8) producer-directors, (9) floor department (floor managers and floor men), (10) staff announcers, and (11) talent.

### Assistant Program Manager

*Functions.* The assistant program manager assists the program manager in all tasks. Since the program manager is usually involved in administrative work, the assistant program manager concentrates more on the supervision of actual station productions. Sometimes the assistant program manager does all the film buying for the station.

*Interaction:* with the assistant chief engineer about technical production requirements; with producer-directors about station policies and special directing procedures; and with all major programming people directly under his supervision.

### Production Manager (Production Coordinator)

*Functions.* The production manager coordinates all local production activities. He issues weekly production schedules, indicating all studio activities, such as setup time, rehearsal times, on-the-air times, and strike times. He also schedules all producer-directors, talent, announcers, and floor personnel. He frequently prepares rough cost estimates for new shows and special events, such as special remote telecasts. This cost estimate must include, among other things, (a) talent fees, (b) salaries for engineering and production crews, including anticipated overtime, (c) expenses for necessary production equipment, and (d) expenses for scenery and graphic arts.

*Interaction:* with programming about new shows; with engineering about required and available studio and remote facilities; with traffic about proper scheduling; and, of course, with all production personnel that he personally supervises.

## Continuity Department

*Head:* continuity director. He is responsible to the assistant program manager for all continuity acceptance and continuity writing.

*Functions.* The continuity department receives and checks all commercial copy before it is released on the air. It has the right to reject commercial copy and commercial presentations. Its criteria for continuity acceptance are usually the general rules as indicated in the NAB Television Code (see Chapter 12) as well as specific station policies.

The continuity department supervises very carefully the commercial copy, the length of the commercial, and the manner of commercial presentation. Should you ever have a doubt about whether a certain program or commercial complies with the Television Code or with your station's policies, consult the continuity department or, of course, your program manager.

The continuity department frequently assists producer-directors in all matters of copyright clearances. It also writes all station breaks and public service announcements. In small stations, continuity is often in charge of script duplication and distribution.

*Interaction:* with the general manager, sales manager, and program manager about station policies and program acceptance procedures; with the sales and traffic departments about commercial copy; and with production personnel about small commercial props, etc.

## Education and Public Affairs Department

*Head:* education director. He is responsible to the assistant program manager. The education director acts as liaison between the station and educational institutions such as local schools, discussion groups, and clubs. As public affairs director, he works with such groups as churches and charitable organizations. The education director is usually the only employee of the department.

*Functions.* The education director (who, in small stations, handles all the assignments himself) supervises and edits most noncommercial programming. He frequently writes, produces, and directs educational and public affairs shows. He also mails educational promotion material to specific educational institutions. Thus, he informs teachers about upcoming educational programs and supplies them with the necessary background material.

*Interaction:* with the program department about show ideas and scheduling; and with traffic and engineering about desired show time and technical facilities.

## News Department

*Head:* news director or news editor. He is responsible to the assistant program manager. The news director is in charge of all news activities. He supervises the entire news staff, including producers and writers, news photographers, news film editors and newscasters, sportscasters, weather girls, etc. Television news departments frequently use the services of free-lance news photographers, or "stringers." These stringers are usually working in neighboring areas, covering all newsworthy events for the particular station. Larger stations may even employ part-time correspondents who report news events from major national or even international cities.

*Functions.* The news department presents news, sports, and weather reports (and farm reports in rural areas).

*Interaction:* with programming and traffic about scheduling; with film about film editing; and with engineering about special events coverage. The news department is, of course, in constant contact with outside news agencies, and also with the police department, fire department, city hall, hall of justice, chamber of commerce, and many other civic institutions.

## Film Department

*Head:* film director or film supervisor. He is responsible to the assistant program manager. The film director is in charge of all film editing, which is usually done by two or more film editors (depending on the size of the station and the amount of film used).

*Functions.* The film department edits all film and prepares the film for on-the-air presentation. Preparation includes the screening of all films received, the cutting and splicing of feature films as well as the commercial inserts, and the editing of all locally produced films. Small stations usually require a comparatively large film editing department, since a great amount of programming is filled by film.

*Interaction:* with programming (film buyer, producer-directors, news department, continuity); with sales; and with traffic. All film editing is done according to the daily log.

## Art Department

*Head:* art director. He is responsible to the assistant program manager. He is in charge of set design and set construction, all properties, and the preparation of all graphic art. He supervises one or two graphic or scenic artists, the number depending on the size of the station.

*Functions.* The art department creates and prepares all on-the-air art work, such as title cards, telops, slides, and charts. Members of the art department design, and usually construct and paint, all necessary scenery. In small stations, the members of the art department frequently double as floor men. The art department also prepares graphic art for station promotion and publicity, such as newspaper ads, station letterheads, and special brochures.

*Interaction:* with producer-directors about scenery and graphic art for new shows; with the production manager about special setup schedules; with the floor crew about scenery construction and prop storage, and also about setup and strike procedures; and with promotion and publicity about the preparation of promotional material.

## Producer-directors

Producer-directors are responsible to the production manager and the assistant program manager.

*Functions.* The producer-director produces and directs shows. Sometimes the directors are also assigned to direct live, film, or tape inserts within a live show; this is sometimes called "directing residue." Residue directing also includes timing film segments while the film is on the air and supervising the proper insertion of slides, telops, and tape clips during station breaks. If live commercial cut-ins are not used, routine residue directing is usually handled by master control personnel or sometimes by computer.

*Interaction:* with programming about new shows; with continuity about script distribution and continuity acceptance; with traffic about proper scheduling and log information; with art department about scenery and graphics; with talent about special show procedures; with production manager about proper scheduling; and with engineering about necessary technical facilities.

## Floor Department

The floor department consists of floor men and floor managers. Floor men are sometimes called stage hands, grips, or facilities men; floor managers are sometimes referred to as stage managers or floor directors. All members of the floor department are directly responsible to the production manager, and ultimately responsible to the assistant program manager.

*Functions.* In small stations, floor men are alternately assigned to floor manager's duties by the production manager. Usually one floor manager is in charge of one program or program series, another of a different program or series.

*Interaction:* with the director about immediate show problems; with studio engineers about special production requirements; with continuity about commercial properties and scripts; with the production manager about scheduling; and with the art director about setups and props.

*The floor manager* is the vital link between the control room and all studio activities. He directs all production people on the floor under the immediate supervision of the director in the control room. In general, the floor manager relays all the director's cues to studio personnel, including performers and actors as well as floor men and other production personnel. At rehearsal and show times, the floor manager is in full charge in the studio. The floor manager's job is often more demanding and complex than that of the director, especially during remote operations. Because of the floor manager's importance in television production, and because most directors will start as floor men or floor managers, a list of some of the major duties and procedures of the floor manager may be helpful here.

*Production preparation.* Unfortunately, the floor manager is not called often enough into important preliminary production meetings. This is a great handicap not only to the floor manager, who has no chance for adequate preparation, but also to the producers and directors, who could frequently benefit from the floor manager's expert and firsthand knowledge of certain physical production problems in studio and remote locations. However, if the production manager is farseeing enough to schedule you into one of the production meetings, you must know what preliminary preparations to consider. The following outline may serve as a guide for your production preparations.

*Preliminary meeting.*
1. Location of show. Local or remote? Which studio?
2. Show format. What type of show is it?
3. Number of performers or actors and their principal activities.
4. Technical facilities:
    *a.* Scenery and properties: How complex is the over-all setup? What properties do you need? If commercial properties are involved, what are they? When do they arrive?

    *b.* Graphic materials: What studio cards are needed? Any special charts, maps, graphs?

    *c.* Special effects: Are any special studio effects intended? If so, what kind?

    *d.* Camera: How many cameras are used? (This is especially important for remote operation, where one floor man for each camera is generally considered essential.) Are special camera dollies used? Do they need special dolly operators?

    *e.* Microphones: If floor men are working as microphone boom operators, how many booms are used?

    *f.* Lighting: If the floor staff is in charge of studio lighting, what type of lighting is required? Any special lighting effects? What are the basic performance areas?

5. Floor staff. How many floor men will you need?

Quite obviously, you cannot expect to have all these questions answered at one preliminary production meeting; you should, however, gather all this information before going into rehearsal.

*Rehearsal.*

1. Read the script carefully.

2. Mark all cues that concern the floor crew. Indicate all necessary set and properties changes.

3. Get the floor plan from the art department. Discuss specific setup requirements and set decorations with the art director.

4. Contact your director and discuss the entire show with him. Ask the director for his marked script so that you can copy his markings. A good knowledge of what the director intends to do will help you considerably in your floor managing.

5. Try to have the entire setup completed on schedule so that the studio can be lighted before the run-through.

6. Make sure that all properties and graphics are properly placed. Watch for out-of-sequence and upside-down studio cards.

7. Before the start of every rehearsal, give a short briefing to all floor men so that everyone understands his specific assignment.

8. If the program is video taped, have your identification slate and chalk ready.

9. Keep floor-marking material on hand, such as red chalk or light-colored masking tape.

10. Check all intercommunication phones.

11. If you are to assist the director in timing the show, make sure your stop watch is wound and works properly.

12. Have the talent ready by scheduled rehearsal time.

13. During the rehearsal, be firm but tactful with all talent, espe-

cially with new people who are not yet accustomed to your studio procedures.

14. Demonstrate your basic cuing system to all new talent. Ask the performer or actor what specific cues he may want.

15. When scenery or properties have to be changed or moved during the rehearsal, mark all positions of flats, furniture, and hand props before you move them. This way you can replace them in the same positions.

16. Keep the studio as quiet as possible during all rehearsal procedures.

17. After the rehearsal, make sure the studio floor is swept before going on the air. Cigarette butts or even a match can seriously interfere with smooth dollying.

18. Discuss all necessary changes with the director. Re-mark your script, if necessary.

*On-the-air-performance.*

1. Just before air time, quickly check the following items: (a) set, (b) set dressing, (c) properties (especially commercial setups), (d) studio cards (the sequence of the cards may have been disturbed during rehearsal), (e) dress and make-up of talent, (f) sequence of idiot sheets, (g) intercom phones, (h) position of floor men.

2. Ask the director about who will get the first cue.

3. Give broad, direct cues firmly but not frantically, quickly but smoothly. Nervous cuing may generate a noticeable nervousness in the performer.

4. Always stand where the talent can see you without having to look for you.

5. Make sure the talent has seen your cue. Usually, you can see the performer glance quickly at your hand.

6. Look alert and interested to the performer, but don't get involved in his presentation to a point where you forget your floor managing duties.

7. If you floor manage a simple two-camera show, you work in general between the two cameras. If you work with more than two cameras, you work between the two most active cameras, preferably close to the wide shot camera.

8. Anticipate all happenings as much as you possibly can. You should be ready for most major cues before the director gives you the cue.

9. Be careful not to get in front of a camera. Even if the camera is not on the air at that moment, you never know when it will be punched up. Watch especially the wide angle lens cameras.

10. Be careful not to get your earphone cable in front of moving equipment or tangled up in the scenery.

11. Don't stand in front of floor lights.

12. Don't stand in front of the floor monitor. Try to position the monitor so that the talent can always clearly see the monitor screen.

13. If you hold idiot sheets, make sure they are in the right order. Read along with the talent and change each sheet just before the end of the last line so that the talent can continue reading without having to wait for the card change.

14. Remain calm, even if the director begins to panic. In this situation, you are the only one who can help the talent to get through the particular crisis. Never let the control room confusion disturb you to a point where you begin to relay the confusion to talent and other studio personnel.

15. Whatever happens, remain calm and tactful.

*Post-show activities.*

1. Make sure the set gets struck properly after each show.

2. All props must be returned to the right places. There is no good or bad method for striking a set. In general, you should start by removing all furniture and set dressings before you strike the flats and other structural set pieces.

3. Write out all necessary production reports.

*The floor men* usually set up scenery, dress the sets, take care of all scenic and commercial properties, and, at the end of the program, strike all scenery and properties. In small stations they frequently operate the microphone boom and sometimes even take care of all studio lighting. In union stations, however, engineers do these more technical jobs. During the show, floor men may help to operate special camera dollies, keep the camera and microphone cables from getting tangled up, and assist the performers by holding idiot sheets. They also work easel cards and all mechanical special studio effects. In small stations, they may also construct and paint scenery and properties and do occasional make-up jobs.

## Staff Announcers

The staff announcer is responsible to the assistant program manager.

*Functions.* The staff announcer announces all logged program continuity, including all station breaks, short public service announcements, and commercials, usually over slides, telops, and silent films. He also introduces and closes shows from the announcing booth. He sometimes announces in front of the camera.

*Interaction:* with programming and master control about all specific announcing duties; with traffic about certain log information.

## Talent

All staff performers are usually responsible to the assistant program manager.

*Functions.* The talent performs in front of cameras in particular shows or program series, such as daily newscasts. Staff performers are usually developed into station personalities.

*Interaction:* with all programming departments.

# ENGINEERING

*Head:* chief engineer. He is in charge of all engineering matters and frequently of all building maintenance. The engineering department is composed of (1) assistant chief engineer, (2) studio supervisor, (3) studio engineers, (4) master control engineers, (5) transmitter supervisor, (6) transmitter engineers, (7) technical maintenance engineers, and (8) building maintenance employees.

## Assistant Chief Engineer

*Functions.* The assistant chief engineer assists the chief engineer in all technical matters. He is usually responsible for all technical operations, including such procedures as remote surveys and cost estimates.

*Interaction:* with program manager and production coordinator about special technical requirements.

## Studio Supervisor

The studio supervisor is responsible to the assistant chief engineer.

*Functions.* The studio supervisor's function is very similar to that of the production manager. He coordinates all technical studio and remote activities, and schedules all engineering personnel.

*Interaction:* with the production manager and frequently with producer-directors.

## Studio Engineers

All studio engineers are responsible to the studio supervisor.

*Functions.* In small station operation, studio engineers are usually split into different studio crews, each crew consisting of the T.D., the video engineer (sometimes combined), the audio engineer, the boom operator (sometimes handled by the floor men), and the cameramen. The crew members rotate from week to week or from show to show so that everyone will perform different duties on different occasions.

One engineer may be the technical director for one show, the camera-man for the next, and the audio engineer for another. Each crew is headed by a crew chief. In larger stations, the crew chiefs are usually assigned permanently as technical directors. The technical director or one of the cameramen acts as lighting engineer when the studio light-ing is not done by the floor crew.

*Interaction:* mainly among other members of the engineering person-nel and with floor crews.

### Master Control Engineers

All master control engineers are responsible to the studio supervisor.

*Functions.* The master control crew chief and his crew perform all master control operations. These include (a) master switching, (b) operating all facets of the film chain, and (c) operating the video tape machines (sometimes a special video tape engineer is assigned to this job). In small stations, the master control engineers also act as film directors, which means that they switch commercial inserts and station breaks without the help of a special director.

*Interaction:* with transmitter engineers about picture quality and operational matters (everything that goes on the air); with traffic about certain log changes; with studio and remote engineers about special line hookups; with the telephone company about network and remote feeds; and with programming about film and video taped shows.

### Transmitter Supervisor

The transmitter supervisor is responsible to the assistant chief engineer.

*Functions.* He supervises all transmitter activities, including the technical operation as well as the program monitoring.

*Interaction:* with studio supervisor about special line feeds; with the telephone company about remote and network feeds; and with traffic and master control about certain log information.

### Transmitter Engineers

The transmitter engineers are responsible to the transmitter supervisor.

*Functions.* These engineers maintain and operate all transmitter facilities. They also monitor and log every program second that is aired. And they list all discrepancies that occur between the master control log and the actual programming.

*Interaction:* with master control and traffic about log information; and with all engineering personnel about technical problems.

### Technical Maintenance Engineers

The technical maintenance engineers are responsible to the studio supervisor.

*Functions.* They maintain all electronic television equipment.

*Interaction:* mainly with all engineering personnel concerning technical problems.

### Building Maintenance Employees

There are usually one or two people who are directly responsible to the assistant chief engineer.

*Functions.* The building maintenance employees maintain building and all nonelectronic installations. The building maintenance supervisor is usually responsible for shipping and receiving and for all station vehicles.

*Interaction:* with engineering about special building assignments; and with programming and other station personnel about transportation.

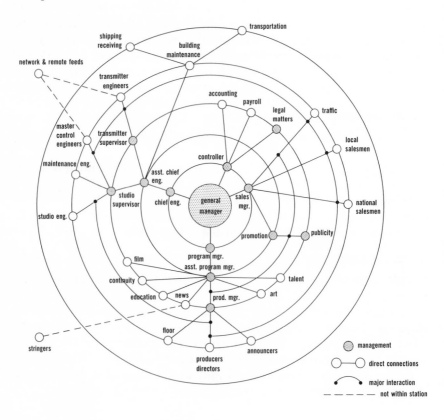

## SUMMARY

A television station is divided into four big departments: (1) business, (2) sales, (3) programming, and (4) engineering. All these departments are under the direct supervision of the general manager.

The individual departments are divided as follows:

### Business:

Controller or treasurer.
Departments: accounting and payroll.

### Sales:

Sales manager, local and national salesmen.
Promotion department, under the supervision of the general manager or, more often, the sales manager.
Publicity department, under the supervision of the promotion department.
Traffic department, under the immediate supervision of the sales manager.

### Programming:

Program manager, assistant program manager, and production manager.
Program manager and assistant program manager are directly responsible for the following program departments: continuity department, education and public affairs department, news department, film department, art department, producer-directors, floor department, staff announcers, and talent.

### Engineering:

Chief engineer, assistant chief engineer, and studio and transmitter supervisors.
These people are responsible for all studio, transmitter, master control, and maintenance engineers.
The assistant chief engineer is also responsible for the building maintenance, for shipping and receiving, and for station transportation.

## EXERCISES

1. You are to direct a sports remote. What station personnel must you contact for more information and for production and engineering coordination?

2. You are directly contacted by the sponsor of your show. He wants you to put on a special film commercial that he did not want to send "through all the channels and red tape" of your station. A quick screening reveals that the commercial seems to violate certain rules of the NAB Television Code and of your station's policies. What would you do?

3. Your floor manager tells you (the director) that a certain logged commercial has been cancelled. With whom should you confirm this cancellation?

4. You realize just before air time that you have neglected to check your log against the master log for certain corrections. With whom should you quickly check for log changes concerning your program?

5. Your floor manager asks you about the arrival of certain commercial properties. You don't know anything about them. What would you suggest for him to do?

6. You decide to use three film clips and one tape insert within your live program. Whom should you notify about these video inserts?

7. You are asked to direct a network news cut-in from your local station. The network representative asks you to give him an idea of the approximate cost of the remote operation. Who should help you in this matter?

8. You intend to hire a special writer for your proposed program. With whom should you check before you do the actual hiring?

9. During the initial blocking of your special college drama show, you realize that you need a third camera. Whom do you contact in this matter?

10. You are asked by the county fair official whether you would like to televise parts of the county fair. The fair promises to be the best fair ever. With whom do you have to make the necessary arrangements to get the remote approved and set up?

# Glossary

*This glossary is not intended to be an exhaustive vocabulary of technical television terms. It includes only those terms and abbreviations most frequently used in small and large stations throughout the country.*

*AAAA:* American Association of Advertising Agencies.

*A-B rolling:* (1) Preparation of a film for printing. All odd-numbered shots are put on one reel (A-roll), with black leader replacing the even-numbered shots. The even-numbered shots, with black leader replacing the odd-numbered shots, make up the B-roll.

(2) Electronic A-B rolling means that on one film chain an SOF film is projected, while on the second film chain a silent film is projected. The films can be intermixed (A-B rolled) through the television switcher.

*AC:* Alternating current; electrical energy as supplied by normal wall outlets.

*Academy Leader:* Piece of film with special markings (numbers ranging from 8 to 3, each 1 second apart) used for cuing up the attached film in the projector and for film picture alignment.

*Account:* Specific sales contract between the television station and an advertising agency or sponsor.

*Acetate:* (1) Cellulose acetate, usually called "cell": a transparent plastic sheet used in preparation of graphic material.
(2) Film base.

*A.D.:* Assistant or Associate Director.

*Ad-lib:* Speech or action that has not been scripted or specially rehearsed.

*Affiliate:* Independent station having a program contract with a network.

*AFTRA:* American Federation of Television and Radio Artists (talent union).

*AGMA:* American Guild of Musical Artists (union).

*AGVA:* American Guild of Variety Artists (union).

*Animation:* Process of filming a number of slightly different cartoon drawings to create the illusion of movement.

*Ann. or Anncr.:* Abbreviation for Announcer.

*Aperture:* Diaphragm opening of a lens; usually measured in *f*-stops.

*Arc:* Slightly curved dolly in or out.

*ASCAP:* American Society of Composers, Authors, and Publishers; collects royalties for performance of copyrighted material.

*Aspect ratio:* Height and width of a television picture: three units high and four units wide.

*Audio:* Electronic reproduction of audible sound. Audio refers to the sound accompanying the "video" or visual portion of a television program.

*Audition:* Testing of a talent's abilities; the talent usually performs in front of a television camera, and the performance is judged by station and agency personnel.

*A-wind:* Reel of tape or film with oxide or emulsion coating (dull side) facing toward hub or inside of reel; this is the most common type of wind.

*Back light:* Illumination from behind the subject and opposite the camera.

*Background light:* Illumination of the set and set pieces such as back-drops; sometimes called a set light.

*Back-timing:* Timing of a program from the end of the program to the beginning; back-timing helps the director and talent to pace the show properly and finish it at the scheduled time.

*Balance:* (1) Video: a pleasing picture composition—that is, a satisfying distribution of objects within the television frame.
(2) Audio: a proper mixing of different sounds.

*Balop:* (1) Balopticon, a television opaque projector.
(2) Opaque or transparent slide used in the balop machine.

*Barn doors:* Metal flaps mounted in front of a spotlight to control the spread of the light beam.

*Base:* (1) Base light: even, nondirectional level of studio illumination. Desired base-light levels: for image-orthicon and Plumbicon monochrome cameras, 75–100 foot-candles; for vidicon cameras, 150–250 foot-candles; for color cameras, 285–500 foot-candles.
(2) Film base: the material of which motion picture film is made; the light-sensitive emulsion is then superimposed on the film base.

*B.G.:* Background; an audio term; "music to B.G." means to fade the music and hold under as a background effect.

*Black:* Darkest part of the gray scale, with a reflectance of 3 per cent; called TV black, "to black" means to fade the television picture to black.

*Blocking:* Working out the physical movement of performers and all mobile television equipment.

*BMI:* Broadcast Music, Inc.; collects royalties on copyrighted music performed on television and radio.

*Book:* (1) TV scenery term: a twofold flat.
(2) To decrease the angle of an open twofold.

*Boom up or down:* Raising or lowering the microphone boom or camera boom.

*Broad:* A square-shaped floodlight, generally used in TV color lighting or in the motion picture industry.

*Burn-in:* Image retention of the camera pickup tube; if a camera is focused too long on an object with strong contrast, the picture tube retains a negative image of this object, although another object is being photographed.

*Bus:* (1) Video: Rows of buttons on a video switching panel.
(2) Audio: A common central circuit that receives from several sources or feeds to several separate destinations; a "mix bus" collects the output signals from several mixing controls (pots) and feeds them into one master volume control.

*Busy:* The picture, as it appears on the television screen, is too cluttered.

*B-wind:* Reel of tape or film with oxide or emulsion coating (dull side) facing out or away from the reel hub.

*Camera:* Television camera, which consists of camera tube and accessory equipment, viewfinder, and lenses.

*Camera chain:* Television camera and associated equipment, consisting of power supply and sync generator.

*Camera light:* Small spotlight, called inky-dinky, mounted on the front of the camera; used as additional fill light. (Frequently confused with Tally Light, which is the red light in front of the camera indicating when the camera is on the air.)

*Camera rehearsal:* Rehearsal with cameras, microphones, and all other studio equipment under actual telecasting conditions.

*Camera left and right:* Directions given from the camera's point of view; opposite of *stage left and right,* which are directions given from the actor's point of view (facing the audience or camera).

*Cans:* Earphones.

*Cap:* (1) Lens cap; a rubber or metal cap placed in front of the lens to prevent light or dust from hitting the lens.
(2) Electronic device that eliminates the picture from the camera pickup tube.

*Cardioid:* Heart-shaped microphone pickup pattern.

*Cast:* (1) All actors and performers appearing in front of a camera as a group.
(2) To select actors and performers for a particular telecast; large stations maintain a special casting director.

*CATV:* Community Antenna Television; also called Cable Television; a system in which home receivers get their signal from a coaxial cable connected to a master antenna; a monthly fee is charged by the CATV companies for this service.

*CCTV:* Closed-circuit television.

*Cell:* See Acetate.

*Cheat:* To angle the performer or object toward a particular camera; not directly noticeable to the audience.

*Chroma key:* Special electronic matting process, achieved by using the blue camera signal of a color camera.

*Chrominance channels:* Channels in the color camera for red, green, and blue signals.

*Client:* Person or agency advertising on television.

*Clip:* (1) Short piece of film or tape, generally used as a brief program insert.
(2) To cut off abruptly the audio portion of a program.

*Closed circuit:* Television program that is distributed to specific television receivers but not telecast to the public.

*Close-up:* Object or any part of an object seen at close range and framed tightly.

*Coax:* Coaxial cable; one cable concentrically shielded by another cable.

*Cold light:* Fluorescent light.

*Color:* (1) Atmosphere; "color shots" are intended to acquaint the television audience with the atmosphere of the happening.
(2) Color television.

*Color temperature:* Relative redness or blueness of incandescent light, as measured in degrees of Kelvin; television lighting instruments have a range of 3000–3400° K.

*Compatible color:* Color signals that can be received as black-and-white pictures on monochrome television sets. Generally used to mean that the color scheme has enough brightness contrast to reproduce on monochrome television with a good gray-scale contrast.

*Composite:* Complete video signal with the sync pulse.

*Continuity:* (1) Even, logical succession of events.
(2) All material presented between shows.
(3) Continuity Department, in charge of commercial acceptance and continuity writing.

*Contrast:* Contrast between black and white; especially important for colors used on television, which may have strong color contrast but little black-and-white contrast; the contrast ratio is not to exceed 20 : 1, with a range of from 3%–60% reflectance.

*Control room:* Room, adjacent to the television studio, from which the program is coordinated.

*Copy:* All material to be read on the air.

*Cover shot:* Wide-angle shot giving basic orientation of place and action; covers a great area.

*Cradle head:* Cradle-shaped camera mounting head.

*Crane:* (1) Special camera dolly enabling the camera to move from close to the studio floor to about ten feet above the floor (depending on the crane used).
(2) To move the camera boom up or down.

*Crawl:* Graphics (usually credit copy) that move slowly up the screen; usually mounted on a drum, which can also be called a "crawl."

*Credits:* List of names of persons who participated in the creation and performance of a telecast; usually at end of program.

*CU:* Close-up.

*Cucalorus:* Shadow pattern projected on a scenic background by means of a special cut-out placed in front of a strong spotlight; sometimes called a "kookie."

*Cue:* (1) Signal to start action.
(2) White or black dots on film, indicating the end of the film.

*Cut:* (1) Instantaneous switch from one camera to the other.
(2) Director's signal to interrupt action (used during rehearsal).

*Cut-in:* Insert from another program source, such as a network cut-in during a local show.

*Cyc:* Cyclorama; a U-shaped continuous piece of canvas for backing of scenery and action.

*Dead:* Equipment not turned on or not functioning, such as a "dead mike" or a "dead camera."

*Definition:* Degree of detail in television picture reproduction.

*Depth:* Third dimension.

*Depth of field:* Field in which all objects, located at different distances from the camera, appear in focus; depth of field is dependent upon focal length of lens, *f*-stop, and distance between object and camera.

*Depth Staging:* Staging technique that divides the stage into a definite foreground, middleground, and background.

*Dichroic mirror:* Mirror-like color filter that singles out red light (red dichroic filter) and blue light (blue dichroic filter) in the color camera.

*Dimmer:* Controls the brightness of the light; three basic types of dimmers are resistance dimmers, transformer dimmers, and electronic dimmers.

*Director:* Coordinator of all production elements before and during the on-the-air telecast.

*Dish:* Parabolic reflector for microwave transmitting unit; sometimes called dish-pan.

*Dissolve:* Gradual transition from one picture to another whereby the two pictures overlap briefly.

*Distortion:* (1) Optical: near objects look large, far objects look comparatively small; achieved with wide-angle lenses.
(2) Electronic: exaggeration of either height or width of the television picture.
(3) Audio: Unnatural alteration or deterioration of sound.

*Dolly:* (1) Camera support that enables the camera to be moved in all directions.
(2) Moving the camera toward (dolly in) or away (dolly out or back) from the object.

*Double system sound:* Picture and sound portion are photographed on separate films and later combined on one film through printing.

*Downstage:* Toward the stage apron or the camera.

*Dress:* (1) What people wear on camera.
(2) Dress rehearsal: final camera rehearsal.
(3) Set dressing: necessary set properties.

*Drop:* Large, painted piece of canvas used for backing.

*Dry run:* Rehearsal without cameras and, usually, without any other electronic equipment.

*Dub:* Transcription of a sound track.

*Dubbing:* Transcribing a sound track from one recording medium to another, such as dubbing a film sound track on audio tape.

*Dutchman:* (1) A strip of canvas pasted over the hinges of a flat.
(2) A strip of wood hinged into a threefold so that the flat can be properly folded.

*Dynamic:* A pressure microphone receiving sound waves on a pressure sensitive diaphragm; this rugged microphone is extensively used in television operation.

*ECU:* Extreme close-up; same as *XCU.*

*Editing:* (1) Emphasizing the important and de-emphasizing the unimportant.
(2) In film and video tape: cutting out unwanted portions and gluing the desired pieces together into a continuous show.

(3) In live television: selecting from the preview monitors the picture that is to go on the air.

*Electronic editing:* Inserting or assembling of program portions on video tape through electronic means whereby the tape does not have to be physically cut.

*Electronic film transfer:* Kinescoping of a program from video tape to film.

*Elevation:* Drawing showing the vertical planes of a floor plan.

*Ellipsoidal spot:* Spotlight with a very defined beam (usually for special effects lighting).

*Emulsion:* Light-sensitive layer put on the motion picture film base.

*Equalizer:* Audio device that changes the original microphone frequency reponse to compensate for acoustical problems.

*Essential area:* Picture area that shows on a home receiver.

*Establishing shot:* Orientation shot, usually a long shot.

*E.T.:* Electrical transcription. Similar to a record except that it is produced solely for radio and television stations.

*ETV:* Educational television.

*Fact sheet:* A run-down of particular items that must be covered during the telecast (generally used for ad-lib commercials); also called a *run-down sheet.*

*Fade:* (1) Audio: decrease in volume.
(2) Video: picture either goes gradually to black (fade to black) or appears gradually on the screen from black (fade in).

*Feed:* Signal transmission from one program source to another, such as a network feed or a remote feed.

*Feedback:* (1) Video: wild streaks and flashes on the monitor screen caused by accidental re-entry of a video signal into the switcher and subsequent overamplification.
(2) Audio: piercing squeals from the loudspeaker, caused by the accidental re-entry of the loudspeaker sound into the microphone and subsequent over-amplification of sound.
(3) Communication: reaction of the receiver of a communication back to the communication source.

*Field:* One-half of a complete scanning cycle; two fields are necessary for one television picture frame; there are 60 fields per second, or 30 frames per second.

*Field lens:* Usually a long-focal-length lens for remote pickups.

*Fill:* Additional program material in case the show runs short.

*Fill light:* Additional light to brighten shadow areas.

*Film clip:* Short piece of film; usually run within a live show.

*Film loop:* Piece of film with its ends spliced together; this loop runs through the projector continuously and can be used for special effects or for dubbing.

*Fixed service:* Short-range television transmission on the 2500 megacycle band; generally used for closed-circuit television transmission.

*Flare:* Dark flashes caused by light reflections off polished objects.

*Flash:* Very short shot or sequence.

*Flat:* (1) Piece of standing scenery (wood frame with muslin cover).
(2) Even, not contrasting; usually refers to lighting; flat lighting is a very diffused lighting with soft shadow areas.

*Flip card:* Title cards of same size that can be changed by flipping one after the other off the easel.

*Floodlight:* Nondirectional, diffused light, in contrast to the directional spotlight.

*Floor:* Studio, or studio floor.

*Floor manager:* In charge in the studio during production; a vital link between the director and talent; cues talent, and supervises all floor activities during telecast; also called stage manager or floor director.

*Floor men:* Studio production crew in charge of setup, set dressing, and other important production jobs during the telecast; also called stage hands, facilities men, or grips.

*Floor plan:* Diagram of scenery and properties in relation to the studio floor area.

*Fluorescent light:* Cold light produced by gas-filled glass tubes.

*Fly:* Objects and scenery hanging from above.

*Focal length:* Distance from the optical center of the lens to the surface of the camera tube. Focal lengths of lenses are measured in millimeters or inches. Short-focal-length lenses have a wide angle of view, long-focal-length lenses have a narrow angle of view (telephoto lenses).

*Focus:* Picture is in focus when it appears sharp and clear on the screen.

*Follow focus:* Rotating the camera focus control to maintain a sharp image while following a moving subject.

*Footage:* Length or portion of a film; sometimes used qualitatively: good footage, bad footage.

*Foot-candle:* International unit of illumination: the amount of light produced by a single candle on a portion of a sphere one foot away; equal to one lumen per square foot.

*Format:* Type of television script indicating the major programming steps; generally contains a fully scripted show opening and closing.

*Friction head:* Camera mounting head that counterbalances the camera weight by a strong spring.

*f-stop:* Calibration on lens indicating the diaphragm opening; the larger the *f*-stop, the smaller the diaphragm opening; the smaller the *f*-stop, the larger the lens opening.

*Fully scripted:* A television script indicating all words to be spoken and all major video information.

*Gain:* Level of amplified sound; "riding gain" means to keep the volume at a proper level.

*Gen lock:* Locking the synchronizing generators from two different origination sources, such as remote and studio; prevents rolling of picture.

*Ghost:* Undesirable double image on screen; caused by signal reflection in poor reception areas.

*Gobo:* A scenic foreground piece through which the camera can shoot, thus integrating foreground and background.

*Go to black:* Picture is gradually faded out; same as fade to black.

*Group shot:* Camera framing to include a group of people.

*Gray scale:* Scale indicating intermediate steps from TV black to TV white; maximum steps: 10; good gray scale: 7 steps; poor gray scale: 5 or less.

*Green scale:* Same as gray scale; the grays, however, are produced by photographing green on monochrome television; green gives a better gray scale than any other color, including different grays.

*Grip:* See Floor men.

*Halo:* Dark flare around a very bright or highly reflecting object.

*Hand props:* All small props handled by the performer.

*Head room:* The space between the top of the screen and the framed object.

*Helical scanning:* Diagonal scanning pattern of the video signal of single- or dual-head video tape recorders; also called *slant track.*

*High band color:* High carrier frequency in color video tape recording; reduces electronic interference.

*High key:* High-intensity illumination.

*Holy factor:* Additional illumination to fill in shadow "holes"; especially important in color lighting.

*Hot:* Hot microphone or hot camera: instruments are turned on.

*Hot spot:* Undesirable concentration of light in one spot; especially noticeable in the middle of a rear screen projection.

*IATSE:* International Alliance of Theatrical Stage Employees (union).

*IBEW:* International Brotherhood of Electrical Workers (engineering union).

*Iconoscope:* Old model television pickup tube; no longer in use.

*I.D.:* Station identification.

*Idiot sheet:* Cue sheet for talent, usually held by floor man.

*Image-orthicon:* Very sensitive camera pickup tube.

*Incandescent light:* Hot light, produced by glowing filaments; used for all television lighting.

*Intercom:* Intercommunication system among studio and control room personnel.

*Intersync:* Accessory to the video tape recorder; allows the smooth integration of various video sources.

*In the can:* Finished television recording, either on film or video tape; the show is now "preserved" and can be rebroadcast at any time.

*Instant replay:* Key action (as in sports) recorded on special tape recorders and specially designated cameras, and immediately played back, sometimes in slow motion.

*I-O:* Image-orthicon.

*Iris:* Adjustable lens-opening mechanism; same as lens diaphragm.

*Jack:* (1) Stage brace to hold up flat.
(2) A socket or phone-plug receptacle (female).

*Key:* (1) Lighting: intensity of illumination; low key (low intensity) and high key (high intensity).
(2) Key light: principal source of illumination; sometimes called modeling light.
(3) Electronic effects: special control signal used in electronic matting.

*Kicker light:* Light coming from the side and back of the object.

*Kill:* Eliminate certain parts or actions.

*Kine:* Kinescope recording.

*Kinescope:* Television program filmed directly from a kinescope tube.

*Kookie:* See Cucalorus.

*Lapel:* Small microphone worn as a lapel "button."

*Lavaliere:* Small microphone worn around the neck; sometimes called *lapel,* or *lav.*

*Lens:* Optical lens, essential for projecting an image on the television pickup tube; lenses come in different focal lengths and different speeds.

*Lens turret:* Round plate in front of a camera holding up to five lenses, each of which can be rotated into "shooting position."

*Level:* (1) Audio: voice level (volume).
(2) Video: white and black picture level, measured in volts.

*Lighting:* Television lighting, which employs the photographic lighting principle of key light (principal light source), back light, and fill light.

*Light level:* Light intensity, measured in foot-candles.

*Light plan:* Basic layout of lighting instruments and the general direction of the lighting beam.

*Limbo:* Any set area used for shooting small commercial displays, card easels, etc., having a plain light background.

*Line monitor:* See Master monitor.

*Lip sync:* Synchronization of sound and lip movement.

*Live:* (1) Direct transmission of a studio program at the time of the origin.
(2) Indicates that a camera or microphone is in active use.

*Log:* Second-by-second breakdown of a day's program schedule.

*Logo:* Station-identification symbol.

*Loop:* See Film Loop.

*LS:* Long shot; includes a large field of view.

*Low key:* Low intensity illumination; usually used for mood effects.

*Lumen:* The basic quantity of light produced by one candle on one square foot.

*Luminance channel:* Monochrome channel in a color camera that gives the color picture its crispness and color separation; also supplies the monochrome signal.

*Magnetic track:* Magnetic sound track on film; a small audio tape running alongside the film frames, opposite the sprocket holes.

*Make-up:* (1) Facial make-up: used to enhance, correct, and change facial features. (2) Film make-up: combining several films on one big reel.

*Mark:* Small piece of masking tape (often color coded) placed on the studio floor to indicate positions of performers and scenery.

*Master control:* Central control center for all telecasts; all master switching from different program sources is done in master control.

*Master monitor:* Monitor that shows only the pictures that go out on the air.

*M.C.:* (1) Master of ceremonies. (2) Master control.

*Microwave:* Wireless transmission of television signals from one point to another in line of sight.

*Mike:* Microphone.

*Mixer:* (1) Audio control console. (2) Audio operator.

*MM or mm:* Millimeter, a thousandth of a meter (European measuring unit); 25mm equal 1 inch.

*Modeling light:* Principal source of light; same as Key Light.

*Monitor:* (1) Television receivers used in the television studio and control rooms. (2) Loud speakers used in TV control room for program sound.

*MS:* Medium shot (between close-up and long shot).

*Multiplexer:* System of movable mirrors or prisms that directs images from several projection sources into one stationary television film camera.

*NAB:* National Association of Broadcasters.

*NABET:* National Association of Broadcast Employees and Technicians (engineering union).

*NET:* (1) Network. (2) National Educational Television.

*Off-camera:* Performance or action that is not seen on camera, such as narration over film.

*On the nose:* (1) On time. (2) Correct.

*Optical track:* Optical sound track; variations of black and white photographed on the film and converted into electrical impulses; there are two kinds of optical track: variable density and variable area.

*Oscilloscope:* Electronic measuring device showing certain electronic patterns on a small screen.

*P.A.:* Public address loudspeaker system.

*Pace:* Over-all speed of performance.

*Pan:* Horizontal turning of the camera.

*Pantograph:* Expandable hanging device for lighting instruments.

*Patching:* Interconnecting audio, video, or light cables into a common circuit.

*Pattern projector:* Ellipsoidal spotlight that can project cucalorus patterns.

*PBL:* Public Broadcast Laboratory; experimental educational-television programming.

*Pedestal:* (1) Special camera dolly that permits a raising and lowering of the camera.
(2) A special oscilloscope picture, indicating the white level of a television picture.

*Periaktos:* A triangular piece of scenery that can be turned on a swivel base.

*Perspective:* (1) All lines converging in one point.
(2) Sound perspective: far sound must go with far picture, close sound with close picture.

*Pickup:* Origination of picture and sound by television cameras and microphones.

*Pin:* Sharpening of the lighting beam by pulling the lightbulb-reflector assembly away from the lens.

*Plot:* Story line.

*POT:* Potentiameter; volume control knob or fader lever on audio control consoles.

*Pre-empt:* Telecasting time made available for a special event, regardless of the regularly scheduled program.

*Preview:* Viewing a performance or a section of a performance before it is released on the air.

*Primary movement:* Movement in front of the camera.

*Process shot:* Photographing foreground objects against a background projection.

*Producer:* Creator and organizer of television shows; usually in charge of all financial matters.

*Props:* Properties; objects used for set decorations and by actors and performers.

*PTV:* Public Television (Educational Television).

*Pylon:* Triangular set piece, similar to a pillar.

*Quartz-iodine:* Highly efficient light instrument with a quartz-iodine lightbulb that emits a very bright incandescent light.

*Quick study:* Actor or performer who can accurately memorize complicated lines and blocking within a very short time; especially important for television talent.

*Racking:* (1) Changing lenses.

(2) Operating the focus knob on the camera (thereby racking the camera tube closer or farther away from the stationary lens).

*Rack-through focus:* Moving the focus control on a camera from one extreme position to the other.

*Rear screen:* Translucent screen onto which slides are projected from the rear and photographed from the front.

*Reel:* (1) Film spool.

(2) Film on spool.

*Remote:* Telecast originated outside the studio.

*Reverberation:* Audio echo; adding echo to sound via an acoustical echo chamber or electronic sound delay; generally used to "liven" sounds recorded in an acoustically dull studio.

*Ribbon:* Ribbon microphone; very sensitive to shock and wind; should not be used outdoors.

*R.P.:* Rear screen projection; also abbreviated as R.S.P. or B.P. (back projection).

*Resolution:* Degree of detail reproduced on the television screen; similar to Definition.

*Return:* Narrow flat lashed to a wider flat at approximately a 90-degree angle.

*Riser:* Small platform.

*Run-down sheet:* See Fact Sheet.

*Running time:* Continuous time from the beginning to the end of a show.

*Run-through:* Rehearsal.

*SAG:* Screen Actors Guild (union).

*Scanning:* The movement of the electron beam from left to right and from top to bottom on the television screen.

*Scanning area:* Picture area that is reproduced by the camera and relayed to the studio monitors, but which is reduced by television transmission on the home screen.

*Scenery:* Flats and other scenic objects that help to set the locale for a television show.

*Scoop:* Television floodlight.

*Secondary movement:* Movement of the camera.

*SEG:* Screen Extras Guild (Union).

*Semi-scripted show:* Type of television script indicating only the approximate dialogue and action for a particular show.

*Servo lens system:* Electrical system on a zoom lens that drives the zoom and focus controls of the lens.

*SESAC:* The Society of European Stage Authors and Composers; collects royalties on performance of all material it has copyrighted.

*Set:* Proper arrangement of scenery and properties to indicate the locale and/or mood of a show.

*Shading:* Adjusting picture contrast; controlling color and black and white levels.

*Shared I.D.:* Title card with commercial copy in addition to the station identification call letters.

*Shot box:* Box containing various controls for presetting zoom speed and field of view; usually mounted on the camera panning bar.

*S.I.:* Station identification (sometimes: sponsor identification).

*Signature:* A specific video and/or audio symbol characteristic of one particular show.

*Silent:* Silent film, or sound film run silent.

*Single system:* Sound recording device frequently used for television news film; sound and picture are simultaneously recorded on one film.

*Slant track:* See Helical scanning.

*Slide:* Transparent pictures between glass plates, usually 2 × 2 inches; for rear screen projectors 3 × 4 or 4 × 5 inches.

*SMPTE:* Society of Motion Picture and Television Engineers.

*Snow:* Electronic picture interference; looks like snow on the television screen.

*SOF:* Sound on film.

*Solid state:* Use of transistors instead of vacuum tubes.

*SOT:* Sound on video tape.

*Space staging:* Arrangement of scenery to indicate foreground, middleground, and background, with room for movement of talent and camera.

*Splice:* The spot where two pieces of film or tape are cemented together.

*Spot:* (1) Short commercial.
(2) Lighting instrument that produces a sharp beam of light.

*Spotlight:* Lighting instrument that produces a sharp beam of light (contrary to floodlight).

*Spread:* To enlarge the light beam by pushing the lightbulb-reflector assembly toward the lens.

*Sprockets:* Small, evenly spaced perforations in the film; single sprockets: holes are in only one side of the film; double sprockets: holes are on both sides of the film; most film is single-sprocket film.

*SR:* Sound reinforcement; loudspeakers used for studio audience.

*Station break:* Interruption of a show to give station identification.

*Stock shot:* Film or photographs of well-known landmarks. Also a collection of actions frequently used in film work, such as a traffic shot, moving clouds, crowded streets.

*Storyboard:* A number of drawings and accompanying text indicating the major points of a proposed show; especially used in shooting motion pictures.

*Stretch:* Slow down.

*Strike:* Remove certain objects; remove scenery after the show.

*Strip light:* Several lightbulbs arranged in a strip, used for lighting the cyclorama.

*Super:* Superimposition; simultaneous showing of two or more full pictures on the same screen.

*Sweep:* (1) Curved piece of scenery.
(2) Electronic scanning.

*Sweep reversal:* Electronic scanning reversal; results in a mirror image (horizontal sweep reversal) or in an upside-down image (vertical sweep reversal).

*Switcher:* (1) Engineer who is doing the switching from camera to camera.
(2) A panel with certain buttons that allows switching from one camera to another.

*Sync:* Synchronization; the simultaneous projections of picture and sound; also, the electronic pulses of picture transmission and receiver must be synchronized to produce a stable image on the television screen.

*Sync generator:* Part of the camera chain; produces electronic synchronization pulses.

*Sync roll:* Vertical rolling of a picture caused by switching from remote to studio, thereby momentarily losing synchronization; also noticeable on a bad video tape splice.

*Take:* (1) Signal for a "cut" from one camera to the other.
(2) Motion picture expression, now used in television recording; "good take": the successful completion of the recording of the show or part of the show; "bad take": unsuccessful recording—another "take" is required.

*Take-up reel:* Reel that takes up film or tape from the supply reel. Must be the same size as the supply reel in order to maintain proper film or tape tension.

*Talent:* Collective name for all television performers and actors.

*Talkback:* Speaker system that connects the control room with the studio.

*Tally light:* Small red light on the camera, indicating when the camera is on the air.

*Tape:* Plastic ribbon, approximately 1/1000 inch thick, varying in width from 1/4 inch to 2 inches; the tape is coated with iron oxide (dull side); it is used to record magnetic impulses from video or audio sources.

*Target:* Light-sensitive front surface of the camera pickup tube, which is scanned by an electron beam.

*T.D.:* Technical director; in charge of technical studio crew. Usually does the switching during a telecast.

*Telecine:* Television film and slide projection equipment, or room where the equipment is located.

*Telephoto lens:* Long-focal-length lens.

*Teleprompter:* Brand name: TelePrompTer; mechanical prompting device; paper roll with copy is mounted in front of the camera, easily visible to the talent.

*Telop:* Opaque photograph or drawing projected by the telop projector.

*Telop projector:* Opaque television projector, similar to the balop.

*Tempo:* Speed of individual show segments within the over-all show pace.

*Tertiary movement:* Movement created by a sequence of shots from two or more cameras.

*Test pattern:* Special design that aids camera picture alignment.

*Tilt:* Pointing the camera up and down.

*Title drum:* Large drum on which title sheets can be fastened for credit supers; same as Crawl.

*Titles:* Any graphic material shown on camera; more specifically, studio title cards or slides.

*Tongue:* Move camera with boom from left to right or from right to left.

*Transcription:* (1) Any kind of recording.
(2) A record made for broadcast use only; same as E.T.

*Traveler:* A large curtain, similar to a theatre curtain, which opens horizontally from the middle or from one side.

*Truck:* Lateral movement of the camera dolly and camera.

*TVR:* Television recording; refers to a kinescope recording; usually called a kine.

*Two-shot:* Framing that includes two people or objects.

*UHF:* Ultra High Frequency, television transmission channels above channel 13.

*Unit set:* Standardized interchangeable scenery.

*Variable-focal-length lens:* Zoom lens.

*VHF:* Very High Frequency, televison transmission on channels 2 through 13.

*Video:* Picture portion of a telecast.

*Video engineer:* Controls the camera pictures before they are sent on the air; also called the shader.

*Video tape:* Plastic tape for recording video and audio portions of a telecast.

*Video tape recorder:* Electronic recording machine that records and plays back television shows or portions of shows.

*Vidicon:* Special camera tube that is less sensitive but more durable than the I-O tube; frequently used in closed-circuit operation and in television film cameras.

*Viewfinder:* Small television set on top of the camera in which the cameraman can see the picture he is photographing.

*VTR:* Video tape recording.

*VU meter:* Volume Unit meter; audio meter indicating the volume level of sound.

*Walk-through:* Type of television rehearsal, usually preceding the camera rehearsal, where production and engineering crews and talent briefly "walk through" major actions.

*Warm up:* Getting the studio audience in the proper spirit.

*WFM:* Wave Form Monitor; a small tube (oscilloscope) that visually indicates the black-and-white video signals; often called "scope."

*Wipe:* Electronic effect whereby one picture seems to push the other picture off the screen.

*XCU:* Extreme close-up; same as ECU.

*Zoom:* Gradual changing of the focal length of the lens; gives an effect of dollying without moving the camera.

*Zoomar:* Brand name of zoom lenses.

*Zoom lens:* Variable-focal-length lens.

# Additional Reading

CHAPTER 1

Bretz, Rudy, *Techniques of Television Production,* 2nd edition. New York: McGraw-Hill Book Co., Inc., 1962. Includes informative chapters on the camera, the cameramen, camera handling, and lenses.

Chester, Giraud, Garnet R. Garrison, and Edgar E. Willis, *Television and Radio,* 3rd edition. New York: Appleton-Century-Crofts, Inc., 1963. Discusses beginning studio techniques. Describes some television equipment.

Fink, Donald G., *Television Engineering*. New York: McGraw-Hill Book Co., Inc., 1952. Explains the basic electronic functionings of television cameras. Good introduction for those interested in television engineering.

Jones, Peter, *The Technique of the Television Cameraman*. London: Focal Press, 1965. Explains in detail the various forms of camera handling. Includes some material on framing and picture composition. Uses British television terminology rather than American.

Millerson, Gerald, *The Technique of Television Production*. New York: Hastings House, Publishers, Inc., 1961. Devotes some chapters to the physical and electronic characteristics of the television camera, camera mountings, and camera lenses.

## CHAPTER 2

Bretz, Rudy, *Techniques of Television Production*, 2nd edition. New York: McGraw-Hill Book Co., Inc., 1962. Contains a good chapter on basic optical characteristics of lenses.

*Journal of the Society of Motion Picture and Television Engineers*. See the index to this trade journal for up-to-date articles on television optics.

Millerson, Gerald, *The Technique of Television Production*. New York: Hastings House, Publishers, Inc., 1961. Discusses the basic optical characteristics of turret lenses.

Spottiswoode, Raymond, *Film and Its Techniques*. Berkeley and Los Angeles: University of California Press, 1951. Contains a good explanation of optical characteristics of film lenses; applies directly to television turret lenses.

## CHAPTER 3

Hubbell, Richard, *Television Programming and Production*. New York: Rinehart and Co., Inc., 1956. Although the book is generally outdated, the section on audio aesthetics and the discussion of the basic functions of television audio and their relationship to emotional responses from the viewer are still quite valid.

Millerson, Gerald, *The Technique of Television Production*. New York: Hastings House, Publishers, Inc., 1961. Contains a short but good section on audio aesthetics.

Nisbett, Alex, *The Technique of the Sound Studio*. New York: Hastings House, Publishers, Inc., 1962. Deals with some important aspects of audio recording. Numerous illustrations.

Oringel, Robert S., *Audio Control Handbook*, revised edition. New York: Hastings House, Publishers, Inc., 1956. Good basic text on audio equipment, such as turntables, microphones, tape recorders, filters, and remote equipment. Includes a glossary of audio terminology.

## CHAPTER 4

Arnheim, Rudolf, *Art and Visual Perception*. Berkeley and Los Angeles: University of California Press, 1954. Contains an excellent section on the basic aesthetics of light.

Bowman, Wayne, *Modern Theatre Lighting*. New York: Harper & Brothers, 1958. Good text on theatre lighting practices with many diagrams and drawings. Includes a good discussion of lighting aesthetics.

*Journal of the Society of Motion Picture and Television Engineers*. From 1955 to date. Special reprints of articles on monochrome and color television lighting practices are available from the Society.

Millerson, Gerald, *The Technique of Television Production*. New York: Hastings House, Publishers, Inc., 1961. Discusses some of the basic lighting principles and aesthetics of television lighting.

Note: CBS and BBC have training films available describing their latest television lighting techniques.

## CHAPTER 5

Auerbach, Arnold, *A Brief History of Sculpture*. New York: Studio Publications, 1952. Designed for quick reference to the major periods of sculpture from prehistoric to modern times.

Berckelaers, Ferdinand Louis (Seuphor, Michel, pseud.), *The Sculpture of This Century*. New York: George Braziller, Inc., 1960. Excellent guide to modern sculpture and spacial expressions. Includes a good bibliography.

Burris-Meyer, Harold, and Edward C. Cole, *Scenery for the Theatre*. Boston: Little, Brown and Co., 1951. Good reference to all facets of theatre production. Outstanding discussion of scenery construction. Contains many illustrations and work drawings.

Fletcher, Sir Banister, *A History of Architecture on the Comparative Method*, 17th edition. New York: Charles Scribner's Sons, 1961. Excellent text, with over 4,000 illustrations. Gives an encompassing picture of all types of architectural forms from ancient to present times.

Janson, H. W., *History of Art*. Englewood Cliffs, N.J.: Prentice-Hall, Inc., 1962. An excellent survey of the major visual arts from the beginnings of history to the present day. Many good illustrations and a comprehensive list of books for further reading.

Levin, Richard. *Television by Design*. London: The Bodley Head, 1961. Gives some examples of television scene design from blueprint to studio setting. Also contains many pictures of typical television sets from all over the world.

## CHAPTER 6

*Alphabet Thesaurus: A Treasury of Letter Designs.* New York: Reinhold Publishing Corp., 1960. Comprehensive collection of letters and styles of printing from every culture for every use. Many good illustrations of type.

Bretz, Rudy, *Techniques of Television Production,* 2nd edition. New York: McGraw-Hill Book Co., Inc., 1962. Good discussion of graphic materials and some special graphic effects for television.

Dair, Carl, *Design with Type.* New York: Farrar, Straus and Cudahy, Inc., 1952. Concise approach to various styles of type, their structure and integration.

Hofmann, Armin, *Graphic Design Manual.* New York: Reinhold Publishing Corp., 1965. Gives many fine examples of up-to-date graphics.

Kepes, Gyorgy (ed.), *Education of Vision.* New York: George Braziller, Inc., 1965. This volume of the *Vision and Value* series contains several excellent articles discussing creative approaches to design. Many illustrations.

## CHAPTER 7

Bretz, Rudy, *Techniques of Television Production,* 2nd edition. New York: McGraw-Hill Book Co., Inc., 1962. Devotes three chapters to a discussion of various special television effects.

Hansen, Marylyn J., "Four Projects Investigating Live Animation in Graphics for Television and Film." Unpublished Master's thesis, Department of Radio-Television-Film, San Francisco State College, 1964. Includes some interesting ideas on title animation and other special effects for television.

Wittlig, Paul F., "New Horizons in Studio Production," *Journal of the Society of Motion Picture and Television Engineers* (September 1959). Discusses several electronic and mechanical studio effects. Also, see later editions of the *Journal of the SMPTE* for articles on special effects.

## CHAPTER 8

Gaskill, Arthur L., and David A. Englander, *How to Shoot a Movie Story.* New York: Morgan and Morgan, 1960. This little book contains excellent information on shot composition, sequence, and pictorial continuity.

Levitan, Eli L., *Animation Art in the Commercial Film.* New York: Reinhold Publishing Corp., 1960. Easy-to-understand, richly illustrated text on the most important phases of film animation techniques.

Lindgren, Ernest, *The Art of the Film,* revised edition. New York: The Macmillan Co., 1963. Comprehensive discussion of film aesthetics. The chapters on film editing are especially valuable.

Mascelli, Joseph V., *The Five C's of Cinematography*. Hollywood: Cine/ Graphics Publications, 1965. This is an excellent, richly illustrated book in which the five "C's" of cinematography are discussed: camera angles, continuity, cutting, close-ups, and composition. Most of the information is also applicable to television photography.

Spottiswoode, Raymond, *Film and Its Techniques*. Berkeley and Los Angeles: University of California Press, 1951. Highly detailed, quite technical discussion of motion picture production. Excellent reference.

Wiegand, John Lee, "Cutting Feature Film for Television," *Journal of the Society of Motion Picture and Television Engineers* (July 1960). Discusses feature film editing problems, such as holding story line and continuity, types of cuts, and when and what may be cut. Also, see current editions of the *Journal of the SMPTE* for articles on video tape.

## CHAPTER 9

Boleslavsky, Richard, *Acting: The First Six Lessons*. New York: Theatre Arts Books, 1949. Good and interesting approach to acting theory. Includes discussion of concentration, emotion, characterization, and rhythm.

Hyde, Stuart W., *Television and Radio Announcing*. Boston: Houghton Mifflin Co., 1959. Excellent text on all major phases of television performing; includes pronunciation, voice and diction, commercial announcements, newscasting, interviewing, sportscasting, and the documentary. Contains many good exercises. An accompanying record is also available.

Lewis, Bruce, *The Technique of Television Announcing*. New York: Hastings House, Publishers, Inc., 1966. Contains some good sections on announcing techniques for television.

Rosenstein, S., L. Haydon, and W. Sparrow, *Modern Acting: A Manual*. New York and Los Angeles: Samuel French, 1936. A concise but intensive analysis of many facets of acting theory. Lists numerous exercises.

Stanislavski, Constantin, *An Actor Prepares*. New York: Theatre Arts Books, 1956. Excellent discussion of all phases of acting. A "must" in every actor's library.

## CHAPTER 10

Barton, Lucy, *Historic Costume for the Stage*. Boston: Walter H. Baker Co., 1935. Discusses in detail each major period of costuming for the stage. Also includes good suggestions on how to make costumes.

Corson, Richard, *Stage Makeup*. New York: Appleton-Century-Crofts, Inc., 1949. Good discussion of all major facets of make-up, including color and pigment, equipment for make-up, character analysis, and modeling with plastic masks.

Hansen, Henny Harald, *Costumes and Styles: The Evolution of Fashion from Early Egypt to the Present.* New York: E. P. Dutton & Co., 1956. Useful pictorial history of costumes.

Kehoe, Vincent J. R., *The Technique of Film and Television Make-Up.* New York: Hastings House, Publishers, Inc., 1957. Thorough treatment of film and television make-up materials and procedures. Includes discussions of make-up equipment, TV gray scale, and corrective and character make-up for monochrome and color television. Contains many pictures and diagrams.

Seki, Hidemitsu, and Akira Kodama, "New Type of Make-up Material for Color Motion Pictures and Color Television," *Journal of the Society of Motion Picture and Television Engineers* (June 1960). Technical discussion of new make-up materials.

Strenkovsky, Serge, *The Art of Make-up.* New York: E. P. Dutton & Co., 1956. Uses anatomy, painting, and geometry to discuss the theory and techniques of make-up. Stage, screen, and still-photography make-up techniques are described. Richly illustrated.

Wilcox, Ruth Turner, *The Mode in Hats and Headdress.* New York: Charles Scribner's Sons, 1946. Good text, well illustrated. Covers styles from ancient Egypt to World War II.

## CHAPTER 11

Chester, Giraud, Garnet R. Garrison, and Edgar E. Willis, *Television and Radio,* 3rd edition. New York: Appleton-Century-Crofts, Inc., 1963. Devotes a section to the television studio and control room.

*Design for ETV: Planning for Schools with Television.* New York: Dave Chapman, Inc., Industrial Design for Educational Facilities Laboratories, 1960. Popular approach to the discussion of television viewing in the classroom.

Hungerford, Arthur, "Studio and Control Equipment," *Understanding Television,* ed. Robert L. Hilliard. New York: Hastings House, Publishers, Inc., 1964. A concise description of the more common production equipment.

## CHAPTER 12

*Producing*

Ashley, Paul P., *Say It Safely,* 3rd edition. Seattle: University of Washington Press, 1966. Describes in simple, nontechnical language the legal limits in publishing, radio, and television.

Hilliard, Robert L. (ed.), *Understanding Television.* New York: Hastings House, Publishers, Inc., 1964. An easy introduction to most aspects of television production.

Klapper, Joseph T., *The Effects of Mass Communication.* New York: The Free Press, 1960. An excellent summary of important studies on mass media and mass communication effects.

Wainwright, Charles A., *The Television Copywriter.* New York: Hastings House, Publishers, Inc., 1966. A book primarily for the writer of television commercials; however, it contains many good sections on production problems and procedures.

Wright, Charles R., *Mass Communication: A Sociological Perspective.* New York: Random House, Inc., 1959. An extremely concise, excellent overview of the most important mass communication theories.

*Directing*

Arnheim, Rudolf, *Art and Visual Perception.* Berkeley and Los Angeles: University of California Press, 1954. A comprehensive treatment of all facets of visual perception, such as shape, form, space, light, and balance.

Battin, Tom C., "Directing," *Understanding Television,* ed. Robert L. Hilliard. New York: Hastings House, Publishers, Inc., 1964. A concise, highly informative treatment of the most important aspects of television directing.

Davis, Desmond, *The Grammar of Television Production.* London: Barrie and Rockliff, 1960. Contains many examples of framing, composition, and camera placement. Although not a true grammar of TV production, this little book contains valuable information for directors.

Dean, Alexander, and L. Carra, *Fundamentals of Play Directing,* revised edition. New York: Holt, Rinehart and Winston, Inc., 1965. Fundamental text on play directing for the stage. Includes several illustrations of major blocking.

Dietrich, John E., *Play Direction.* Englewood Cliffs, N.J.: Prentice-Hall, Inc., 1953. Analyzes the major aspects of play direction, such as the motivational units, stage movement, and tempo.

Dolman, John, Jr., *The Art of Play Production.* New York: Harper & Row, Publishers, Inc., 1946. Good treatment of play directing aesthetics. Includes rhythm, emphasis, balance, harmony, grace, etc.

Heffner, Hubert C., *Modern Theatre Practice: A Handbook of Play Production.* New York: Appleton-Century-Crofts, Inc., 1959. Part Two explains the duties of the director in stage directing, such as rehearsals, director-actor relationship, pace, tempo, and timing. Especially useful for reference.

Millerson, Gerald, *The Technique of Television Production.* New York: Hastings House, Publishers, Inc., 1961. Several chapters deal with some aspects of television aesthetics, such as framing, composition, editing, shot continuity, screen directions, and the importance of sound. A valuable book for directors.

*Writing*

Barnouw, Erik, *The Television Writer.* New York: Hill and Wang, Inc., 1962. Contains many examples of scripts. Chapter 1 is a comprehensive introduction to numerous aspects of television writing.

Bluem, A. William, *Documentary in American Television: Form, Function, and Method.* New York: Hastings House, Publishers, Inc., 1965. Contains much valuable material on the general structure and form of television documentaries.

Hilliard, Robert L., *Writing for Television and Radio,* 2nd edition. New York: Hastings House, Publishers, Inc., 1967. Gives valuable information on the writing for various program categories, such as news and sports, special events, and plays.

MacGowan, Kenneth, *A Primer of Playwriting.* New York: Doubleday and Co., Inc., 1951. Although this small, excellent book is not written specifically for television, it provides a wealth of material basic to the understanding of dramatic writing.

Willis, Edgar E., *Writing Television and Radio Programs.* New York: Holt, Rinehart and Winston, Inc., 1967. A well-organized book that discusses the various aspects of dramatic writing, such as the nature of drama, theme, plot, and characters, as well as more technical aspects of broadcast writing, such as designing the script.

### CHAPTER 13

Atkins, Jim, Jr., and Leo Willette, *Filming TV News and Documentaries.* Philadelphia, Pa.: Chilton Book Co., 1965. Describes major phases of filming television news and documentaries.

Wimer, Arthur, and Dale Brix, *Radio and TV News Editing and Writing,* 2nd edition. Dubuque, Iowa: William C. Brown Co., Publishers, 1963. A helpful workbook with many news exercises.

Wood, William A., *Electronic Journalism.* New York: Columbia University Press, 1967.

### CHAPTER 14

Chester, Giraud, Garnet R. Garrison, and Edgar E. Willis, *Television and Radio,* 3rd edition. New York: Appleton-Century-Crofts, Inc., 1963. Devotes one chapter to the "inside of the station." It gives a good personnel chart of a network television station.

Lawton, Sherman P., *The Modern Broadcaster.* New York: Harper & Row, Publishers, Inc., 1961. Part One discusses some fundamental aspects of station organization.

Roe, Yale (ed.), *Television Station Management.* New York: Hastings House, Publishers, Inc., 1964. Contains several good articles on the various management and business aspects of television operation.

Summers, Robert E., and Harrison B. Summers, *Broadcasting and the Public.* Belmont, Calif.: Wadsworth Publishing Co., Inc., 1966. An excellent treatment of the history of U.S. broadcasting and the current program practices.

# Index

antalge LARRY KANE for camera work